TECHNIQUES AND APPLICATIONS OF NEURAL NETWORKS

ELLIS HORWOOD WORKSHOP SERIES

A.P. Ambler, M. Abadir & S. Sastry

D.R. Avresky

R. Beale & J. Finlay

W. van der Hoek, J.-J. Ch. Meyer, Y.H. Tan & C. Witteveen

T. E. Nagle, J.A. Nagle, L.L. Gerholz & P.W. Eklund

J. Treur & T. Wetter

**ECONOMICS OF DESIGN AND TEST FOR
ELECTRONIC CIRCUITS AND SYSTEMS
HARDWARE AND SOFTWARE FAULT TOLERANCE
IN PARALLEL COMPUTING SYSTEMS
NEURAL NETWORKS AND PATTERN RECOGNITION
IN HUMAN–COMPUTER INTERACTION
NON-MONOTONIC REASONING AND
PARTIAL SEMANTICS
CONCEPTUAL STRUCTURES:
Current Research and Practice
FORMAL SPECIFICATION OF
COMPLEX REASONING SYSTEMS**

TECHNIQUES AND APPLICATIONS OF NEURAL NETWORKS

P.J.G. LISBOA
Department of Electrical Engineering and Electronics
University of Liverpool

M.J. TAYLOR
Department of Computer Science
University of Liverpool

ELLIS HORWOOD
NEW YORK   LONDON   TORONTO   SYDNEY   TOKYO   SINGAPORE

First published in 1993 by
Ellis Horwood Limited
Campus 400, Maylands Avenue
Hemel Hempstead
Hertfordshire, HP2 7EZ
and Market Cross House, Cooper Street
Chichester, West Sussex, PO19 1EB, England
A division of
Simon & Schuster International Group

Printed and bound in Great Britain
by Bookcraft, Midsomer Norton.

British Library Cataloguing in Publication Data

A catalogue record for this book is available
from the British Library
ISBN 0-13-062183-8

Library of Congress Cataloging-in-Publication Data

Available from the publisher

1 2 3 4 5   97 96 95 94 93

CONTENTS

INTRODUCTION   P.J.G. Lisboa and M.J. Taylor   **15**

THEORY

**1   THE STATISTICAL INDEPENDENCE OF NETWORK   21
GENERALISATION: AN APPLICATION IN SOFTWARE
ENGINEERING**

1.1	INTRODUCTION	22
1.1.1	Generalisation	23
1.2	SIMULATION STUDIES	24
1.2.1	General Method and Architecture	24
1.2.2	Study 1: Random Seed	25
1.2.3	Study 2: Random Unique	27
1.2.4	Study 3: Methodological Diversity	29
1.3	CONCLUSIONS	31

**2   MODELLING PROBABILITY DENSITY FUNCTIONS FOR   35
CLASSIFYING USING A CMAC**

2.1	INTRODUCTION	35
2.2	THE CEREBELLAR MODEL ARTICULATION	
	CONTROLLER	36
2.2.1	Design of the Model	36
2.2.2	Advantages Over Other Models	37
2.2.3	Shortcomings of the CMAC Model	38
2.3	IMPROVING THE MODEL	38
2.3.1	Controlling the Generalisation	38
2.3.2	Making the Response More Uniform	39
2.3.3	Multi-class CMAC	40
2.3.4	Training Algorithm	40
2.4	PERFORMANCE EVALUATION	41
2.4.1	Testing Method	41
2.4.2	Test Data	42
2.4.3	Discussion	44
2.5	CONCLUSION	44

**3   A NEURAL NETWORK SIMULATION OF VISUAL   47
      PROCESSES INVOLVED IN SCENE ANALYSIS**

3.1   THEORETICAL BACKGROUND   48
3.1.1   Traditional A.I. Scene Analysis   48
3.1.2   Psychological Evidence   50
3.2   HARMONY THEORY   52
3.2.1   Harmony Theory Design   52
3.2.2   Merit of the Approach   53
3.2.2.1   Problem-Dependent Characteristics   53
3.2.2.2   Parallel-Serial Implementational Differences   54
3.3   NETWORK IMPLEMENTATION   54
3.3.1   The Lower Layer   54
3.3.2   The Upper Layer   55
3.3.3   Connectivity and General Parameters   56
3.4   RESULTS   58
3.5   CONCLUSIONS   61

MEDICAL APPLICATIONS

**4   TUMOUR CLASSIFICATION USING ^{1}H NUCLEAR   63
      MAGNETIC RESONANCE SPECTROSCOPY, PRINCIPAL
      COMPONENT ANALYSIS AND A NEURAL NETWORK**

4.1   INTRODUCTION   64
4.2   METHODS   65
4.2.1   Tumour and Tissue Extracts   66
4.2.2 ^{1}H Nuclear Magnetic Resonance Spectroscopy   67
4.2.3   Data Sets Studied   67
4.2.4   Principal Component Analysis   68
4.2.5   Cluster Analysis   68
4.2.6   Artificial Neural Network   68
4.3   RESULTS   70
4.3.1   PC Analysis and Cluster Analysis   70
4.3.2   Sample Classifications with an Artificial Neural Network   71
4.4   DISCUSSION   74

5   CLASSIFICATION OF CHROMOSOMES USING   77
A COMBINATION OF NEURAL NETWORKS

5.1   INTRODUCTION   77
5.2   CLASSIFICATION OF CHROMOSOMES   80
5.2.1   Network Training Algorithm   80
5.2.2   Use of the MLP for Chromosome Classification   81
5.2.3   Optimisation of the MLP Classifiers   82
5.2.4   Classification Performance   84
5.3   SECOND STAGE CLASSIFICATION USING A
         COMPETITIVE NETWORK   87
5.4   DISCUSSION   88

6   APPLICATIONS OF ARTIFICIAL NEURAL NETWORKS   93
TO FETAL MONITORING DURING LABOUR

6.1   INTRODUCTION   94
6.1.1   The Cardiotocogram   95
6.1.2   Detection of Fetal Heart Beats   97
6.2   NEURAL NETWORK CLASSIFICATION OF THE CTG   98
6.2.1   Methods   98
6.2.2   Results   99
6.3   NEURAL NETWORK DETECTION OF THE QRS
         COMPLEX   99
6.3.1   Methods   99
6.3.2   Results   102
6.4   DISCUSSION AND CONCLUSIONS   104

FORECASTING

7   MANAGING EXCHANGE RATE PREDICTION   109
STRATEGIES WITH NEURAL NETWORKS

7.1   INTRODUCTION   109
7.2   COMPUTER TRADING STRATEGIES   110
7.2.1   Moving Averages   110
7.2.2   Mean-Value   111
7.3   EXPERIMENTAL SET UP   112
7.3.1   System Architecture   112
7.3.2   Training and Test Sets   113
7.4   RESULTS   113
7.5   DISCUSSION   115
7.6   CONCLUSION   115

**8   TREND ANALYSIS OF REMOTE STANDBY   117
GENERATING SETS USING PARAMETER-
ESTIMATION NEURAL NETWORKS**

8.1	INTRODUCTION	**118**
8.1.1	In Search of Power	**118**
8.1.2	Remote Condition Monitoring	**118**
8.1.3	Condition Based Maintenance	**120**
8.2	DATA ACQUISITION	**123**
8.3	DATA-NORMALISATION USING NEURAL NETWORKS	**125**
8.3.1	Parameter Estimation Using Back-Propagation	**125**
8.3.2	Implementing the Parameter Estimation Neural Network	**126**
8.3.3	Neural Model Testing	**129**
8.3.4	Measuring Errors in the Neural Model	**130**
8.4	A KNOWLEDGE-BASED SYSTEM	**130**
8.5	CONCLUSIONS	**132**

INDUSTRIAL MEASUREMENT AND CONTROL

**9   NEURAL NETWORK BASED ELECTRONIC NOSE   135
USING CONSTRUCTIVE ALGORITHMS**

9.1	INTRODUCTION	**136**
9.2	THE RCE MODEL	**137**
9.2.1	Topology of the Network	**138**
9.2.2	Training	**138**
9.3	ALPAYDIN'S MODEL	**141**
9.4	THE RV ALGORITHM	**142**
9.4.1	Model	**142**
9.4.2	Steps Involved in the Algorithm	**143**
9.5	RESULTS AND COMMENTS	**144**
9.5.1	Data-bases Used to Train the Network	**144**
9.5.2	Previous Experiments Performed Using a 3-Layer	
	Back-Propagation Network (One Hidden Layer)	**145**
9.5.3	Results Obtained with the RCE Algorithm	**146**
9.5.4	Results Obtained with Alpaydin's Algorithm	**148**
9.5.5	Results Obtained with the RV Algorithm	**150**
9.6	CONCLUSION	**152**

10 DETECTION AND IDENTIFICATION OF   **155**
POTENTIOMETRIC FLOW INJECTION ANALYSIS PEAKS

10.1	INTRODUCTION	**155**
10.1.1	Applications of Neural Network Technology to Analytical	
	Chemistry	**156**
10.1.2	Flow Injection Analysis	**158**
10.1.3	Potentiometry	**159**
10.1.4	Potentiometric Flow Injection Analysis	**161**
10.2	EXPERIMENTAL METHOD	**162**
10.3	RESULTS	**163**
10.3.1	Using the NT5000 Software	**163**
10.3.1.1	Variation of MSE with Noise Level and Number of Neurons in	
	the Hidden Layer	**165**
10.3.1.2	Variation of MSE with Peak Height and Number of Hidden	
	Layer Neurons	**167**
10.3.1.3	Variation of MSE with Baseline Shifting as a Function of	
	the Number of Neurons in the Hidden Layer	**167**
10.3.1.4	Discussion of Results	**168**
10.3.1.5	Further Training	**168**
10.3.2	Using NeuralWorks II	**170**
10.3.2.1	Comparison of Training and Testing Set Errors	**171**
10.3.2.2	Variation of Vector Length and Angle Formed with the Unit	
	Vector During Training	**173**
10.4	CONCLUSION	**177**

11 IDENTIFICATION OF LIGHTING FLICKER SOURCES   **183**
USING A NEURAL NETWORK

11.1	INTRODUCTION	**183**
11.2	FLICKER PATTERNS AND DATA COLLECTION	**185**
11.2.1	Motivation	**185**
11.2.2	Derivation of Flicker Patterns	**186**
11.3	THE NEURAL NETWORK PARADIGMS	**187**
11.3.1	The Back-Propagation Algorithm	**187**
11.3.2	The Kohonen Self Organising Feature Map	**190**
11.4	METHOD	**190**
11.4.1	Preprocessing of Data	**190**
11.4.2	The Networks	**192**
11.5	RESULTS	**193**
11.6	CONCLUSIONS	**196**

12 A NEURAL NET CONTROLLER FOR NAVIGATION AND 199 OBSTACLE AVOIDANCE FOR NON-HOLONOMIC MOBILE ROBOTS USING SENSORY INFORMATION

12.1	INTRODUCTION	200
12.1.1	Mobile Robot Navigation	200
12.1.2	Human Navigation Behaviour	201
12.2	THE NAVIGATION SYSTEM	201
12.2.1	Overall Structure of the System	201
12.2.2	Symbolic World Description	202
12.2.3	Place and Path Classification	203
12.2.4	Local Navigation and Obstacle Avoidance	203
12.3	LOCAL NAVIGATION USING BACK-PROPAGATION THROUGH TIME	204
12.3.1	Control System Structure	204
12.3.2	The Vehicle Emulator Net	205
12.3.3	The Environment Emulator Net	206
12.3.4	Controller Training Using Position States	207
12.3.5	Controller Training Using Distance Values	209
12.4	NEURAL NET CONTROLLERS FOR LOCAL NAVIGATION	210
12.4.1	Learning to Keep Distance	210
12.4.2	Learning to Follow a Wall	210
12.4.3	Learning to Avoid Obstacles	211
12.4.4	Learning to Turn and Go Straight Ahead on Crossroads	212
12.4.5	Generalisation to Unknown Environments	213
12.5	ENVIRONMENT PREDICTION	213
12.6	CONCLUSION	215
12.6.1	Summary	215
12.6.2	Future Research	216

IMAGE PROCESSING

13 MEASURING THE SIZE DISTRIBUTION OF EMULSION 219 DROPLETS IN AN IMAGE USING KOHONEN'S SELF ORGANISING FEATURE MAP

13.1	INTRODUCTION	220
13.1.1	Image and Ruler	220
13.1.2	Malvern Mastersizer	220
13.1.3	Brightfield Imaging	221
13.1.4	Differential Interference Contrasting (DIC)	221
13.2	SIZE DISTRIBUTION USING KOHONEN SOMs	221

13.3	DESCRIPTION OF THE SYSTEM	**223**
13.3.1	Preprocessing the Images	**224**
13.3.2	Training the Kohonen SOMS	**226**
13.3.3	Running the System	**227**
13.4	RESULTS	**228**
13.5	CONCLUSION	**232**

14 LOCATION OF FACIAL FEATURES USING A   **235**
BOLTZMANN MACHINE TO IMPLEMENT
GEOMETRICAL CONSTRAINTS

14.1	REVIEW	**236**
14.1.1	Neural Feature Extraction	**236**
14.1.2	Exploiting Knowledge to Prune the Search Space	**237**
14.2	GENERALITIES ABOUT BOLTZMANN MACHINES	**239**
14.2.1	Dynamics of Sequential Boltzmann Machines	**239**
14.2.2	A Learning Algorithm for the Weights of a Boltzmann Machine	**240**
14.3	THE PARAMETERISED BOLTZMANN MACHINE	**241**
14.3.1	Structure of the Network	**242**
14.3.1.1	The Links Between the Different Units	**242**
14.3.1.2	The Energy Function	**243**
14.3.2	The Modified Boltzmann Learning Algorithm	**246**
14.4	DISCUSSION OF THE MODEL AND RESULTS	**247**
14.4.1	Discussion of the Model	**247**
14.4.2	Results	**249**
14.5	CONCLUSION	**251**

APPLICATION ENVIRONMENTS

15 USING NEURAL NETWORKS IN A   **253**
CAD/CAM APPLICATION

15.1	INTRODUCTION	**253**
15.2	CONCURRENT ENGINEERING	**254**
15.3	THE APPLICATION	**256**
15.3.1	The Scenario	**258**
15.4	INTEGRATING NEURAL NETWORKS IN A CAD/CAM SYSTEM	**258**
15.4.1	The Data Representation	**258**
15.4.2	Integration of Neural Networks	**260**
15.5	CURRENT WORK AND CONCLUSION	**261**

16   A SELF ORGANISING LOGIC NEURAL NETWORK FOR   263
PATTERN COMPLETION TASKS

16.1	INTRODUCTION	263
16.2	SYSTEM DESCRIPTION	264
16.2.1	Adaptive Algorithm Description	265
16.2.2	Separation of Similar Patterns	267
16.2.3	Application to Pattern Completion Tasks	267
16.3	SIMULATION RESULTS	268
16.3.1	Random Noise Experiments	270
16.3.2	Black Line Deformation	271
16.3.3	White Line Deformation	273
16.4	DISCUSSION	274

17   IMPLEMENTING AN ASSOCIATIVE MEMORY   277
ENVIRONMENT

17.1	INTRODUCTION	277
17.2	ADAM	278
17.3	THE ADAM LIBRARY	280
17.3.1	Introduction	280
17.3.2	Example Application	280
17.4	HARDWARE SUPPORT	281
17.4.1	Introduction	281
17.4.2	The DSPVME System	282
17.4.3	ADAM Co-Processor	283

18   NEURAL NETWORKS FOR SYSTEM FAULT   287
MANAGEMENT

18.1	INTRODUCTION	287
18.2	THE FAULT MANAGEMENT PROBLEM	288
18.3	HELP DESKS	289
18.4	SOFTWARE SUPPORT FOR HELP DESKS	290
18.5	NEURAL NETWORKS: A SOLUTION?	290
18.6	A PILOT EXPERIMENT WITH ADAM	293
18.6.1	Representing the Transcripts	293
18.6.2	The Approach Taken	294
18.6.3	Results	295
18.6.4	The Implications of the Study	296
18.7	DESIGN FOR A SUPPORT SYSTEM	297
18.8	SUMMARY	298

CONTRIBUTORS   **301**

INDEX   **305**

INTRODUCTION

Artificial neural networks are an emerging technology which has gained considerable momentum in the early 90's, and whose advance is set to continue throughout the decade. During this period, neural networks are gradually making a transition out of the laboratory bench and into the marketplace, and this book is intended for those readers interested in how far this transition has progressed in the U.K., which application areas it concerns and how it was carried out.

As this technology advances, there is a need for coherence among the many different approaches to neural networks, raising a number of important questions. What are the relative merits of each proposed algorithm? What is the place of this technology in relation to conventional methods? And the most important question of all, is there a niche where pattern recognition methods can provide practical solutions where alternative methods cannot, thus opening up new and potentially profitable markets?

This book grew out of a Workshop on 'Neural Networks: Techniques and Applications' held in Liverpool in September 1992, which brought together a number of practitioners from a wide spread of specialist application areas looking to compare the performance of different neural techniques, for a consensus on how they are best matched with the requirements from particular practical situations and, of course, to identify the classes of problems where neural network methods offer superior performance to that of alternative conventional approaches.

There are here seven different algorithms, applied to a dozen specific applications in eight different application areas. The basic algorithms are the multi-layer perceptron, trained mostly using standard back-propagation but also using back-propagation through time, CMAC, the Boltzmann machine, RCE, Kohonen and the logic or n-tuple neural network.

The application areas are medicine, finance, sensors, condition monitoring, vehicle navigation, feature location in natural images, computer-aided manufacturing and network fault management.

The book is divided into six sections.

THEORY

Biological systems are the inspiration for artificial neural models, and the reason for this is simple - they are much better at pattern recognition than conventional computer architectures, several orders of magnitude faster, and there is a vast number of problems that are accessible using pattern recognition methods. However, it is important to lay solid theoretical foundations at the base of neural network technology, a task very much in its infancy.

Chapter One demonstrates the potential of the flexibility afforded by the multi-layer perceptron for developing independent solutions to problems, offering a different angle on the perennial problem of software reliability. In particular, it clearly shows the relative effects of changing the initial conditions of the network to yield essentially similar solutions, as against using different selections of example data to map out independent decision boundaries.

Chapter Two introduces an old algorithm which is coming back to the fore, the Cerebellar Model Articulation Controller or CMAC for short. It solves at a stroke some of the main difficulties faced by the more commonly used multi-layer perceptron, namely the large amounts of processing time required when training on real-world data. The solution offered by CMAC is primarily in the trade-off between speed and memory requirements familiar to software engineers, but it has other differences too and they are analyzed in this Chapter.

One of the most important and as yet unresolved problems in scene analysis, is the labelling of localised geometrical features in images of three dimensional objects. Chapter Three offers a new solution to that fundamental problem, using a development of the Boltzmann network to create a labelling scheme which is consistent with current psychophysical evidence about the action of mammalian visual system.

MEDICAL APPLICATIONS

Among the areas where pattern recognition methods are known to pay dividends is the analysis of medical signals, since this is one area where accurate and reliable models are particularly difficult to obtain, due to the complexity of the human body. The three Chapters in this section all use real-world data, and therefore serve to illustrate the ability of neural network techniques to tackle real-life problems.

Chapter Four is concerned with spectral analysis, a specialism of interest not only to medicine but also to several branches of engineering. The approach taken combines data pre-conditioning using principal component analysis with the discrimination capabilities of the multi-layer perceptron. This is an area where neural networks offer a distinct advantage over alternative methods, and a systematic comparison with statistical clustering techniques is carried out.

The next Chapter is one where expertise about the task domain is put to good effect using sophisticated coding techniques, developed from the methods conventionally used for that task. The role of the neural network is to generalise the solutions developed for example data, to similar data in the field. The key role carried out by data pre-conditioning is now well established as one of the most important factors in ensuring successful generalisation to data outside of the training set.

The final Chapter in this section is an example of a small number of neural network applications in medicine undergoing large scale clinical trials. It is another case where domain knowledge is imparted into the network partly via the data conditioning which extracts high level features essential to complete the diagnostic process. In addition, it shows how a similar network can be applied at a lower level of data processing to accurately locate the QRS peaks in electrocardiograms.

FORECASTING

Here is a network application that can actually make you money. Chapter Seven describes a neural approach to managing exchange rates trading strategies in the financial markets. The key to the impressive performance of this approach, which outperforms conventional methods while managing substantial investment sums, is in placing the network at the level of information processing where pattern association is most relevant. In this case, the data supplied to the network is derived from sources other than just historical data for that currency, but including information from conventional methods known to help in estimating the position which the trader should take at any moment in time. As a consequence, the network is used not as a time series predictor, but as a strategy advisor.

Keeping with real-world data, the next Chapter describes a relatively straightforward, yet successful, way of ensuring the reliability of remote equipment in a situation where reliability is crucial. This application illustrates the relatively fast development times possible with neural computing without the need for extensive access to expert knowledge.

INDUSTRIAL MEASUREMENT AND CONTROL

This section shows the immense flexibility of neural networks. Similar methods can be used in seemingly disparate applications, and much can be learnt from successful applications in unrelated areas.

Chapter Nine is an example of an area of sensing which has been opened up by the advent of neural computing. Olfaction requires numerous sensors to yield a sufficiently rich response to different signals, but the precise response of each sensor to a particular gas is difficult to characterise precisely. Nonetheless, it is a function easily modelled from example data, and this is the fundamental advantage of the methods used here. It will become just one of several novel sensors that will result from the use of neural computing!

The next Chapter describes an application in analytical chemistry, preceded by a thorough review of the work previously carried out applying neural networks in that area.

This is an example of the more general case that if a response is reproducible, then it can be measured with neural methods, even if knowledge of the response is imprecise or the response is very non-linear. The application described here is combined with a useful analysis of network training.

A classical approach to neuro-computing is to use a self-organising network, for example a Kohonen net, to search for critical features of interest, followed by a supervised network, such as the multi-layer perceptron, to classify them. This approach is well illustrated by the application in Chapter Eleven.

Another example of a difficult unsolved problem for conventional computing is that of autonomous vehicle navigation. Chapter Twelve successfully explores a solution using a group of networks trained by back-propagation through time to help a robot negotiate obstacles in its path, while still carrying out the surprisingly complex task of following on at T-junctions when required to do so. Once again, the choice of inputs to present to the neural network proves to be critical.

IMAGE PROCESSING

The two applications in this section both come from commercial companies, and are of a totally different nature to each other.

In Chapter Thirteen one of the main advantages of using a self-organising algorithm is exploited, namely its ability to classify droplet sizes in an emulsion cream without the requirement for expensive hand-labelling of numerous droplets in example images. The accuracy of this method for measuring droplet size is verified experimentally.

Chapter Fourteen assesses the application of the Boltzmann algorithm to another difficult task, namely accurate location of a number of different features in natural images. This task is carried out hierarchically, starting from a coarse low resolution image. As in Chapter Two, the Boltzmann algorithm is used here to implement known constraints hence using *a priori* knowledge, to limit the solution space.

APPLICATION ENVIRONMENTS

The final section gives a sample of development environments and fast implementations suitable for a number of different applications.

It begins with an application in Computer Aided Manufacturing described in Chapter Fifteen. The aim is to minimise the lead time to produce a new component, by identifying at an early stage design elements which the new piece has in common with previous ones, and utilising this knowledge to transfer over as much manufacturing information from existing pieces as possible.

Next comes an example of an n-tuple, or logic neural network applied as a noise filter. The main advantage of this network, one of a family long in existence, is that it is easy to implement on conventional digital hardware, and fast to train while retaining a large functionality. The application of this network in unsupervised mode is important because it avoids the need for explicit labelling of large amounts of example data.

The implementation of large scale artificial neural networks using conventional digital hardware is also the subject of Chapter Seventeen. The model is based for its implementation on n-tuple networks, and therefore is aimed at achieving fast training times, but it is refined to implement more conventional architectures using 'hidden' nodes to improve generalisation performance. This involves the resolution of the communication bottlenecks that arise as a consequence of the large size networks which this environment is intended to support.

Chapter Eighteen shows an application developed on the environment described in the previous Chapter, which acts as a test of some of its objectives regarding the flexibility of the network architecture, and its training speed. The application consists of developing a buffer system capable of automatically handling a number of routine fault conditions, while transferring more complex cases on to human operators. The main purpose in using a neural network for this task is to build a system capable of intelligent interaction with the user, without requiring complex analytical models either of the user interaction, or the possible faults. Instead, these models are developed by training with example data.

A companion volume to this book, containing some of the remaining quality publications presented at the Workshop, is the April 1993 Special Issue on Neural Networks of the Journal of Microcomputer Applications, published by Academic Press.

ACKNOWLEDGEMENTS

This book contains selected papers from the 'Workshop on Neural Networks: Techniques and Applications' which was held at the University of Liverpool on 7/8 September 1992.

We are grateful for the co-sponsorship of the meeting by the North West Branches of the British Computer Society, the Institute of Electrical and Electronics Engineers United Kingdom and Republic of Ireland Computer Chapter, and the European Association of Microprocessing and Microprogramming.

We also acknowledge the support of the programme committee: Ross Maxwell, St. George's Hospital Medical School; Jon Waite, British Telecom Laboratories and Paul Wilkie, Royal Insurance (UK).

The support of Liverpool University's Department of Computer Science is gratefully acknowledged. In particular, we wish to thank Katrina Houghton who administered the meeting and who, together with Nikki Cattrell, prepared the documentation for the meeting and meticulously prepared the camera-ready manuscript for this book. We also thank Joan Jones for her assistance.

P.J.G. Lisboa and M.J. Taylor
University of Liverpool, March 1993

Chapter 1

The Statistical Independence of Network Generalisation: an Application in Software Engineering

Noel E. Sharkey and Derek Partridge

Department of Computer Science, University of Exeter, U.K.

Overview

A connectionist implementation of the "Launch-Interceptor" problem is presented that shows the promise of neural network techniques as an innovative technology for the production of reliable software. One conventional approach to software reliability is to incorporate effective redundancy by using a number of different versions of a program in the hope that the versions will fail on different examples. However, a usable and effective framework for adding redundancy has proved extremely elusive. As [KL86], and [AT92] have shown, the problem is that even independently developed versions of the same software tend to fail on the same inputs, i.e. they do not, in fact, exhibit much independence. Adopting a different approach, we explored the problem of creating programs that fail independently by exploiting a well known fact about Multi-layer Perceptrons trained with Back-Propagation: nets started from different initial conditions (or damaged) tend to develop different solutions to the same problem [e.g. Den87, KP90]. This has mainly been discussed in terms of differences in the hidden unit representations of the training data and never in terms of the *statistical* independence of the solutions. Our aim was to examine differences in generalisation that arise from changes in the initial random conditions of nets or from training nets on different samples of the training sets.

1.1   INTRODUCTION

There are essentially two ways to achieve highly reliable software: generate provably correct algorithms, or incorporate effective redundancy. Logic-based verification has been the favoured approach, despite deep-seated problems with implementations of the idea as well as considerable doubts about the practical value of a successful outcome.   Partridge [Par92] summarised the arguments for and against formal verificationism. However, a usable and effective framework for adding redundancy has proved equally elusive. And, although these two approaches are not mutually exclusive, we propose to concentrate on reliability through redundancy, but within a programming paradigm that includes redundancy as an inherent property rather than as a tacked-on afterthought. Within this new paradigm formal guarantees are not abandoned, but they do become manifest as statistics-based quantities rather than logic-based ones.

The aim was to demonstrate the feasibility of constructing a reliable multiversion network programming system. This involved demonstrating the basic feasibility of network-programmed implementations, the version "independence" attainable, and the potential for methodological "diversity" between different network-generation strategies.

Recent experiments [e.g. KL86, AT92] with the traditional multiversion programming approach to reliable software have revealed two significant facts

1.   Independently developed versions of the same software tend to fail on the same inputs, i.e. they do not, in fact, exhibit much 'independence'. Common design faults run across the different versions.

2.   An increase in methodological diversity between versions increases independence, and thus improves the reliability of a multiversion software system.

We treat "neural network technology", or "connectionism", as a new paradigm for software construction, called "network programming." Network programming (i.e. implementing well-defined functions as neural networks) appears to be a methodological extreme, in relation to conventional programming, and thus holds the possibility of greater independence between versions when combined with conventionally programmed versions in a multiversion system. In addition, the nature of network programming (specifically, training rather than conscious design of an algorithm) is such that it may allow us to avoid the major weakness found in conventional versions - common design misconceptions which undermine the independence of separately developed versions. There is thus reason to think that multiversion programming within the network-programming paradigm can result in greater system reliability than when employed solely within conventional programming paradigms. Finally, the multiversion approach to reliable software systems is both difficult and expensive to organize. It requires that a number of independent people (or groups) all duplicate each others program design and development effort. Within the network-programming paradigm, alternative, independent versions will be producible with very little programmer effort, once the basics of the methodology have been clarified.

1.1.1   Generalisation

In all of the studies reported here, we employed simple two-layer nets using the much researched back-propagation learning rule [RHW86]. Such nets may be characterised as automata that sample an input environment and learn, by example, to perform appropriate tasks in response to the input. One big advantage with the back-propagation learning method is that its ability to extract higher order relations in the input environment give it good generalisation properties. The new learning devices have been applied in a wide range of tasks too numerous to relate here. These include text to speech translation [SR86]; syntactic parsing [HK87]; sonar target recognition [GS88]; navigation of a car on a winding road [Pom89]; image compression [CMZ89]; Backgammon [Tes90]; recognising hand-written ZIP codes for the US mail [Lec89].

Earlier devices such as the perceptron would not have been able to learn such tasks because they rely on developing a metric of perceptual similarity on the weights such that perceptually similar inputs will result in similar behaviours. For example, if a task consisted of only two possible behaviours B1 and B2, and if pattern 1 = {111000} resulted in behaviour B1 and pattern 2 = {000111} resulted in behaviour B2, then pattern 3 = {110000} would result in B1, and pattern 4 = {000110} would result in B2. This is because patterns 1 and 3 have a number of common elements, but none in common with patterns 2 and 4.

In contrast, a multilayer net, learning with the generalised delta rule, can devise its own internal metric of similarity so that input environment may be classified according to the functional requirements of the task (rather than perceptual similarity). Thus, two perceptually distinct patterns may be functionally similar and result in similar output behaviour, while two perceptually similar patterns may be functionally distinct and thus result in different output behaviours. For example, a net could be trained to produce output behaviour B1 in response to patterns 1 and 2 from above, B2 in response to patterns 3 and 4. This is a version of the parity problem where nets have been trained to respond in one way to an even number and a different way to an odd number [RHW86]. The net has to extract a higher order rule (parity) that determines the functional similarity of the input patterns.

The internal metric of similarity is encoded on the hidden units and functions as a representation of the semantics of the task and the structure of the input patterns [Sha92, Sha91]. It is the distributed superpositional nature of the internal representations that give the new nets much of their generalisation abilities. Essentially the input to hidden weights are used to draw a decision hyperplane on each hidden unit and then the output hyperplanes determine which pattern class an input belongs to [SS92].

The property of multi-layer weights of most interest here concerns the way in which decision hyperplanes are formed from different initial random starting positions. It has been known for some time that multilayer nets, running back-propagation learning, when started from different random initial conditions, with the same training set, tend to develop different solutions to the same problem [e.g. Den87]. But there is no research on how different generalisations differ statistically. The aim here was to exploit such differences in the construction of a reliable multiversion system. The overall system can be reliable, despite the lack of total reliability in any one version, provided that the occurrence of common errors is minimized. Several statistical frameworks have been developed [see LM89] to measure the "independence" achieved between alternative versions, and the "diversity" achieved between alternative methodologies. The greater these two quantities, the better the 'coverage' of the total system, and coverage is a necessary precursor of system reliability. But added to coverage we need a mechanism for accurately selecting correct outputs. Simple majority vote has been used for this purpose, but network programmed versions, with their 'analogue' functioning, offer the possibility of assigning dynamic reliability measures to individual networks. This possibility will allow us to employ more sophisticated 'voting' mechanisms to generate reliable software systems. We propose to use meta-nets to implement the decision process for a collection of alternative versions, a collection of subnets. In addition, there is a *prima facie* case for supposing that network-programmed versions will improve system reliability when added to conventional multiversion software. The current study, however, is limited to an investigation of version "independence" and methodological "diversity" within the network-programming paradigm.

1.2   SIMULATION STUDIES

We adopted the theoretical model of Littlewood and Miller [LM89] (the most sophisticated model published to date) which provides us with a way to compute methodological "diversity" such that the results will be comparable with those generated in earlier studies on conventionally programmed alternative versions. Three studies of connectionist multiversion systems were carried out. In the first study, the random initial conditions (prior to training) varied over 9 different networks and the training set (100 patterns) was held constant. In the second study, both the random initial conditions and the training sets were varied over 8 networks. Other than these "control" differences, all 17 nets used in the study had identical architectures and identical training parameters. The third investigation examined the statistical "diversity" of the networks from investigations 1 and 2.

1.2.1   General Method and Architecture

Preparation of input sets: Within this feasibility study we implemented only part of the Launch Interceptor problem (the five-page specification is given by Knight and Leveson [KL86]). For this subproblem (essentially the second half of the complete problem), the problem inputs are two vectors and a matrix of values (supposedly derived from radar tracking data), and the output is a decision 'launch' or 'no-launch.'

Input:	Conditions Met Vector (CMV)	15 binary elements
	Preliminary Unlocking Vector (PUV)	15 binary elements
	Logical Connectivity Matrix (LCM)	15x15 ternary elements

Output: Launch or No-Launch decision

For the three studies reported here, a data set, D, consisting of 1130 input/target pairs was generated using the Gold program (this was the standard used in the earlier empirical studies). Next, two sets were chosen randomly: (i) a training (or memorisation) set $M \in D$, and a generalisation test set, $G \in D$, each consisting of an equal number of positive and negative (launch/no-launch) decision classes. All of the simulations were trained on M using back-propagation with a 150-10-1 architecture (error tolerance = 0.1; learning rate = 0.75, momentum = 0.1). They were then tested on G, with no further training, to determine how well each net computed the Launch Interceptor function, LI, such that $LI(G^+) = 1$, and $LI(G^-) = 0$, for all g^+ & $g^- \in G$.

1.2.2   Study 1: Random Seed

In the first study, M, the training set, consisted of 100 randomly chosen pairs (8.8% of D) - 50 launch and 50 no-launch input/output pairs. The same 100 patterns were employed for training all 9 networks. The test set, G, consisted of the remaining 1,030 pairs (91.2% of D). The manipulandum was the seed used to generate the initial random weights for nine independent nets.

Results

Training: The number of training cycles for each net to learn to an error tolerance of 0.1 varied about a mean = 22, with a Standard Deviation = 1.9.

Generalisation: All 9 nets tested on G, exhibited a high degree of generalisation on LI, ranging from 94.5% to 96.4% correct (see Table 1.1). However, the main point was to examine the independence of the network solutions. To do this we calculated the probability of any two net versions failing on a randomly selected input [LM89]. Table 1.2 shows the successes and failures of the individual network versions and Table 1.3 shows the coincident failures.

Ver	1	2	3	4	5	6	7	8	9
gen%	95.9	96.4	95.7	96.0	96.1	95.3	95.7	95.6	94.5

Table 1.1 - Random Seed - Generalisation.

version	failures	successes	prob(fail)	prob(success)
1	42	988	0.0407767	0.959223
2	37	993	0.0359223	0.964078
3	44	986	0.0427184	0.957282
4	41	989	0.0398058	0.960194
5	40	990	0.038835	0.961165
6	48	982	0.0466019	0.953398
7	44	986	0.0427184	0.957282
8	45	985	0.0436893	0.956311
9	56	974	0.0543689	0.945631

Table 1.2 - Random-Seed Version Failures.

We can then calculate the probability that a randomly chosen network will fail on a randomly chosen input [cf. LM89] by

$$E(\theta) = \sum_{\chi} \sum_{\pi} v(\pi,\chi) S(\pi) Q(\chi) = 0.043 \qquad (1.1)$$

where, in the current problem,

$$S(\pi) = \frac{1}{Number\ of\ versions}, \quad Q(\chi) = \frac{1}{Number\ of\ inputs}, \qquad (1.2)$$

$$v(\pi,\chi) = \begin{cases} 1 & if\ program\ \pi\ fails\ on\ input\ \chi \\ 0 & if\ program\ \pi\ succeeds\ on\ input\ \chi \end{cases} \qquad (1.3)$$

This probability is very low given that the *only* difference between the network versions is that the random initial conditions before training varied from version to version. Moreover, the probability of two independent versions failing on a randomly selected input was calculated from the values given in Tables 1.2 and 1.3 [c.f. LM89]: $E(\theta^2) = 0.322$ which is also low.

no. versions	coincident failures	prob(failure)
0	941	0.913592
1	30	0.029126
2	10	0.009708
3	4	0.003883
4	3	0.002912
5	2	0.001941
6	4	0.003883
7	10	0.009708
8	15	0.014563
9	11	0.010679

Table 1.3 - Random-Seed Version Coincident Failures, n=1030.

Ver	1	2	3	4	5	6	7	8
gen%	96.0	94.3	95.4	93.6	91.2	94.0	89.6	92.1

Table 1.4 - Random-Unique Generalisation.

Summary 1: For the current purposes there are four main results from Investigation
1: (i) the nets were very easy to train (mean = 22 cycles); (ii) from a small training
set (100 examples) there was excellent generalisation, the worst performance being
94.5% of 1030 examples that had not been seen by the nets before; (iii) there was a
low probability of failure given a randomly chosen net and a randomly input pattern;
(iv) there was a similarly low probability of two independent versions failing on the
same input pattern.

1.2.3   Study 2: Random Unique

In the second study we wished to find out what the effect would be of training nets
on different sets of the data. Thus 8 net versions of *LI* were created by manipulating
both the random seed and the training pairs in *M*. Each net was trained on a
different $M_i \in D$ (100 patterns) such that $M_1 \cap M_2 \cap \ldots M_8 = \emptyset$.

Initial Conditions: As in the first study, the random initial weights (range -.1 to .1) were varied for each of the 8 networks by using a different random seed for random weight generation.

Results

Training: The number of training cycles for each net to learn to an error tolerance of 0.1 varied about a mean = 35, with a Standard Deviation = 28.18 (the high Standard Deviation results because one of the nets took much longer than the others - 106 cycles).

Generalisation: After training the nets on the 100 examples (each) the other 1030 patterns from the pool were used as a test set to determine how well the nets had extracted the structure of the task. Each net was tested under 8 different threshold criteria differing by 0.1 in the range 0.9-0.1. The generalisation performance on each net was high as shown in Table 1.4, ranging between 89.6% to 96.0%. Table 1.5 shows the successes and failures of the individual network versions and Table 1.6 shows the coincident failures.

Version	failures	successes	prob(fail)	prob(success)
1	41	989	0.0398058	0.960194
2	58	972	0.0563107	0.943689
3	47	983	0.0456311	0.954369
4	65	965	0.0631068	0.936893
5	90	940	0.0873786	0.912621
6	56	974	0.0543689	0.945631
7	106	924	0.1029126	0.897088
8	81	949	0.0786408	0.921359

Table 1.5 - Random-Unique Version Failures.

Again we calculated the probability that a randomly chosen network fails on a randomly chosen input: $E(\theta) = 0.066$, which is comparable to the result in the previous experiment. The probability of two independent versions failing on a randomly selected input was calculated from the values given in Tables 1.2 and 1.3 [cf. LM89], $E(\theta^2) = 0.027$ which is again similar to the previous result.

no. versions	coincident failures	prob(failure)
0	794	0.77087
1	101	0.09806
2	51	0.04951
3	32	0.03106
4	31	0.03009
5	12	0.01165
6	4	0.00388
7	3	0.00291
8	2	0.00194

Table 1.6 - Random-Unique Version Coincident Failures, n=1030.

Summary 2: The results of the second study parallel those of the first and serve to confirm the general significance of our results by their replication within the context of a different network-generation strategy.

1.2.4   Study 3: Methodological Diversity

The final study combined the results from Studies 1 and 2. The two sets of versions generated in Studies 1 and 2 were treated as sets derived from two different methodologies and the Littlewood and Miller [LM89] model was applied to determine the "diversity" between the two network-generation strategies (i.e. random initial condition manipulation *versus* random initial condition and training set manipulation).

Results

From the joint distribution (see Table 1.7), of the two sets of versions, random-unique, 'ru', and random-seed, 'rs', we obtained the probability of simultaneous failure (within both methodologies) on a randomly chosen input, $E\left(\Theta_{ru}, \Theta_{rs}\right) = 0.00279$, the covariance, $Cov\left(\Theta_{ru}, \Theta_{rs}\right) = -0.000038$ and the correlation coefficient, $\rho(\Theta_{ru}, \Theta_{rs}) = -0.0014$.

	1/8	2/8	3/8	4/8	5/8	6/8	7/8	8/8
1/9	0.0028558	0.00144203	0.000904654	0.000876401	0.000339318	0.000113009	8.47567e-05	5.65044-e05
2/9	0.000951869	0.000480643	0.00030153	0.000292114	0.000113098	3.7667e-05	2.82503e-05	1.88335e-05
3/9	0.000380728	0.000192247	0.000120606	0.000116839	4.5237e-05	1.5066e-05	1.12995e-05	7.53302e-06
4/9	0.000285522	0.000144173	9.04467e-05	8.76221e-05	3.39248e-05	1.12986e-05	8.47392e-06	5.64928e-06
6/9	0.000380728	0.000192247	0.000120606	0.0001116839	4.5237e-05	1.5066e-05	1.12995e-05	7.53302e-06
7/9	0.000951869	0.000480643	0.00030153	0.000292114	0.000113098	3.7667e-05	2.82503e-05	1.88335e-05
8/9	0.0014279	0.000721014	0.000452327	0.000438201	0.000169659	5.65044e-05	4.23783e-05	2.82522e-05
9/9	0.00104708	0.000528717	0.00033169	0.000321331	0.00012441	4.14345e-05	3.10759e-05	2.07173e-05

Table 1.7 - Joint Probability Distribution.

This negative correlation, or "diversity", can be seen in Figs. 1.1a and 1.1b where probability of failure within the two network-generation strategies is illustrated graphically. In the optimum case (assuming imperfect programming methodologies) all of the plot points would be on the axes - indicating that inputs which have a non-zero probability of failure within one network-generation strategy are 'covered' by the other strategy. A worst case would be when the other plot points all sit on a line of slope 1 - indicating that they are just as likely to fail in one network-generation strategy as in the other. In Figs. 1.1a and 1.1b it can be seen that our empirical data clusters on the axes and towards the origin, i.e. it resembles the optimum case. Fig. 1.1a clearly illustrates the concentration of data on the axes, and towards the origin. Fig. 1.1b clearly illustrates the lack of data points on the line of slope 1.

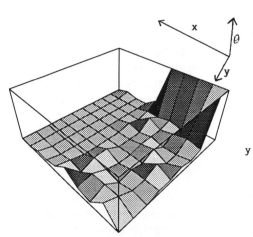

Fig. 1.1a
x: random unique
y: random seed

Fig. 1.1b
x: random unique
y: random seed

Fig. 1.1a is a three-dimensional plot of the probability of failure of each input pattern within the two network-generation strategies - random-unique, and random-seed. The θ for the 'random-unique' strategy is on the x-axis, the θ for 'random-seed' is on the y-axis, and the number of inputs is represented as the height on the z-axis. The largest data points were cut off at 16 to avoid lack of discrimination in the rest of the plot. Fig. 1.1b is a contour plot of the same data as Fig. 1.1a with the θ for 'random-unique' on the x-axis and the θ for 'random-seed' on the y-axis. All θs are in the 0 - 1 range.

Summary 3 The significance of these correlation and covariance values is that they are essentially zero, indicating virtually no correlation between the net generation methodologies. Littlewood and Miller pointed out that it is possible, and desirable, to have negatively correlated methodologies (so that failure of one version on certain inputs will be 'covered' by another). Thus we have demonstrated an independence between sets of versions which has never been obtained within a single methodology.

1.3 CONCLUSIONS

Overall the pattern of results obtained here leads to considerable optimism about the use of a "network methodology" in developing multiversion programs for software reliability. In a task considered to be difficult by the software engineering community, a high degree of generalisation was obtained in both Studies 1 and 2 for all nets (ranging from 89.6% to 96.4%) with extremely short training time (mean = 22 epochs in Study 1, and 35 epochs in Study 2). Moreover, we have shown that networks can evolve statistically independent solutions to functions from different initial condition and training sets.

Because we have yet to discover what the major factors that will lead to diverse net-generation strategies actually are, no significant effort was made to diversify the methodologies employed here (only the initial random weights and the training sets were manipulated). Yet we have found clear statistical evidence of independent failures in generalisation across different nets. In the first investigation, with only a random seed manipulation, the probability of coincident failure was very low, $E(\theta^2) = 0.0322$. This was almost as good as the independence achieved in the second investigation in which both the seed and the data sets were manipulated: $E(\theta^2) = 0.027$. But more importantly, in the final investigation we demonstrated an independence between sets of versions ($\rho(\theta_{ru}, \theta_{rs}) = -0.0014$) which has never been obtained within a single methodology before.

Our preliminary results, which must be treated with extreme caution in view of the exploratory nature of this feasibility study, are most encouraging. However, as they stand they provide evidence for our supposition that the use of the network-programming paradigm will permit system developers to avoid the common-design-fault failures that undermine the validity of conventionally programmed multiversion software systems, and also to go further and devise significant negatively correlated net-generation strategies. Our next major step is to make the process of generalisation itself more transparent [SS92, MS92] to enable more systematic manipulations of different network versions.

ACKNOWLEDGEMENTS

We would like to thank the ESRC (Grant R000 23 3441) for funding this research. Paul Day ran all of the simulations funded by a small research grant from the University of Exeter Research Committee.

REFERENCES

[AT92]   Adams, J.M. and Taha, A., An Experiment in Software Redundancy with Diverse Methodologies, in *Proceedings of the 25th International Conference on Systems Sciences, Hawaii,* 1992.

[CMZ89]   Cottrell, G.W., Munro, P. and Zipser, D., Image Compression by Back-Propagation: An Example of Extensional Programming, in *Models of Cognition: A Review of Cognitive Science,* Sharkey, N.E. (ed.), 208-40, Norwood, N.J., Ablex, 1989.

[Den87]   Denker, J., Schwartz, D., Wittner, B., Solla, S., Howard, R., Jackel, L. and Hopfield, J.,   Large Automatic Learning Rule Extraction and Generalisation, *Complex Systems,* 1, 877-922, 1987.

[GS88]   Gorman, R.P. and Sejnowski, T.J., Analysis of Hidden Units in a Layered Network Trained to Classify Sonar Targets, *Neural Networks,* 1, 75-89, 1988.

[HK87]   Hanson, S.J. and Kegl, J., PARSNIP: A Connectionist Network That Learns Natural Language Grammar from Exposure to Natural Language Sentences, in *Proceedings of the 9th Annual Conference of the Cognitive Science Society, Seattle, Washington,* 106-19, 1987.

[KL86]   Knight, J.C. and Leveson N.G., An Experimental Evaluation of Independence in Multiversion Programming, *IEEE Trans. on Software Eng.,* SE-12(1), 1986.

[KP90]   Kolen, J.F. and Pollack, J.B., Back-Propagation is Sensitive to Initial Conditions, *Technical Research Report 90-JK-BPSIC,* Ohio State University, 1990.

[Lec89]   Le Cun, Y., Boser, B., Demker, J.S., Henderson, D., Howard, R.E., Hubbard, W. and Jackel, L.D., Back-Propagation Applied to Handwritten Zip Code Recognition, *Neural Computation*, 1, 541-51, 1989.

[LM89]   Littlewood, B. and Miller, D.R., Conceptual Modelling of Coincident Failures in Multiversion Software, *IEEE Trans. on Software Eng.*, 15(12), 1989.

[MS92]   Mundy, D. and Sharkey, N.E., Type Generalizations on Distributed Representations, in *Cybernetics and Systems Research*, Trappl, R. (ed.), 1327-34, Kluwer Academic Publishers, Dordrecht, The Netherlands, 1992.

[Par92]   Partridge, D., *Engineering Artificial Intelligence Software*, Intellect Books, Oxford, 1992.

[Pom89]   Pomerleau, D.A., An Autonomous Land Vehicle in a Neural Network, in *Advance in Neural Information Processing Systems II, San Mateo*, Touretzky, D.S. (ed.), 305-13, Morgan Kaufmann, 1989.

[RHW86]   Rumelhart, D.E., Hinton, G.E. and Williams, R.J., Learning Internal Representations by Error Propagation, in *Parallel Distributed Processing, Vol. 1.*, Rumelhart, D.E., McClelland, J.L. (eds.), 318-64, Cambridge, MA, MIT, 1986.

[SR86]   Sejnowski, T.J. and Rosenberg, C.R., NETtalk: A Parallel Network that Learns to Read Outloud, *Technical Report JHU/EECS-86/01*, John Hopkins University, 1986.

[Sha91]   Sharkey, N.E., Connectionist Representation Techniques, *AI Review*, 5(3), 43-67, 1991.

[Sha92]   Sharkey, N.E., The Ghost in the Hybrid: A Study of Uniquely Connectionist Representations, *AISB Quarterly*, 10-16, 1992.

[SS92]   Sharkey, N.E. and Sharkey, A.J.C., Prestructured Neural Nets and the Transfer of Knowledge, in *Proceedings of 2nd Irish Neural Networks Conference, Belfast*, 1992.

[Tes90]   Tesaura, G., Neurogammon Wins Computer Olympiad, *Neural Computation*, 1, 321-23, 1990.

Chapter 2

Modelling Probability Density Functions for Classifying Using a CMAC

David J. Cornforth and David G. Elliman

Department of Computer Science, University of Nottingham, U.K.

Overview

The Cerebellar Model Articulation Controller (CMAC) network was first proposed by Albus in 1975. The model was inspired by the structure and function of the Cerebellum, the part of the brain responsible for muscle control and motor coordination. Albus' model of the Cerebellum is based on a look-up table. Its speed and accuracy make it a good prospect as a classifier. This chapter proposes some improvements to the CMAC model, which enable it to be used as a modeller of Probability Density Function as input to a Bayesian discriminator.

2.1 INTRODUCTION

Learning falls into two categories, unsupervised and supervised. We are concerned here with the latter. A major part of learning is classification. Classification is therefore ubiquitous for pattern recognition and for Artificial Intelligence. There are many competing classifier algorithms, such as statistical, k-Nearest Neighbour, and various networks paradigms. For any application, some assessment needs to be carried out to determine which type of classifier will be most appropriate for the application. Some of the important attributes are

1. Classification accuracy,
2. Training time,
3. Classification time,
4. Memory usage,
5. Fault tolerance.

This chapter looks at one particular model, CMAC, for although it gives promising results, it has received very little attention until recently. The original CMAC model is described with its advantages and shortcomings. Improvements are then proposed which address the shortcomings.

2.2 THE CEREBELLAR MODEL ARTICULATION CONTROLLER

2.2.1 Design of the Model

The original CMAC model [Alb71, Alb75a, Alb75b, Alb81], is based on the structure of part of the brain known as the cerebellum. The cerebellum is responsible for muscle control and co-ordination. The structure of the cerebellum enables a model to be easily constructed based on look-up tables. Analogue inputs to the model are grouped together in bands by functions known as Hashing functions. These bands are equivalent to the "mossy fibres", or input nerve fibres found in the Cerebellum. Many hashing functions are applied to each input. The bands into which the inputs are grouped are staggered for different hashing functions, so that there is overlap of the bands in different hashing functions. The overlapping of quantising bands is also used in the Fuzzy Associative Memory model, or FAM [Kos92], and is responsible for the generalisation properties of both models. In the case of FAM, the overlapping is achieved by functions which reduce in magnitude at the edges, but in the case of CMAC the amount of overlap is much greater, and is effected by the nature of the multiple functions. An example of these overlapping bands is given in Fig. 2.1, where there are five hashing functions.

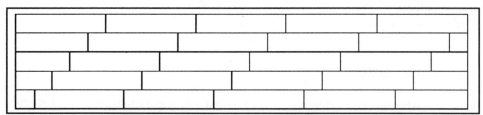

Fig. 2.1. - The quantising regions covered by five hashing functions.

For a two input classifier, this has the effect of dividing the input space into many overlapping squares. For many inputs, these become overlapping hypercubes. Each hypercube is associated with a unique address in a look-up table. Any input will fall into several of these hypercubes, and will therefore form several addresses. The number of addresses formed is equal to the number of hashing functions used.

The addresses produced refer to locations in the output table. The values stored in these locations are modified during training. The error, or difference between classifier output and desired output, is calculated, and a fraction of this is added to each of the values referred to by the addresses. The CMAC model is shown in Fig. 2.2 for an example of four hashing functions.

The model generalises by virtue of the fact that if an input changes slightly, the input may cross the boundary of a square into another. However, as the squares are overlapping, only one boundary will be crossed, only one address will be changed, so the output will change only slightly. The greater the number of hashing functions, the less this change will be, and therefore the greater the region of generalisation.

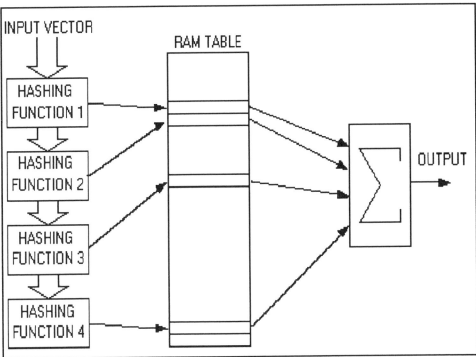

Fig. 2.2. - The CMAC model using four hashing functions.

2.2.2   Advantages Over Other Models

The CMAC model offers many advantages over other classifier models. It is plausible as a simplified biological model. Its training time is very fast, in fact it can be trained in only a few epochs. The epoch time is also fast, as the computation required is very simple. It cannot get stuck in local minima. It can form decision boundaries of arbitrary complexity, and therefore can classify data which is linearly non-separable.

Its classification time is very fast, again because of very simple computation. Its look-up table structure makes it relatively simple to realise in conventional hardware.

2.2.3   Shortcomings of the CMAC Model

The main problems in using CMAC to solve practical problems are

1.   Memory size proportional to power of the input features,
2.   Inflexibility in generalisation regions,
3.   Response not constant over input space,
4.   Different classes represented as points on a scalar range,
5.   Training method has no formal proof of convergence.

The problem of memory size becomes apparent in scaling up the feature set. The number of unique addresses is equal to the number of overlapping hypercubes which are used to divide the input space. This increases in proportion to the power of the number of inputs. For example, if there were only ten overlapping regions along each axis, with fifteen inputs, there would be roughly ten to the power of fifteen addresses for each hashing function. This problem would preclude the use of CMAC in any problem with more than a few inputs.

One method of reducing the memory requirement is the CMAC model implemented by [For90]. This introduces another, intermediate table containing random numbers. These random numbers are added together to form the addresses. With control over the entries in the random table, the size of the output tables can be controlled, and therefore reduced drastically in size. The region over which generalisation is effective tends to be variable but unpredictable, as different parts of the input feature space are mapped onto the same value in the output table.

Another solution to the memory problem is to exploit the fact that very few of the memory locations in the output table are actually used. Therefore, a table can be built which starts with no locations, adding them as needed until training is complete.

2.3   IMPROVING THE MODEL

2.3.1   Controlling the Generalisation

The region over which generalisation is effective tends to remain fairly constant over the whole input space. This is undesirable, since for many problems, training points will be tightly grouped together in some areas, and widely spaced in others.

This can be alleviated by using many hashing functions, so that the region of generalisation can be large, yet the resolution can still be fine. Unfortunately, owing to the fact that the intrinsic response of the CMAC is not constant within one region, this results in very irregular patterns of generalisation. More hashing functions tend to reduce memory requirements, as the quantisation regions are bigger, and cover more of the input feature space. This also has the effect of making the model slower to run. If the number of hashing functions are reduced, some areas of the feature space will be poorly covered if no training vectors occur there. However, the areas poorly covered will be those areas corresponding to the lowest probability of an input vector occurring, so will not significantly affect the performance of the classifier. If the hashing functions are reduced still further, the training set will tend to be over-fitted. In practice there is a broad area in between which gives fast operation, minimum memory usage, and avoids over-fitting the data.

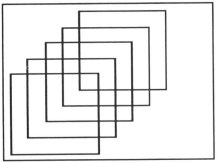

Fig. 2.3a - Albus' original arrangement of hashing function squares.

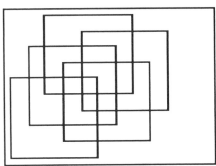

Fig. 2.3b - Parks' arrangement of hashing squares.

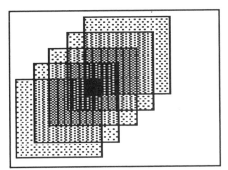

Fig. 2.3c - Contour map of activation for Albus arrangment.

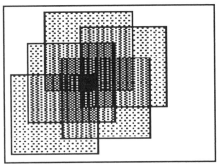

Fig. 2.3d - Contour map of activation for Parks' arrangement.

2.3.2 Making the Response More Uniform

The structure of the hashing functions for CMAC leaves much to be desired, since if all weights of the CMAC model were set to equal values, the output would not be the same over the complete input space. The reason for this is the way in which hashing functions are combined. If the hashing functions are pictured as grids superimposed on top of each other, then the bottom left hand corners of an individual square on each grid would form diagonal lines. The response of the CMAC output alters depending on how far away the input is from these lines, therefore the magnitude of the response forms diagonal stripes. This has prompted the devising of alternative strategies of combining the hashing function squares, such as the one shown in Fig. 2.3 [AMP91]. This scheme, when implemented, results in a nearly circular response around each training point.

2.3.3   Multi-class CMAC

There are two ways to provide multiple class outputs for a CMAC. The first is to designate one point on a scalar range to represent each class. The scalar "nearness" to any point could represent the degree of confidence, or probability of that class. The second is to use a vector, with one axis for each class, and the magnitude along a particular axis being the probability of that class. As a measure of confidence is desirable in pattern recognition, the second method seems more robust. It also simplifies the equations to be solved during training.

2.3.4 Training Algorithm

The training algorithm originally proposed by Albus was to compare the output produced from an input vector with the desired output, then correct each memory location which contributed. This procedure was carried out for each training vector, over a number of cycles, until the average error approached a satisfactory amount. This paper does not seek to present a formal proof of Albus' training scheme, but instead introduces an alternative scheme.

   An iterative algorithm is of value only when the solution is hard to be reached by direct means. Once we have selected the vector class representation as above, the exact value of output is no longer important, only the relative values in each class are. Therefore we do not need to solve a set of simultaneous equations. An output activation proportional to the density of training points at any region in the feature space can be formed by adding contributions from each training point, to the memory cells addresses by that point. This will result in an estimation of the probability density function for each class, and will allow a Bayesian [DH73] test of class membership to be applied. The Bayes' test depends on the model of the Probability Density Function used for its accuracy [HL87]. The model formed by using CMAC in this way will not be restricted to a Normal distribution, but will be able to model arbitrary distributions.

   For the multi-class CMAC, a separate memory table is used to model each class. Each training vector is used to store values in those memory cells which it addresses using the hashing functions, but only in the class to which it is known to belong. The values are designed to form a suitable kernel function, so that the memory table for each class builds up a probability density function in a manner similar to the Parzen window technique [Par62, Jam85]. The training vector only needs to be presented once.

The kernel function is defined by the actual values stored in the memory locations addressed by the hashing functions. All memory locations are set to zero to begin with, and these values are added to the existing contents, so that two points close together will have part of their response added. If the kernel used is a step function, then all memory locations accessed have the same amount added.

With the original Albus scheme of hashing functions, this has the effect of producing square regions of generalisation. There is a tendency to draw diagonal boundaries between classes, in the direction that the hashing functions are arranged.

With Parks' scheme, the regions of generalisation become roughly circular, but diagonal boundaries suffer from a twist distortion, which corresponds to the twist shown in Fig. 2.3d.

The use of a slightly more complicated kernel function corrects this distortion, and produces regions of generalisation which more closely model contours of equal probability. There was little difference observed between linear, cosine and cubic kernels, which agrees with standard texts on the Parzen window estimation method [Fuk87].

2.4 PERFORMANCE EVALUATION

2.4.1 Testing Method

The revised CMAC model was tested against a classifier based on a simple statistical model, the Normal distribution. Training for this model consisted of estimating a mean vector and covariance matrix separately for each class. During testing, vectors were presented and the a posteriori probability for each class calculated from the model, using Bayes' Law. The input vector was assigned to the class with the highest value. The CMAC model implements Bayes' law implicitly, as its estimation of the probability density functions is modified by the number of samples in each class. Tests on the CMAC model were made using different values for the number of hashing functions, and for the number of resolution units each dimension was divided into. These are shown as the /h and /r numbers, respectively. In the first column of each table.

The testing method chosen for the first three data sets below was the leaving-one-out method. For each model, all but one of the vectors available were presented, and it was tested on the one left out. For the Wind data and Fetal data, the volume of data made this impractical, so a cross-correlation method was chosen. The Wind data was divided into 19 groups, and the Fetal data into 20 groups. The classifier was trained on all but one these groups, then tested on the group left out. This was repeated with each group being left out. In this way figures were obtained for the number of samples correctly classified, tabulated in the second column of each table.

The timing tests were obtained by running the first leaving-one-out or cross-validation cycle only. The CMAC model requires an initial operation to index its tables, so this time has been shown in the third column of each table. The remaining two columns show the training and testing time for the models. All the times given are in seconds, and were obtained on a SUN-4 workstation.

2.4.2 Test Data

Fisher's Iris data contains 150 samples of four measurements. The classifier must determine the type of iris from the inputs. The four inputs are sepal length, sepal width, petal length and petal width. The three classes are "Iris Setosa", "Iris Versicolor", and "Iris Virginica". There are 50 samples of each class. Source: [Jam85].

Method	Correct	Setup time	Train 149	Test 1
NORMAL	145 / 150	N A	0.0122	0.00050
CMAC /h15 /r50	143 / 150	0.123	0.106	0.00152
CMAC /h20 /r50	142 / 150	0.165	0.158	0.00305
CMAC /h15 /r100	142 / 150	0.220	0.113	0.00174
CMAC /h20 /r100	140 / 150	0.219	0.144	0.00218

Table 2.1 - Fisher's iris data.

Method	Correct	Setup time	Train 193	Test 1
NORMAL	173 / 194	N A	0.033	0.00061
CMAC /h20 /r50	170 / 194	0.438	0.259	0.00203
CMAC /h25 /r50	165 / 194	0.442	0.373	0.00370
CMAC /h40 /r100	171 / 194	1.168	1.084	0.00373
CMAC /h50 /r100	169 / 194	0.852	0.655	0.00450

Table 2.2 - Biomed data.

The Biomed data contains 194 samples of six measurements. The classifier must determine if the patient is a carrier of a disease or not. The six inputs are blood type, patient age, and four blood measurements. The two classes are "patient is a carrier of disease" and "patient is not a carrier". There are 67 samples of the first class, and 127 samples of the second. Source: Statlib server [SL].

The Spiral data contains 194 pairs of coordinates which represent two interlocking spirals, which make three complete revolutions. The classifier must determine which spiral the input coordinates belong to. There are two inputs, x and y. The two classes are spiral one and spiral two. There are 97 samples for each class. Source: Alexis Wieland of the MITRE Corporation.

Method	Correct	Setup time	Train 193	Test 1
NORMAL	86 / 194	N A	0.005120	0.000391
CMAC /h5 /r100	141 / 194	0.266097	0.045915	0.000627
CMAC /h10 /r100	153 / 194	0.409900	0.090398	0.000985

Table 2.3 - Spiral data.

The Wind data contains 6574 samples of twelve measurements of wind speed from twelve different sites. The classifier must determine which month the measurements relate to. The twelve inputs are the wind speed measurements. The twelve classes are the 12 months in the year. There are 558, 508, 558, 540, 558, 540, 558, 558, 540, 558, 540, 558, samples for January to December, respectively. Source: Statlib server [SL].

Method	Correct	Setup time	Train 6228	Test 346
NORMAL MODEL	812 / 6574	N A	3.78	1.68
CMAC /h10 /r50	929 / 6574	98.8	7.63	2.08
CMAC /h15 /r50	862 / 6574	70.8	11.57	3.00
CMAC /h15 /r100	830 / 6574	178.2	11.75	3.35
CMAC /h20 /r100	816 / 6574	179.0	17.67	5.23

Table 2.4 - Wind data.

The Fetal data is derived from fetal ECG signals obtained during labour. The data contains 7286 samples of seven measurements on ECGs taken from four patients. The classifier must determine which mother the measurements relate to. The seven inputs are P-wave duration, Q-peak to S-peak, P-peak amplitude, Q-peak amplitude, R-peak amplitude, S-peak amplitude and T-peak amplitude. There are 3135, 1645,

2300 and 206 samples respectively. Source: Prof. E.M. Symonds, Queens Medical Centre, Nottingham.

Method	Correct	Setup time	Train 6727	Test 559
NORMAL	6133 / 7286	N A	1.67	0.482
CMAC /h5 /r50	7238 / 7286	21.7	3.13	1.210
CMAC /h10 /r50	7236 / 7286	9.7	5.56	0.950
CMAC /h10 /r100	7242 / 7286	43.5	5.96	1.114
CMAC /h15 /r100	7240 / 7286	24.2	8.37	1.461

Table 2.5 - Fetal data.

2.4.3 Discussion

The CMAC model is about the fastest classifier based on a biological system which can be envisaged. Even so, it appears slow compared with the simple Normal model. It should be noted that as the complexity of the problem increases, this time advantage diminishes. The CMAC, like any other biological model, could be implemented in parallel architecture. The most obvious division of processing would be division by the number of hashing functions. If hardware were available to do this, a clear time advantage would be realised.

As for classifier accuracy, CMAC is worse than the Normal model on trivial problems, such as the first two, as it has inherent quantisation errors. However, on the other problems, CMAC out-performs the simple Normal model. This is due to the fact that CMAC makes no prior assumptions about the distributions of data. It can model arbitrary distributions of data, including multi-modal data. Of course, more complex statistical models can be formed which would allow better modelling of these problems, but these would then incur a speed penalty.

2.5 CONCLUSION

A method is described which utilises the ability of the CMAC to model multivariate functions. Using a windowing technique, the CMAC forms estimates of the Probability Density Function, making no initial assumptions about the underlying distribution or number of modes of the data. This estimation is formed simply by adding pre-defined values into memory cells. The accuracy of the method has been shown to approach that of a normal model, on simple problems, and to surpass it on more complicated problems.   Speed advantages are expected with a parallel implementation.

REFERENCES

[Alb71]   Albus, J.S., A Theory of Cerebellar Function, *Mathematical Biosciences,* 10, 25-61, 1971.

[Alb75a]   Albus, J.S., A New Approach to Manipulator Control: the Cerebellar Model Articulation Controller (CMAC), *Trans. ASME, Series G, J. Dynamic Systems, Measurement and Control*, 97, 220-33, 1975.

[Alb75b]   Albus, J.S., Data Storage in the Cerebellar Model Articulation Controller, *Trans. ASME Series G, J. Dynamic Systems, Measurement and Control,* 97, 228-33, 1975.

[Alb81]   Albus, J.S., *Brains Behaviour and Robotics*, BYTE Books, McGraw-Hill, 1981.

[AMP91]   Edgar An, P.C., Thomas Millar W. and Parks, P.C.P., Design Improvements in Associative Memories for Cerebellar Model Articulation Controllers, in *Artificial Neural Networks,* Vols. 1 and 2, Chapter 345, 1207-10, 1991.

[DH73]   Duda, R.O. and Hart, P.E., *Pattern Classification and Scene Analysis*, John Wiley and Sons, New York, 1973.

[For90]   Forsyth, R., Neural Learning Algorithms: Some Empirical Trials, in *Proceedings of 3rd Conference on Neural Networks and Their Applications, Neuro-Nimes '90, France*, 301-17, 1990.

[Fuk87]   Keinosuke Fukunaga, Bayes Error Estimation Using Parzen and k-NN Procedures, *IEEE Trans on Pattern Analysis and Machine Intelligence,* PAMI-9 (5), 634-43, 1987.

[HL87]   Huang, W.H. and Lippmann, R.P., Comparisons Between Neural Net and Conventional Classifiers, *IEEE First International Conference on Neural Networks, San Diego*, 4, 485-93, 1987.

[Jam85]   James, M., *Classification Algorithms*, Collins, 1985.

[Kos92]   Kosko, B., *Neural Networks and Fuzzy Systems*, Prentice-Hall, 1992.

[Par62]   Parzen, E., An Estimation of Probability Density Function and Mode, *Ann. Math. Statistics*, 33, 1065, 1962.

[SL]   Statlib server is a public domain database available by sending email to Statlib@lib.stat.cmu.edu.

Chapter 3

A Neural Network Simulation of Visual Processes Involved In Scene Analysis

T. Tambouratzis

Department of Mathematics, Agricultural University of Athens, Greece

Overview

Harmony Theory [Smo86] is a particularly suitable tool for implementing in parallel artificial techniques incorporated in the constraint propagation paradigm (for an early example see the electricity problem [Smo86]). The advantages of such an approach have been clearly illustrated in a recent class of Harmony Theory networks [Ta91a, Ta91b, Ta92a, Ta92b] realising the A.I. scene analysis [Huf71, Clo71] task. These were found [Ta91a] to be more efficient than the corresponding serial algorithm [Win84] and to possess a number of interesting implementational characteristics.

In this chapter it is shown that an appropriately structured Harmony Theory network can - besides accommodating most effectively scene analysis - provide a versatile model of human performance on this task, which is capable of directly complying with psychophysical hypothesising and testing.

3.1 THEORETICAL BACKGROUND

3.1.1 Traditional A.I. Scene Analysis

The traditional scene analysis task [Huf71, Clo71] offers a means of ascertaining the main shape characteristics of objects belonging to the "blocks world" (solid objects consisting exclusively of opaque and planar faces which abut creating trihedral and crack-free corners), as these are depicted in their perfect and shadow-free line-drawing representations. According to these conditions

- Four junction-types (L-, Arrow-, Fork- and T-) are permissible for representing the viewed projection of the objects' corners,
- Four labels are acceptable for characterising the scenes' edges: "+", "-", "BO" and "BI" to express convexity, concavity and directed occlusion (segmentation) respectively (illustrated in Fig. 3.1), and
- Eighteen junction-configurations are physically acceptable (shown in Fig. 3.2). These constitute the Huffman-Clowes [Huf71, Clo71] labelling scheme and list the valid configurations of labelled lines which can come together to portray realisable 3-D corners.

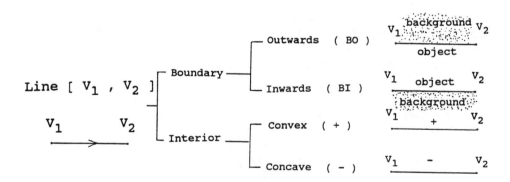

Fig. 3.1 - The four physically possible interpretations (labels) of an oriented line in the line-drawing.

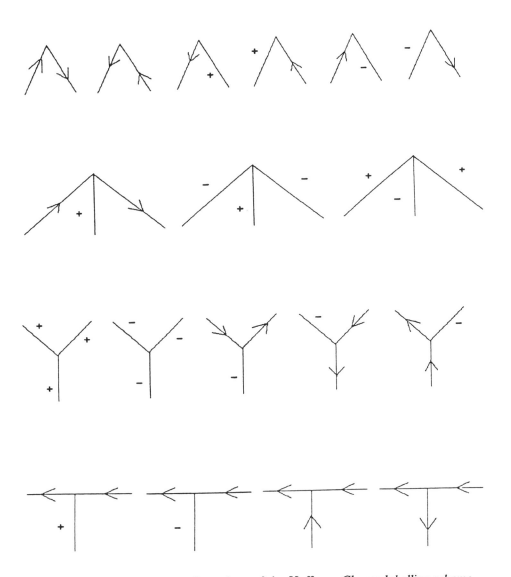

Fig. 3.2 - The 18 junction-configurations of the Huffman-Clowes labelling scheme.

The analysis consists of labelling the lines of the line-drawing which correspond to the edges of the depicted objects in order to expose the nature and relative orientation of the 3-D faces which meet, or appear to do so, at these edges. Labelling proceeds serially (Waltz algorithm [Win84]) by applying constraint propagation on the possible labels of the lines, utilising as constraints the junction-configurations of the Huffman-Clowes [Huf71, Clo71] labelling scheme. Constraint propagation results in successful interpretation if

(a)   a unique label is attributed to each line of the line-drawing, and
(b)   one of the 18 junction-configurations of the Huffman-Clowes labelling scheme is assigned to each vertex so that the junction-types of vertex and junction-configuration coincide.

In traditional scene analysis the criterion for correct interpretation is whether the algorithm succeeds or not. Failure attests a non-labellable scene, i.e. one containing non-physically realisable object(s) or object(s) not complying to the "blocks world" conditions. The location of the violation(s) of (either of) those criteria is immaterial, since it depends greatly on the starting point of the serial algorithm.

3.1.2 Psychological Evidence

It has been supported [Cow88] that a locally applied analogue of the labelling scheme is utilised during the earliest stages of visual processing for recovering the main shape properties of a scene (essential segmentation and convex/concave relationships of abutting surfaces, executed prior to identification). Hence, the line labelling scheme seems to be an appealing starting point for a scene analysis system, provided that an effort is made for the natural processes leading to perception to be simulated.

Any model of visual perception must, however, not only use the same primitives but also the same procedure as the system simulated. An initial requirement is that the implementation must be made to fail in the same manner and at the same location(s) as the naturally intelligent system. In order to achieve this, the starting-point-dependent constraint-propagation procedure of the serial algorithm is not adequate. Instead, for the proposed network implementation, an attempt to determine and incorporate the manner in which lines and vertices are represented in natural scene analysis is made

- Vertex validity needs to be explicitly stated as it discloses the valid junction-configurations used by the labelling scheme. Such a representation adds modelling potential to the simulation since vertices of different junction-types can be assigned diverse importances, as indicated by psychophysical experiments: it has been shown [Wal87] that the vertices of a line-drawing are subjected to graded processing corresponding to their varying perceptual significance. Perceptual significance depends on the number of lines which come together to form the vertex and on the way these lines are joined (junction-type). Experimentation proves that L-junctions are perceptually the most important, followed by Arrow- and Fork-junctions, and ultimately T-junctions. Additionally, it is possible that different junction-configurations within each junction-type may be assigned different importances, depending on their frequency of interpreting a corner's structure.

- Line validity also needs to be explicitly expressed, preferably as compatible labelling from the two ends (connected vertices) of the line. In some impossible line-drawings, it is more appealing psychologically to express impossibility with violations of line validity than with mere violations of vertex validity: the former agrees with human decisions whereas the competing interpretations of the line-drawing alternate, i.e. coexist over time. Such a labelling is depicted in Fig. 3.3, where changes in the interpretation of a line along its length reveal distinct types of labelling incompatibilities and display the two rival interpretations of upper and lower parts of the line-drawing. For the impossible object of Fig. 3.3, the main "problematic" region has been filled in, revealing three bars of which

(a)   the leftmost is spatially acceptable and labelling is also correct.
(b)   the middle one indicates a gradual depth (but not orientation) discrepancy, when compared to the depth of the first bar. Interpretation with explicit use of line validity reveals a line labelling incompatibility.
(c)   the rightmost indicates an orientation change, whereas the bar's surface from "horizontal" becomes "vertical". This is again illustrated by violations in the labelling of the corresponding lines.

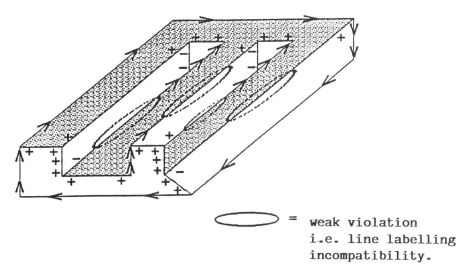

⬯ = weak violation i.e. line labelling incompatibility.

Fig. 3.3 - The "Devil's Fork" [Clo71] impossible line-drawing, with its mostly consistent with human performance labelling.

Explicitly considering line validity has another important advantage besides being able to match the location of violation: psychophysical experiments [Wal87] have proved that line length is a significant factor for perception with perceived contrast increasing with line length for lengths from 60' to 90'. Accordingly, the perceptual significance of a line, its importance for compatible labelling and the degree at which each line is labelled independently from its two ends - all as a function of line length - can be directly incorporated in the scene analysis simulation.

3.2 HARMONY THEORY

3.2.1 Harmony Theory Design

Harmony Theory [Smo86] is a neural network model based on simulated annealing and, as developed by Smolensky [Smo86], it is a mathematical tool for studying dynamic systems which perform perceptual or cognitive tasks evolving in parallel and in time.

The theory is motivated by fidelity in information processing rather than neural modelling, characterised [Smo86, Smo88] as the *subsymbolic paradigm*. This is contrasted with the *symbolic paradigm*, i.e. the theory of symbolic computation in cognitive science, which has been mainly used in Artificial Intelligence. According to Smolensky [Smo88], the most powerful level of description of cognitive systems is lower than the symbolic level and the process of cognition depends upon dynamic properties such as spread of activation and statistical correlation rather than effective procedures and symbol manipulation.

The Harmony Theory network is tailored to implement in parallel the constraint propagation paradigm. The subsymbolic tailoring of this paradigm is implemented in such a way that the network's semantics are particularly transparent, making the network's state at any moment easy to comprehend. To this end

(a)   The probabilistic activation function can only take discrete values, thus conforming with the multistability property of perception [Att71]. It is worth mentioning that the probabilistic nature of Harmony Theory makes the network implementation especially suitable for pattern "completion" tasks, where the system starts with an incomplete, fragmented input and proceeds by filling in the missing information, i.e. the unspecified features of the sensory input, with their mostly likely values.

(b)   The network structure consists of two semantically disparate layers of nodes, each defining a different kind of domain-knowledge. The lower layer contains representational features which stand for the directly detectable primitives of the domain, i.e. elementary hypotheses about the immediately perceived environment. The upper layer comprises knowledge atoms which translate the laws of the problem-domain by encoding relationships among the representational features in order to enforce constraint propagation.

(c)   The flexible, detailed and modular upper layer description dictates that separate sources of domain information and constraint be represented as different levels of environmental knowledge of the upper layer. These levels can only communicate via common representational features and hence constitute sublayers of the network.

(d)   The connectivity is symmetric, logically assigned as well as of a highly structured nature. The restriction of connections between but not within the two layers of nodes produces "vertical" [Smo86] flow of activation (upwards and then downwards during each iteration of the "simulated annealing"-based settling procedure).

(e)   The crystallisation of the network into the state of greatest consistency and coherency is particularly gradual and lucid. In Harmony Theory, each state of the network (collection of activation values for all network nodes) is assigned a quantitative harmony value which denotes the internal consistency ("goodness-of-fit" to the input) of the state. During settling, the "best" state (maximally "harmonious" configuration of network nodes) is reached.

3.2.2 Merit of the Approach

It has been shown [Ta91a, Ta92a] that the A.I. application of constraint propagation in scene analysis can be perfectly tailored by a Harmony Theory network. This is due to two facts: the suitability of Harmony Theory and the corresponding network to the properties of the problem and the superiority of this parallel approach over the traditional sequential implementation.

3.2.2.1 Problem-Dependent Characteristics

(i)   Harmony Theory's top-down mode of representation matched the processing followed in the scene analysis task.

(ii)   Its subsymbolic level of description, located between the neural and cognitive levels, fitted the intermediate-level visual perceptual task of extracting the main 3-D shape properties and solid structure of the depicted objects, prior to identification. The constraints of the Huffman-Clowes labelling scheme (microdecisions of the subsymbolic paradigm) acted as the foundation of simulated annealing which, in turn, created the interpretation (macrodecision).

(iii) The crystallisation of the network translated the interpretation procedure into a "completion" task [Smo86, Ta91a]; the input, which was coded in the network structure, was completed with its interpretation, i.e. with activation values of all network nodes.

(iv)   The positive constraints, as represented by the 18 valid junction-configurations of the labelling scheme, were directly accepted by the simulation, as this kind of network entails no training. This was not problematic from a psychological point of view as for such early visual tasks it is assumed that learning can only be accomplished by positive examples; in fact, these are the only ones encountered in the real world. Furthermore, the lack of training avoids lengthy training schedules for the network, as well as the associated problems of training-set volume, epoch size, order and frequency of presentation and representability of the training patterns.

3.2.2.2 Parallel-Serial Implementational Differences

(v) The interpretation of the scene was reached *effortlessly* and *elegantly* in the network implementation. The simulation automatically strived for the state of greatest harmony, which was

- a violation-free state for labellable scenes,
- the state of least violations for non-labellable scenes. In this case, *no backtracking* and eventual halting (as in the serial Waltz algorithm) were performed.

(vi) The direct differentiation of the semantics and the "vertical flow" of activation

- obliterated the initial depth-first search [Mac73] performed prior to the execution of the serial Waltz algorithm [Win84] in order to reduce the search-space, and
- produced an implementation directly amenable to *Parallel Hardware realisation* [Ta92a].

(vii) For *decomposable* scenes [Ta91a], while each part was labelled in turn by the serial algorithm, the network was partitioned in sub-networks which *simultaneously* and *independently* interpreted the segmented sub-scenes (additivity under decompositions property [Smo86]).

3.3 NETWORK IMPLEMENTATION

The presented Harmony Theory network implementation followed the generally accepted conventions which apply to traditional A.I. scene analysis as well as the requirements made in Section 3.1.2.

3.3.1 The Lower Layer

The representational features encoded the directly perceived elements of the line-drawings, i.e. the lines. Here, the representation of each line was made as follows: in order to allow for the modelling of psychological findings (graded interpretation of a line from its two ends), pairs of "opposite" oriented lines were used to express each original line of the scene. This resulted in eight (4 labels x 2 "opposite" oriented lines) representational features for fully expressing each labelled line (see lower part of Fig. 3.4).

3.3.2 The Upper Layer

The knowledge atoms explicitly stated the imposed constraints among the representational features, i.e. translated the laws and regularities of the problem domain.

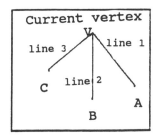

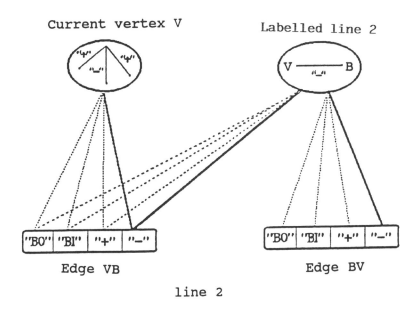

*Fig. 3.4 - Part of the Harmony Theory network for representing vertex V and **line2** of the inset illustration.*

In the present simulation two separate sources of domain information were utilised, coded as different levels of environmental knowledge to be stored in the upper layer. These were

- The *vertex environmental level*, which involved valid labelling of a vertex in the line-drawing by expressing the knowledge embodied in the Huffman-Clowes labelling scheme (top-left part of Fig. 3.4). For each vertex in the line-drawing, as many knowledge atoms were created as there are junction-configurations of the same junction-type (6, 3, 5, 4 for L-, Arrow-, Fork- and T-junctions respectively).

- The *line environmental level*, which encoded the information concerning validly labelled lines, as this was gathered for compatible labels from the component "opposite" edges of each line (see top-right part of Fig. 3.4). Four (one for each possible line label) knowledge atoms were needed for every validly interpreted line in the line-drawing.

In Fig. 3.4, one knowledge atom of each environmental level was depicted. For the vertex level to fully encode vertex **V**, two more knowledge atoms should be created (representing the remaining two junction-configurations of Arrow-junctions). For all three knowledge atoms, appropriate connections should also be made to the 8-tuples of representational features expressing **line1** and **line3**. As a result, these three knowledge atoms would be connected to the same representational features as the one illustrated; it would be the excitatory/inhibitory nature of connectivity which would differentiate the semantics of these knowledge atoms, encoding the distinct valid labelling of the connected lines (for more details see the following section).

Regarding the line environmental level and in order to fully incorporate knowledge about acceptable labels for **line2**, three more knowledge atoms should be stored: two representing directed occlusions for **line2** ("BO" label for oriented line **VB**, "BI" for edge **BV**; "BI" for oriented line **VB**, "BO" for edge **BV**) and the third representing the possibility of **line2** being a convex line ("+" labels for both constituent oriented lines). Again, all four knowledge atoms should be connected to the same representational features but with dissimilar connections to them.

3.3.3 Connectivity and General Parameters

In Harmony Theory, connections are enforced only between semantically related nodes of different layers ("vertical" flow of activation). These can take positive (excitatory connection) or negative values (inhibitory connection), whose magnitude (weight) is mathematically determined [Smo86] prior to the network's settling procedure. For the present task, connectivity was realised as illustrated in Fig. 3.4, with positive connections drawn as bold lines and negative ones as broken lines.

Due to the fact that connections cannot be adjusted via training in a Harmony Theory network, the "strength" parameter is assigned to each knowledge atom. This takes positive integer values which allow the frequency of occurrence of the constraint in the domain and hence represent the probabilistic importance of the information contained in each node to be expressed. In other words, the ability of the Harmony Theory network to convey the relative importance of the knowledge atoms is provided by their configuration of strengths. By setting them appropriately the simulation's efficiency and accuracy of performance can be investigated via coordination of the knowledge of different environmental levels as well as that of various knowledge atoms, be they of the same or diverse environmental levels; consequently the network's flexibility can be demonstrated.

Concerning the vertex environmental level, varying strengths could be attached to

- knowledge atoms representing vertices of different junction-types, signifying their distinct psychological significance, and
- knowledge atoms representing the same vertex, indicating the frequency of occurrence of each candidate junction-configuration.

Regarding the line environmental level, distinct strengths could be assigned to

- knowledge atoms of different lines (strength values proportional to their lengths) in order to encode the psychological hypotheses of line validity as a function of length, and
- knowledge atoms expressing the degree to which lines are considered independently from their two ends.

It is believed that such adjustments would provide the simulation with further potential as a model of human performance.

Under the present network construction, the simulation's strength values could vary in complexity from the simplest case where only the relative strengths of the two environmental levels were modified (uniform strength values for knowledge atoms within the same environmental levels were assigned), to the most complex one where strengths were adjusted according to all the psychological hypotheses mentioned above. For the latter, interpretation should proceed (gradual settling of the simulation as implicit priority setting according to perceptual significance of the natural system) and be performed (end-state reaching as decision making) as in the natural (visual) perception.

In this piece of research the simplest case is discussed in detail, the target being to render the model maximally efficient. Thus, finding the appropriate strengths of the knowledge atoms was reduced to extracting suitable relative strengths for the nodes of the two environmental levels of the upper layer. To this end, the parameter **r** was introduced, which specified the relative strength value of the two environmental levels:

$$r = \frac{\textbf{strength of vertex level knowledge atoms}}{\textbf{strength of line level knowledge atoms}}$$

For setting the optimal strength configuration the dichotomisation method was used. Starting from two extreme **r** values for which performance was not coordinated (the maximum indicating that the vertex environmental level was much too emphasised compared to the line environmental level, the minimum the opposite), the simulation was progressively tested on new **r** values, each equalling the average of the last two used values which were found closest to optimum performance. The method was terminated when performance could not be improved upon.

The settling procedure consisted of 2,900 iterations of (vertical) activation with the temperature of the network being lowered from a high of 5 to a low of 0.001 (for more details see the identical settling procedure in [Ta91a]). During each trial the simulation was run 10 times for each **k** value ranging from 0.4 to 0.7 with a step of 0.1. A number of trials investigating the network's general performance was also executed with **k** values outside this range.

The value of **Q** [Ta91a] ranged in the interval [0.875, 1.25] for the tested line-drawings of Fig. 3.5. These were of various properties [Ta92b], in order to ensure accurate performance evaluation.

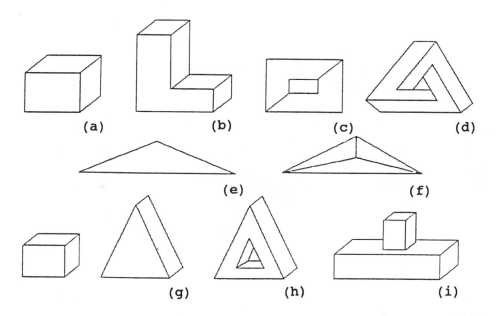

Fig. 3.5 - The microworld of line-drawings used for testing the network.

3.4 RESULTS

(i) The dichotomisation method employed the initial extreme **r** values of $1(=1/1)$ and $2.333(=7/3)$ for which performance was uncoordinated. In both cases one environmental level (the vertex level for the former value, the line level for the latter) became too powerful relative to the other, resulting in numerous and unnecessary violations of knowledge of the "weakened" environmental level. The state of greatest harmony was not always reached due to the unbalanced influence of the two sources of information.

Next, the **r** values of $1.666(=(1+2.333)/2)$ and $1.333(=(1+1.666)/2)$ were tested, with the last one being found to optimally balance the two environmental levels.

(ii)   Subsequent testings with strength configurations close to the optimal **r** (within the "optimal" range [1.25, 1.45]) showed that the simulation continuously strived for the maximally harmonious state(s). The non-maximally harmonious states, which were occasionally visited due to the probabilistic nature of the Harmony Theory network, differed in the way violations were expressed: depending on whether **r** was above or below the optimal value, the proportion of violations of the line and vertex environmental levels involved in the non-maximally harmonious state varied demonstrating a continuum of performance in the number of violations of either kind. Information from distinct sources (environmental levels) was not accurately integrated and more importance was attached to one or the other environmental level at the expense of an unnecessary number of violations of the other kind.

The general observations concerning the suitability of the original Harmony Theory network for executing the scene analysis task (see Section 3.2.2) were made for the model with the maximally efficient **r** value as well as for the ones whose **r** parameter belonged to the optimal interval. These performance characteristics were

(iii) The notion of maximum harmony was pursued during the testings, and the end-state of greatest consistency with the explicitly stored precompiled knowledge was attained, subject only to probabilistic errors which were due to Harmony Theory's probabilistic activation function [Smo86].

(iv)   The *"inverse" thresholding* role [Ta91a] of the parameter **k** was prominent. Below the [0.4, 0.7] range of **k** there was a high probability for entire lines (pairs of "opposite" oriented lines) - and a lower one for solitary oriented lines - to remain unlabelled, while above it confined neighbourhoods of entire lines were subject to multiple labelling.

The distribution of local harmony maxima was roughly equal from the lowest **k** values and hence the *oscillation factor* [Ta91a] property of **k** was not demonstrated here.

(v)   During settling, the gradual crystallisation of the nodes' activation states was monitored by the nodes' respective connectivities and amounts of ambiguity. Locations of greatest constraint and/or least ambiguity were the first to settle (from the lowest **k** values) at their interpretation and "guided", to a certain extent, subsequent labelling of locations of reduced constraint and/or increased ambiguity. For parts of the scene between which little or no constraint flowed - caused either by the junction-type's lack of constraint (e.g. T-junctions) or by the scene's topological characteristics (e.g. a large number of adjacent L-junctions or indeed objects with no common lines in their line-drawing representation), the corresponding sub-networks settled (almost) independently demonstrating thus the additivity under decompositions property.

The T-junction problem, which involves problematic labelling of the vertice's baseline due to its ambiguity in labelling, was alleviated under the present network construction and strength assignment (within the optimal range). The inverse thresholding characteristic of **k** assisted compatible labelling of these lines and as the parameter increased the flow of activation through T-junctions was facilitated. However, the flow of activation from such neighbourhoods was still restricted, producing occasional symmetry-breaking failures at the object-level [Ta91a] whereas the loosely connected parts received mutually incompatible interpretations.

(vi)   Because of the network's augmented (compare to the other Harmony Theory network constructions of [Ta91b]) and modular upper layer *balance of informational power* (**Q** ≈ 1) was accomplished. By having a roughly equal number of nodes in the two layers of the network, flow of activation and constraints could be more easily and efficiently propagated. This was responsible for the network's resistance to probabilistic errors, the limited multiple labelling at high **k** values, the facilitation of labelling T-junctions' baselines as well as the inverse thresholding property and attenuated oscillation factor.

(vii)   The rise in the number of knowledge atoms also provided the construction with *redundancy*. Redundancy increases the ability of a simple distributed memory to cope with degraded input patterns [Wil81]: a big number of nodes and connections denotes that single node activations become less important in themselves, while they collectively communicate the same information. Consequently, a violation of stored information is negligible when distributed over the total network and hence can be rectified by the corrective influences of the other node activations. The increased interpretational power and accuracy of the simulation supported Harmony Theory's implicit *principle of "performance through transparency and redundancy"*, whereas the larger the set of knowledge atoms, the greater the potential power of the cognitive system [Smo86] (also see [Ta91b] for an empirical confirmation).

(viii)   The graceful degradation property of the Harmony Theory network for network size and the characteristics referring to symmetry-breaking failures were identical to those encountered at [Ta91a].

(ix)   The modular structure of the domain inherent knowledge (dual representation of the problem domain into discrete environmental levels) made the simulation very *flexible*, since by simply adjusting the relative strengths of the two environmental levels, the effects of the constraints concerning line and vertex validity could be considerably modified. It is anticipated that more fine-grained adjustments of the strength values within as well as between layers will create even more interesting effects in performance and will render the simulation suitable for modelling psychophysical findings concerning human performance on the task.

3.5 CONCLUSIONS

The *transparency* and *modularity* of the representation of the task (due to the existence of distinct but interacting environmental levels) led to *flexibility* of the simulation. The network's performance could be monitored and greatly modified in order to achieve maximum interpretational accuracy, simply by varying the strengths of the (knowledge atoms of the) two environmental levels, i.e. by altering the degree of interaction and importance of the two sources of information.

Alternatively, by taking into account existing psychological hypotheses concerning scene analysis, the network could be additionally adjusted so as to simulate human performance. For instance, the degree at which the nature of each line is judged independently from its two ends as well as the perceptual significance of a line (and hence its importance in compatible labelling) as a function of its length [Wal87] could be integrated in the network, simply by appropriately modifying the strengths of the knowledge atoms belonging to the line environmental level and coordinating them with those of the vertex environmental level. The same is true for knowledge atoms encoding information about vertex validity (for vertices of different junction-types as well as for junction-configurations of the same junction-type but of different perceptual significance). Furthermore, the manner of decision making (temporal spread of the interpretation via microdecisions of the subsymbolic level) could be simulated by the correct configuration of strength values, i.e. importance and priority assignment of the microdecisions leading to the interpretation (macrodecision).

The network construction (representation of the problem domain) also furnished the parallel implementation with *redundancy* of the encoded information ; resulting from the increase in the number of knowledge atoms [Ta91b] this produced an improvement in the network's performance (greater accuracy and robustness, less probabilistic errors, etc.).

The presented Harmony Theory network implementation of the scene analysis task was thus shown to constitute a superior tool for scene analysis, which was also found flexible enough to have the potential to incorporate, simulate and test various hypotheses concerning the interpretation process, as this is believed to be executed by naturally intelligent systems, due to its transparent, redundant and modular design.

REFERENCES

[Att71]   Attneave, F., Multistability in Perception, *Scientific American*, 225, 63-71, 1971.

[Clo71]   Clowes, M.B., On Seeing Things, *Artificial Intelligence*, 2, 79-116, 1971.

[Cow88] Cowie, R., Impossible Objects and the Things We Do First In Vision, *British Journal of Psychology*, 79, 321-38, 1988.

[Huf71] Huffman, D.A., Impossible Objects as Nonsense Sentences, *Machine Intelligence*, 6, 295-323, 1971.

[Mac73] Mackworth, A.K., Interpreting Pictures of Polyhedral Scenes, *Artificial Intelligence*, 4, 121-37, 1973.

[Smo86] Smolensky, P., Information Processing in Dynamical Systems: Foundations of Harmony Theory, in *Parallel Distributed Processing: Foundations, Vol. 1*, Rumelhart, D.E., McClelland, J.L., (eds.), 194-281, MIT Press, Cambridge MA, 1986.

[Smo88] Smolensky, P., On The Proper Treatment of Connectionism, *The Behavioral and Brain Sciences*, 11, 1-74, 1988.

[Ta91a] Tambouratzis, T., An Implementation of a Harmony Theory Network for Interpreting Line-Drawings, *Network: Computation in Neural Systems*, 2, 443-54, 1991.

[Ta91b] Tambouratzis, T., Harmony Theory Networks for Scene Analysis, in *Artificial Neural Networks*, Kohonen, T., Makisara, K., Simula, O., Kangas, J. (eds.) 1743-46, North-Holland, Amsterdam, 1991.

[Ta92a] Tambouratzis, T., A Parallel Translation of the Waltz Algorithm for Analysing Line-Drawings, in *Artificial Neural Networks-II*, Aleksander, I., Taylor, J., (eds.), 533-56, North-Holland, Amsterdam, 1992.

[Ta92b] Tambouratzis, T., The Economy/Performance Issue in Harmony Theory Networks, in *Artificial Neural Networks-II*, Aleksander,I., Taylor, J., (eds.), 537-40, North-Holland, Amsterdam, 1992.

[Wal87] Walters, D., Selection of Image Primitives for General Purpose Visual Processing, *Computer Vision, Graphics and Image Processing*, 37, 261-98, 1987.

[Wil81] Willshaw, D.J., Holography, Associative Memory and Inductive Generalisation, in *Parallel Models of Associative Memory*, Hinton, G.E., Anderson, J.A., (eds.), 83-104, Erlbaum, N.J., Hillsdale, 1981.

[Win84] Winston, P.H., *Artificial Intelligence*, Addison-Wesley, Massachusetts, 1984 (2nd edition).

Chapter 4

Tumour Classification Using ^{1}H Nuclear Magnetic Resonance Spectroscopy, Principal Component Analysis and a Neural Network

Ross J. Maxwell, Sian L. Howells, Andrew C. Peet and John R. Griffiths

St. George's Hospital Medical School, University of London, U.K.

Overview

The practical application of an artificial neural network to the classification of tumours and normal tissues is discussed. The classification scheme presented here is based on the analysis of ^{1}H nuclear magnetic resonance (NMR) spectroscopy data from excised rat tissues, prepared by chemical extraction. It is anticipated that the nature of a tumour or tissue would be reflected in the pattern of its chemical components: NMR spectroscopy provides simultaneous measurement of many of these chemicals.

We have employed two intermediate stages in the analysis of the NMR data; (1) a relatively crude digitisation of the region of the spectrum containing information about most of the low molecular weight tissue components, and (2) principal component analysis. In this way, the original data (16K data points per spectrum) are represented by 10 to 15 principal component scores with the additional advantage that some sources of noise are removed. The principal component scores were used as the inputs to a semilinear feedforward network with back-propagation of error.

The data processing scheme was found to be extremely effective for learning the training sets used in this study. Classification of new samples (not included in the learning) was also very successful. The network architecture typically involved 3 hidden layers of 20 to 30 nodes each and 8 or 9 outputs. This architecture was found to be better (i.e. giving fewer errors when classifying new samples) than when 1 or 2 hidden layers were used. In all cases we were able to distinguish correctly between tumours and normal tissues. As expected, the main problems occurred with the classification of samples which were not adequately represented in the training set.

We anticipate that these methods could help in the diagnosis and prognosis of human disease based on NMR (or other) analysis of tissue biopsies and/or urine and blood samples. Since NMR methods are available for making non-invasive biochemical measurements on patients, it is possible that this information could be processed in a similar way, although the diagnostic potential may be restricted by the limited detail in NMR spectra obtained *in vivo*.

4.1   INTRODUCTION

It is now possible to obtain ^{1}H Nuclear Magnetic Resonance (NMR) spectra non-invasively from patients. This technology has become clinically available largely as a spin-off from the application of NMR imaging in medical diagnosis. However, it is not yet clear how the biochemical information present in the spectra can provide some clinical benefit such as diagnosis, selection of a certain treatment or prediction of treatment response.

We have obtained ^{1}H NMR spectra of animal tissue and tumour extracts so as to understand the biochemical basis and potential value of clinical observations. The NMR spectra are comprised of signals from many low molecular weight biochemical components (metabolites) present in the tissues and tumours. Most metabolites contribute several signals and it is anticipated that disease states will perturb combinations of metabolites in a complex way. The conventional approach to analysing data of this type has been to assign the signals from a certain subset of metabolites (chosen to be "important") and to determine which of them is altered in disease or in response to some treatment. We have attempted to develop automated methods for analysing the NMR data which use the full information content of the spectra without the need for *a priori* decisions about which metabolites may be important.

We have previously applied the pattern recognition techniques of principal component (PC) analysis and cluster analysis to the processing of these ^{1}H NMR spectra [HMG92]. PC analysis resulted in a reduction in the dimensionality of a dataset of 70 samples each with 180 variables (NMR peak heights) in that it could be adequately described (i.e. accounting for 95% of the variance) with just 15 principal components. Cluster analysis of the training set (using 15 PC scores for each sample) gave good separation of each tissue and tumour type and suggested that this reduced dataset could form the basis for a classification of test samples. However, the attempted classification of these test samples based on the clustering hierarchy (i.e. nearest neighbour location in the dendrogram) was found to be only partly successful [HMG91, HMPG92]. This is probably because an atypical sample can cause bad branching decisions in traversing the dendrogram. Such problems may generally be attributed to the fact that cluster analysis is a form of unsupervised learning. For classification purposes a supervised learning method, such as neural network computing, may be more appropriate. Artificial neural networks have been used for the analysis of spectroscopic data [WLT90] and for the interpretation of laboratory data (including some NMR data) in cancer diagnosis [AW92]. We now report the application of a neural network computing approach to the classification of samples based on their ^{1}H NMR spectra.

4.2 METHODS

The overall scheme for data processing is summarised in Fig. 4.1.

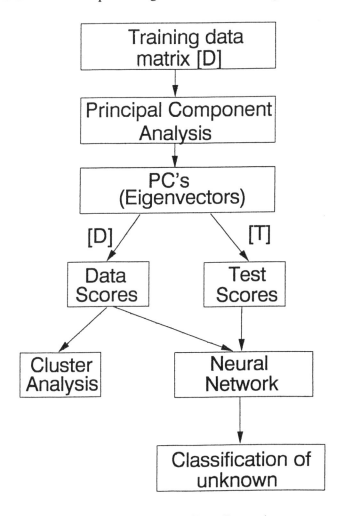

Fig. 4.1 - Scheme for Data Processing.

4.2.1   Tumour and Tissue Extracts

Five of the tumours were from established cell lines grown subcutaneously in the flanks of a variety of rat strains. Morris hepatoma lines H7777 (poorly differentiated and fast growing) and H9618A (well differentiated and slower growing) were grown in male or female Buffalo rats; a pituitary tumour (GH3 prolactinoma) in Wistar-Furth rats; Walker 256 carcinosarcoma in female Wistar rats; LBDS$_1$ fibrosarcoma in male BD9 rats. Chemically-induced primary mammary tumours developed in female Ludwig-Olac rats following injections of methyl-nitrosourea. Normal tissues (liver, spleen and kidney) were obtained from rats (which did not have tumours) of each of these different strains. Tissues and tumours were frozen in liquid nitrogen, extracted using 6% perchloric acid, neutralised with potassium hydroxide and then freeze-dried. This procedure results in minimal breakdown of low molecular weight metabolites. Macromolecules (e.g. proteins and DNA) and lipophilic components will be precipitated out during the extraction and will not contribute to the NMR signals.

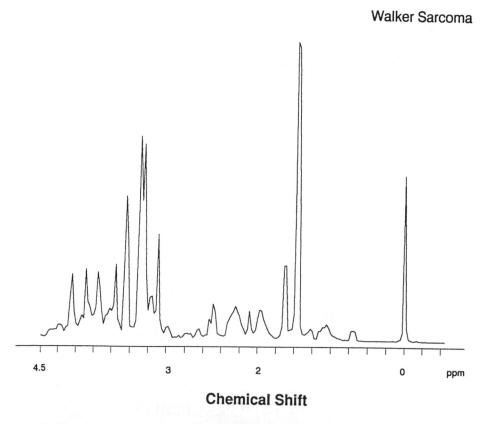

Walker Sarcoma

Chemical Shift

Digitisation : 4.5 - 0ppm at 0.025ppm intervals

Fig. 4.2 - Example of ^{1}H NMR spectrum from a tumour extract.

4.2.2 ¹H Nuclear Magnetic Resonance Spectroscopy

^{1}H NMR spectra were obtained at 25°C on a Bruker AM-400 spectrometer after dissolution of 70mg of freeze-dried material in 0.5ml D_2O and readjustment to pH 6.80 ± 0.05. A typical spectrum from a tumour extract is shown in Fig. 4.2. The signal at 0ppm is from sodium 3'-(trimethylsilyl)-1-propane sulphonate (TPS) which was added for chemical shift and quantification referencing. Data acquisition involved a pulse repetition time of 10s, a spectral width of 8kHz and collection of 16K data points.

NMR signals were acquired in the time domain but converted by Fourier Transformation into the frequency domain. Note that the frequency axis of the NMR spectrum is also known as the chemical shift axis since it is the chemical environment of each ^{1}H nucleus which influences the resonance frequency of its NMR signal. By convention, this chemical shift axis is scaled in parts per million (ppm) to account for the operating frequency of the spectrometer.

Although the sample is dissolved in deuterated water, some water is often introduced during pH adjustment and the signal from these water protons is largely eliminated by selective presaturation at 4.7ppm. This minimises distortion of the baseline such that we have only applied a linear baseline correction in the range (4.5 to 0.0ppm) over which signal heights were measured. It should be noted that, under our experimental conditions, the concentrations of the metabolites in the samples are proportionate to the area under each NMR signal. However, the presence of large numbers of overlapping signals makes it difficult to accurately measure the areas under many of the NMR peaks so we decided to use an algorithm which measured the maximum peak height within each narrow (0.025ppm) window in the spectrum. A line broadening function was applied to each spectrum to ensure that the width of the (unsuppressed) water peak would have been the same (4Hz) in each case. 180 peak heights were normalised with respect to the TPS reference peak and therefore reflect the pattern of metabolite concentrations in each sample.

4.2.3 Data Sets Studied

Four datasets have been used in this analysis, as summarised in Table 4.1. Training set A (70 samples) is that described previously [HMPG92] and this has been supplemented with some additional samples (giving training set B) to better represent all the classes present in the test set. The test set, X, comprises 22 samples not included in the training sets A or B.

The complete data set, C, (119 samples) includes almost all the tumour data and a random selection of the normal tissue data. Samples were deliberately excluded from this dataset only when cluster analysis showed them to be outliers AND subsequent observation of the spectra indicated errors in sample preparation (see Section 4.3.1). Learning was repeatedly performed on 118 out of the 119 samples and was followed by classification of the remaining sample each time. This 'leave-one-out' regime enabled us to use as many samples as possible for learning. The principal components used were those obtained from training set A.

Class	A (Train)	B (Train)	C	X (Test)
Fibrosarcoma	10	10	16	2
Pituitary tumour	4	6	10	4
Walker sarcoma	7	7	8	1
Hepatoma H7777	10	10	13	2
Hepatoma H9618A	9	9	12	2
Spleen	10	10	16	2
Kidney	10	10	16	2
Liver	10	10	16	2
Mammary tumour	0	5	12	5
Total	70	77	119	22

Table 4.1

4.2.4 Principal Component Analysis

SAS version 6.03 under SunOS running on a Sun workstation was used for PC analysis. PCs were generated via a correlation matrix.

4.2.5 Cluster Analysis

Cluster analysis was run on the SAS package as an exploratory examination of the data, i.e. to investigate whether the PC scores could provide some discrimination between the various sample classes. PC scores used in cluster analysis were standardised to unit variance. Several clustering algorithms are available but we preferred to use Ward's method [Wa63]. This takes into account every sample at each stage in the analysis and attempts to reduce the loss of information when samples are combined into a cluster. Ward's method imposes the least restrictions on the clusters expected and for this reason it appears to be the most suitable. The dendrogram shown in Fig. 4.3 demonstrates the output of cluster analysis.

4.2.6 Artificial Neural Network

PC scores were calculated for each sample (by matrix multiplication of the PC vectors by the peak heights) and used as inputs to a semilinear feedforward net consisting of

77 samples, using 11 principal components

Key:

F = Fibrosarcoma
P = Pituitary tumour
W = Walker sarcoma
H = Hepatoma H7777
G = Hepatoma H9618A
L = Liver
K = Kidney
S = Spleen
M = Mammary tumour

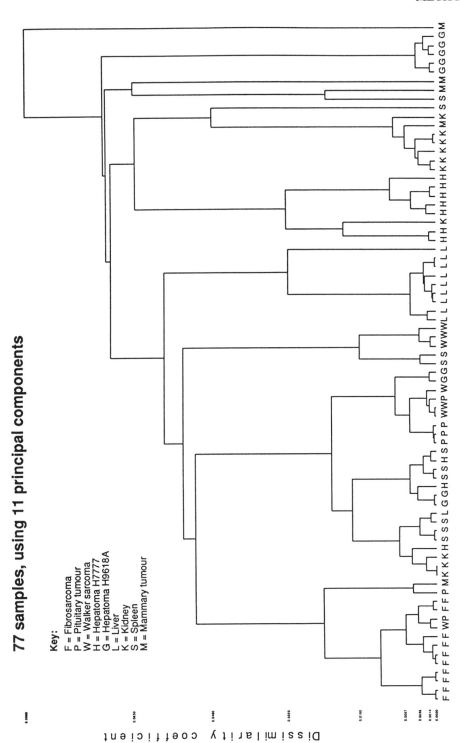

Fig. 4.3 - Dendrogram for training set B.

20 or 30 nodes in each of 3 hidden layers. Each sample was allocated 8 output scores (training set A) or 9 output scores (sets B and C which additionally include mammary tumours) of either 0.9 (class membership) or 0.1 (non-membership). Learning of weights and thresholds involved the Generalised Delta Rule with back-propagation of error [Pao89]. Learning was terminated when the normalised system error was <0.001. PC scores were calculated for further samples (the test set) which had not been included in the original PC analysis or the learning. Application of a net with its learned thresholds and weights to these new data provided outputs indicative of class membership.

4.3   RESULTS

4.3.1   PC Analysis and Cluster Analysis

The results of cluster analysis of dataset B using 11 PC scores are shown in Fig. 4.3. Analysis of dataset A gave similar results [HMPG92]. Samples are clustered together based on their proximity within the hypervolume described by the PC scores (in this case, an 11-dimensional space). Samples close together in this space will form a cluster with a low dissimilarity coefficient, i.e. they are considered to be very similar.

There is good clustering of many of the samples, suggesting that this dataset should form a suitable basis for sample classification. Some samples are seen to cluster with samples of other classes. This imperfect clustering probably accounts for the inadequacy of classification methods based on the clustering hierarchy or on nearest neighbour analysis [HM93]. Note also that some classes, especially the mammary tumours, form clusters only with relatively large dissimilarity coefficients. The diffuse distribution of mammary tumour data may result in difficulties in classification and probably arises from the more heterogeneous biological origins of these tumours (they are primary tumours and not cell lines).

The use of factor analysis methods such as principal component analysis can result in a reduction in the error contained in the dataset, as described by Malinowski [Ma87]. The important PCs will describe the "pure" data (error free) plus an error term ("imbedded error"), further PCs will consist only of an additional error term ("extracted" error). We have used cluster analysis to help select the appropriate number of principal components to use for a given dataset. There tends to be an improvement in the clustering of samples of the same class as the number of principal components increases. For these datasets, the clustering stabilises at between 10 and 15 PCs, usually when about 95% of the total variance is accounted for.

A further application of cluster analysis is in the identification of outliers. The original NMR spectra of samples showing anomalous clustering behaviour were re-examined. In a few cases, these were found to have spurious peaks (from contaminating solvents) or unusually broad lines (inadequate elimination of lipophilic or macromolecular components). Four tumours (1 pituitary and 3 mammary tumours) and 2 spleens were identified on this basis: these were the only samples deliberately excluded from database C. It is likely that the careful elimination of outliers from the training sets will improve the performance of any classification method.

4.3.2   Sample Classification with an Artificial Neural Network

Adequate learning (giving a normalised system error < 0.001) was accomplished in less than 30 mins per training set on a Sun SPARC-1. The network architectures for training sets A and B were optimised by gradually increasing the number of hidden layers and nodes per hidden layer until the outputs from the test set had stabilised. The classification results for training sets A and B with comparable optimised networks (3 hidden layers of 30 nodes each) are shown in Table 4.2. Virtually all of the samples which were well represented in a training set were correctly classified. The only exception was one kidney which is classified as a liver from A; depending on the exact architecture of the network this sample was classified either as a liver or a kidney. It is possible that unreliably classified samples such as this could be identified by running more than one realisation of the learnt neural network.

The results for network architectures of 1 or 2 hidden layers were similar except that a few (1-3) of the test samples that were correctly classified with 3 hidden layers were wrongly classified when using fewer hidden layers. The wrongly classified samples varied depending on the exact architecture of the network (number of nodes). We concluded that the network with 3 hidden layers produced outputs for test samples which were more often correct as well as being more stable. It is possible that the choice of convergence criterion (i.e. normalised system error < 0.001) could have affected the optimum network architecture. For example, if we had chosen a much more stringent convergence criterion this may have resulted in 'over-learning' of the training set and possibly a lack of generalisation to new (test set) samples. The extent of this problem may be different for different network architectures but we have not investigated this.

It should be noted that it is impossible for the mammary tumours to be correctly classified by learning of training set A, since it includes no examples of this class. The best result that could have been anticipated would have been that they would have been unclassified. However, all 5 mammary tumours were convincingly and incorrectly classified as fibrosarcomas. This presents a problem in the practical application of such a method in medical diagnosis since it has to be anticipated that samples from classes which are new to the network will be encountered. However, it is encouraging that in no case was there confusion between tumours and normal tissues. Even the hepatomas (which originate from liver) were correctly classified. As expected, there was an improvement in the classification of pituitary tumours when using B, in which they were better represented (6 instead of 4 samples). Some of the mammary tumours were correctly classified from B but 2 were not. These failures could arise from (i) the small number of mammary tumours in B, (ii) the relatively heterogeneous nature of this tumour class, or (iii) because the "mammary" tumours are primary, they are not necessarily all mammary tumours. No histological examination was performed on these tumours but previous studies have shown that although a majority of the tumours induced by this method are mammary adenocarcinomas some are of other classes.

Sample	Training Set A	Training Set B
Pituitary tumour	Correct	Correct
Hepatoma H7777	Correct	Correct
Hepatoma H9618A	Correct	Correct
Hepatoma H7777	Correct	Correct
Walker sarcoma	Correct	Correct
Hepatoma H9618A	Correct	Correct
Fibrosarcoma	Correct	Correct
Fibrosarcoma	Correct	Correct
Liver	Correct	Correct
Liver	Correct	Correct
Spleen	Correct	Correct
Spleen	Correct	Correct
Kidney	Wrong: Liver	Partly correct
Kidney	Correct	Correct
Pituitary tumour	Partly correct	Correct
Pituitary tumour	Unclassified	Partly correct
Pituitary tumour	Correct	Correct
Mammary tumour	Wrong: Fibrosarcoma	Correct
Mammary tumour	Wrong: Fibrosarcoma	Partly correct
Mammary tumour	Wrong: Fibrosarcoma	Correct
Mammary tumour	Wrong: Fibrosarcoma	Wrong: Fibrosarcoma
Mammary tumour	Wrong: Fibrosarcoma	Wrong: Fibrosarcoma
% Correct	64	77

Table 4.2 - Classification of test dataset.

Class	Correct	Partly correct	Unclassified	Wrong
Fibrosarcoma	15	1	0	0
Pituitary tumour	8	2	0	0
Walker sarcoma	8	0	0	0
Hepatoma H7777	13	0	0	0
Hepatoma H9618A	10	2	0	0
Spleen	15	1	0	0
Kidney	15	1	0	0
Liver	14	2	0	0
Mammary tumour	8	1	2	1
% of total	89.1	8.4	1.7	0.8

The network learnt from 118 samples at a time and classified the omitted sample

Basis of classification:

Correct: Required output > 0.75 (target 0.90). All other outputs < 0.25 (target 0.1)
Partly correct: Required output < 0.75 but with highest score
Unclassified: No outputs > 0.75
Wrong: Incorrect output > 0.75

Table 4.3 - Classification of 119-sample dataset (C).

The most impressive results were obtained when the largest dataset (C, 119 samples) was used for learning (Table 4.3). This provided a rigorous test of the classification method since it included all tumour samples that we have measured with the specific exception of those outliers discussed in Section 4.3.1. Learning with all but one of these samples at a time also ensured that the largest possible number of samples was included. The only wrong or unclassified samples were mammary tumours, probably for one or more of the reasons discussed in the previous paragraph or because no mammary tumour data were used in obtaining the principal components used for this database.

4.4 DISCUSSION

The use of neural network computing following principal component analysis of ^{1}H NMR data was found to be an effective and reliable method of classifying samples which were adequately represented in the training dataset.   Problems were encountered for tumour types which had very few examples in the training set or which were not represented at all.   However, in no case was a tumour wrongly classified as a normal tissue.

Expansion of the database to include the maximum number of samples resulted in a remarkably effective classification method (Table 4.3). Although the data used has been of animal origin, this level of success encourages to believe that an optimised, fully automated classification technique can be developed in a similar way to deal with clinical samples. Given the expected increase in heterogeneity of such samples, we would predict that a larger number of samples per class would be needed before reliability could be achieved.

We intend to expand our database to include a wider variety of tissues and tumours and to test the approach on human tumour data (biopsies plus urine and blood samples). Nevertheless, this classification strategy provides an objective and automated analysis of *in vitro* (and possibly *in vivo*) NMR spectroscopic data and has great diagnostic potential.

REFERENCES

[AW92]   Astion, M.L. and Wilding, P., Application of Neural Networks to the Interpretation of Laboratory Data in Cancer Diagnosis, *Clin. Chem.*, 38 (1), 34-38, 1992.

[HMG91]   Howells, S.L., Maxwell, R.J. and Griffiths, J.R., in *Proceedings of the 11th Annual Meeting of Society for Magnetic Resonance in Medicine*, San Francisco, 600, 1991.

[HMG92]   Howells, S.L., Maxwell, R.J. and Griffiths, J.R., Classification of Tumour ^{1}H NMR Spectra by Pattern Recognition, *NMR in Biomedicine*, 5, 59-64, 1992.

[HMPG92]   Howells, S.L., Maxwell, R.J., Peet, A.C. and Griffiths, J.R., An Investigation of Tumour ^{1}H Nuclear Magnetic Resonance Spectra by the Application of Chemometric Techniques, *Magn. Reson. Med.* (in press).

[Ma87]   Malinowski, E.R., Theory of Distribution of Error Eigenvalues Resulting from Principal Component Analysis with Applications to Spectroscopic Data, *Chemometrics J.*, 1, 33-40, 1987.

[Pao89]   Pao, Y-H., *Adaptive Pattern Recognition and Neural Networks*, Addison Wesley, 1989.

[Wa63]   Ward, J.H., Hierarchial Grouping to Optimise an Objective Function, *J. Am. Statist. Assoc.*, 58, 236-44, 1963.

[WLT90]   Wythoff, B.J., Levine, S.P. and Tomellini, S.A., Spectral Peak Verification and Recognition using a Multilayered Neural Network, *Anal. Chem.*, 62, 2702-9, 1990.

Chapter 5

Classification of Chromosomes Using a Combination of Neural Networks

Phil A. Errington and Jim Graham

Department of Medical Biophysics, University of Manchester, U.K.

Overview

Neural Networks have proved to be useful as adaptable classifiers for a range of applications. In this chapter we investigate the performance of a combination of two network classifiers when applied to classification of chromosomes. The classification is performed in two stages, the first involves a context free classification of chromosomes using a Multi-Layer Perceptron (MLP) trained using error back-propagation. The second stage involves using contextual information to modify the classification results from the first stage. We propose using a competitive neural network for this re-classification.

5.1 INTRODUCTION

Chromosome analysis is routinely undertaken in hospital laboratories for pre-natal diagnosis, monitoring of cancer treatments and the assessment of radiation effects. Classification of the 24 different classes of chromosomes from the 46 chromosomes appearing in microscope images of a cell is a common requirement of this analysis [Par71]. The task requires specially trained staff and is labour intensive [LGG81]. This has led to some considerable interest in its automation [CM76, Gra87, GP87, LIL80, LGG81, LGM86, PNM82, ZJA86].

Various methods have been proposed for automatic classification of chromosomes from visual data [CW73, CM76, Gra73, Gra76, Gra82, GTK89, LIL80, LLG76, LGG81, LPG80, NNW66, NGH75, PG89, Pip91, TG86]. Each method must cope with high degrees of variability both in shape and contrast of the ribbon like chromosomes in such images (Fig. 5.1).

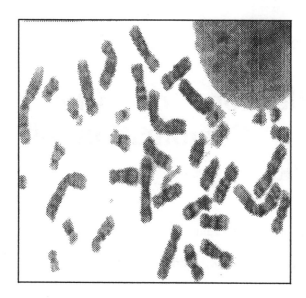

Fig. 5.1 - An image of a metaphase cell showing G-banded chromosomes.

Standard statistical approaches to classification require the extraction of shape and density features which, to perform effectively, need to be specific to the cell culture preparation methods. One issue separating many of the methods is that of representing the banding pattern which appears along each chromosome when suitably stained. Often intuitively defined features are used for its representation and it is these which may not be readily adaptable to changes in the preparation methods. This may prove a significant drawback considering the current climate of continual adjustment and enhancement in the preparation of cell cultures.

An artificial neural network offers the possibility of an adaptable classifier for chromosomes [Jen90]. Of particular interest are the feature extraction properties such models exhibit, which allow unrefined information to be presented to the classifier rather than specific intuitively defined features. This is reflected in our classification approach, as we use an artificial neural network to extract features from the raw grey level banding profile taken along the length of the chromosome. This profile is relatively easy to extract from a chromosome image (Fig. 5.2). Additionally we use two other features representing the chromosome length and the position of its centromere (a characteristic constriction in the chromosome, see Fig. 5.2). This chapter presents and compares the performance of an artificial neural network with a statistical classifier and discusses how the performance of the network classifier may be enhanced with the use of further neural networks.

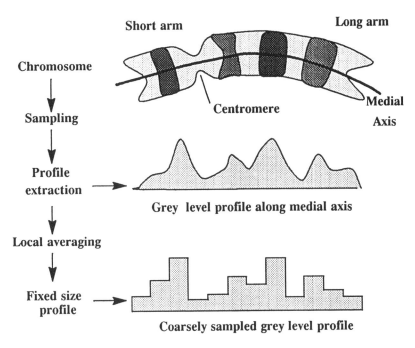

Fig. 5.2 - An example of an extraction of a fixed length profile from a chromosome.

Three extensive data sets of annotated measurements from G-banded chromosomes are used in our study, originating in Copenhagen, Edinburgh and Philadelphia. These have been used in previous classification studies using statistical methods [Gra80, Gra82, Jen90, NNW66, PG89, Pip91, TG86, ZJA86]. They cover a range of data quality, each set consisting of a large number of chromosome density profiles (Fig. 5.2) extracted from images of cells in the metaphase stage of cell division. Of the three data sets the Copenhagen set is considered the highest visual quality, as its chromosomes were carefully measured by densitometry of photographic negatives from selected cells of high quality. The other two data sets were taken from routine material with no attempt to remove measurements errors arising from overlapped or bent chromosomes. The Philadelphia set is considered the poorer of these two, as the nature of the slide preparation method results in direct chorionic villus samples providing cells of significantly poorer visual quality than in the case of peripheral blood. Details of the three data sets appear in Table 5.1.

It should be noted that the chromosomes are all from normal human cells and not from those exhibiting abnormalities. Such cells are expected to contain 46 chromosomes of 24 classes. These 46 chromosomes consist of 22 pairs of classes 1 to 22, with either one X and one Y chromosome (in male cells) or a pair of X chromosomes (in female cells).

Data set	Tissue of origin	Digitisation method	Number of Chromosomes	Data quality
Copenhagen	Peripheral blood	Densitometry from photographic negatives	8106	Good
Edinburgh	Peripheral blood	TV Camera	5469	Fair
Philadelphia	Chorionic villus	CCD line scanner	5817	Poor

Table 5.1 - Details of the three data sets used.

5.2 CLASSIFICATION OF CHROMOSOMES

In our approach, classification takes place in two stages. The first involves classification of a chromosome independent of other chromosomes in a cell. For this task the Multi-Layer Perceptron (MLP) was selected. The bulk of our work has been to modify and optimise classifiers built from this design of neural network.

During all classification experiments we use both a training and test set of data. Each of these sets is selected from approximately half of the data set under study. Two experiments are conducted, one with one half of the full data set as training data and then in a subsequent experiment as test data. Similarly the role of the other half of the data set is reversed. The classification rates we present are the mean classification rates over the two experiments.

5.2.1 Network Training Algorithm

Preliminary work had shown the MLP to be a promising classifier for chromosome data [Jen90] compared with other network topologies. For training our MLPs we chose a modification of the back-error propagation algorithm of Rumelhart, Hinton and Williams [RHW86]. Our modification of the standard algorithm as described in [RHW86] involves the use of a gradual reduction in gain (or learning rate). Initially the gain value in our network is set at a standard value (e.g. 0.1). As training proceeds two measures are monitored to select when a decrease in the gain term is required. These measures are the network classification error rate for the training data and the sum of the output node error signals for all of the training examples. The gain term is halved if the classification error rate does not decrease after 4 passes of the training data through the network. The gain is also halved if the sum of error signals increases by 10% over that observed on the previous pass of the training data set. This second measure (which is a scaled measure of the r.m.s. error between desired and actual outputs) prevents the network weights oscillating wildly with too high an original gain value, it is unlikely that such increases in the summed error signal will occur after the first few training passes.

The gain reduction mechanism permits larger values of gain to be initially used to allow considerable alteration in network weights, while allowing smaller more refined adjustments later in training for optimal classification performance. Fig. 5.3 shows a typical training curve for network error signal and classification performance using Copenhagen data.

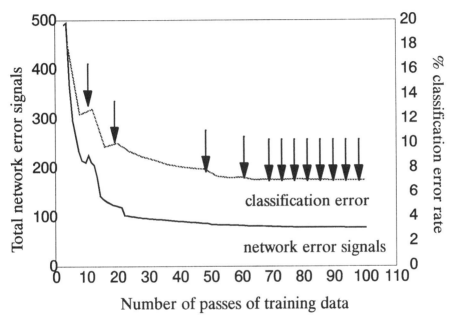

Fig. 5.3 - The reduction in total error signals and classification error rates as training proceeds. Arrows show positions where gain was halved.

Other algorithms (reviewed in [Fah88]) have not yet been investigated for our MLP training, if training time becomes an issue it may be necessary to adopt one of these.

5.2.2   Use of the MLP for Chromosome Classification

The number of banding profiles for individual chromosomes in the data sets varies considerably. Examples with up to 140 samples are present, although most chromosomes have approximately 90 samples. To maintain consistent inputs to the MLP the chromosome profiles are scaled to a constant length and local averaging is used to produce a fixed number of averaged samples along the chromosome length (Fig. 5.4). These averaged inputs are presented to the MLP input nodes. If extra features are used these are presented alongside the banding profile at extra input nodes.

The network is trained so that the highest output denotes the category of the input pattern. As there are 24 classes of chromosome, 24 output nodes are required. A variable number of hidden nodes are used in one or two layers (see below).

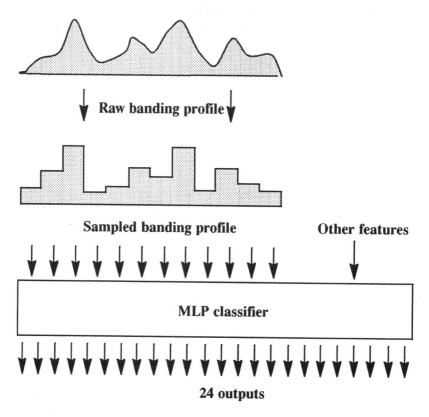

Fig. 5.4 - Presentation of classification features to the MLP.

5.2.3 Optimisation of the MLP Classifiers

We have conducted a number of experiments to optimise our MLPs, using banding samples as the only inputs. The first stage of the optimisation involved testing the sensitivity of a particular network topology to changes in the value of the gain and momentum parameters. After varying the values of these parameters between 0.1 and 0.9 (involving 81 separate experiments in two halves) it was discovered that medium and high values of gain (greater than 0.6) and high momentum (e.g. 0.8, 0.9) resulted in unstable classifiers, while if the gain value was initially low (0.1) near optimal classification performance could be achieved with the entire range of momentum values. The result of the experiment was to select the best combination, in terms of training time efficiency, of gain and momentum which produces optimal classification performance. This combination was found to be an initial gain of 0.1 and a constant momentum value of 0.7.

Selection of an optimal topology for our problem was the next task. Although there are theoretical guidelines to the number of hidden nodes required for a classification problem [Bau88, HH91, SA91], these involve knowing something about the expected variability of the input data. As chromosome classification requires the network to cope with highly variable data, we selected the optimal topology for the MLP by experimentation.

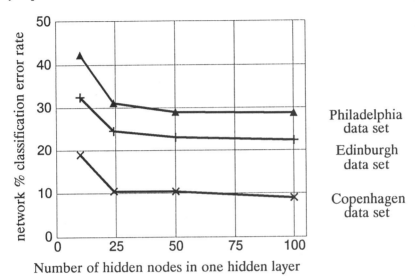

Fig. 5.5 - *The variation in classification performance of networks with different numbers of hidden nodes in one hidden layer, tested with three data sets.*

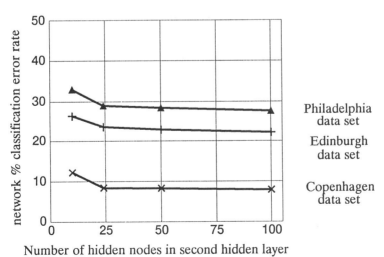

Fig. 5.6 - *The variation in classification performance of networks with different numbers of hidden nodes, in their 2nd hidden layer. Experiment performed with 100 nodes in the first hidden layer and tested with three data sets.*

Topology testing was performed with a fixed number of input nodes accepting banding inputs and 24 output nodes, one for each class of chromosome. Fifteen input samples were presented to the inputs as these had proved effective at representing the banding profile information in a preliminary study [Jen90]. A variety of topology combinations of hidden nodes were tried. Initially a single hidden layer of nodes was used, with topologies involving 10, 24, 50 and 100 hidden nodes. The performance of these classifiers is shown in Fig. 5.5, which shows that the classification performance increases with increasing network complexity. Experiments with a second layer of hidden nodes were also conducted to evaluate the effect of their extra discriminating ability. The number of nodes in the first layer was set at 100 to reflect the best performing single hidden layer network. The results of trying 10, 24, 50 and 100 nodes in a second hidden layer network is shown in Fig. 5.6. This shows that there is very little variation in performance with increasing numbers of second hidden layer nodes. This is interesting as the training and classification times of the larger nets are far greater than those with fewer hidden nodes.

5.2.4   Classification Performance

Once a good choice of topology and network parameters were made, the main advance in the performance of the classifier was achieved by including two extra features representing the length and centromere position. The centromere divides the chromosome into a long 'arm' and a 'short' arm. The ratio of the length of the short arm to that of the whole chromosome is called the centromeric index, and can be used as a representation of the centromere position, which varies depending on chromosome class. Length values are normalised to remove the effects of considerable inter-cell variation.

Three methods of including the centromeric index and length features were tried. The first involved each feature as an extra input along with banding inputs in a large MLP. The second used both features along with the banding information, but by far the most effective method was the use of an MLP pre-classifier (see Fig. 5.7).

Using the centromere position and chromosome length alone it is possible to classify the chromosomes into 7 broader groups, corresponding to the 'Denver' classification [Den60]. The pre-classifier was built to perform this broader classification, accepting the two features as inputs and producing likelihoods of membership of the 7 broader groups as outputs. This 7 group information was passed, together with the banding inputs, to a second MLP trained to produce the 24 class classification.

The optimisation of the MLP pre-classifier was performed in a similar manner to that discussed above; a number of topologies involving 2 inputs and 7 outputs were tried. The best performing of these topologies and their performance at classifying the 24 chromosome classes into the corresponding 7 Denver groups is shown in Table 5.2.

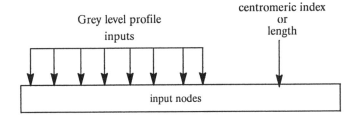

Method 1 : Profile plus single feature

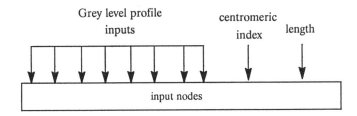

Method 2 : Profile plus pair of features

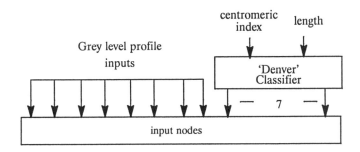

Method 3 : Profile plus pre–classified features

Fig. 5.7 - Different methods of inclusion of the centromeric index and length features.

Data set	Network Topology	Error rate for classifying into 7 groups
Copenhagen	2-14-7	5.4%
Edinburgh	2-14-7	10.1%
Philadelphia	2-14-7	14.6%

Table 5.2 - Classification error rates of the best Denver classifiers used for pre-classification.

The performances of the three inclusion methods for the centromere position and length features are shown in Table 5.3, which indicates that a succession of two MLPs, the first performing a broad classification, later refined by a second using extra data, can outperform a single layer MLP working on all the data.

Features Used	Data set		
	Copenhagen	Edinburgh	Philadelphia
Banding pattern alone	8.8%	22.3%	28.6%
Banding and normalised length	8.4%	19.4%	27.6%
Banding and centromeric index	7.7%	21.0%	26.5%
Banding, length and centromeric index	6.9%	18.6%	24.6%
Banding, and 'Denver' groups	5.8%	17.0%	22.5%

Table 5.3 - Classification error rates of networks using 15 grey level banding inputs with different representations of centromere and length features.

Using this combination of classifiers, chromosomes are classified according to the highest MLP output, and the overall performance compares favourably with statistical classifiers. Table 5.4 compares the error rates for the three data sets we use with those of the best statistical classifier working under context free conditions on the same data [Pip91]. As can be seen the neural network classifier outperforms this statistical classifier.

Data Set	Classification error rate.	
	Network Classifier	Parametric Classifier [Pip91]
Copenhagen	5.8%	6.5%
Edinburgh	17.0%	18.3%
Philadelphia	22.5%	22.8%

Table 5.4 - Comparison of classification error rates for a neural network classifier using both banding and Denver group inputs with a highly optimised parametric classifier.

5.3   SECOND STAGE CLASSIFICATION USING A COMPETITIVE NETWORK

The first classification stage works on individual chromosomes classified in isolation; no contextual information is used. The approach also relies on the highest MLP output representing the correct class of chromosome; information contained in the other MLP outputs is not considered. We propose to use a second stage of classification where the other MLP outputs are examined and used. Also in the second stage of classification we wish to apply context in the form of the number of chromosomes expected in each class when a cell of chromosomes is classified. We are investigating the application of a competitive network to both of these tasks.

From an MLP's output vector it is possible to select not only the most likely class, but secondary and less likely classes, using the second highest output, the third highest etc., [Wan90, RRK90]. By considering all the MLP outputs, it may be possible to correctly classify chromosomes misclassified on the basis of highest MLP output alone. To test the feasibility of this approach we have trained a competitive network using chromosomes misclassified by the MLP and used it as a post-classifier for a separate test set of misclassified chromosomes.

The competitive network we chose to use is a single layer topology of competitive nodes trained using a 'Winner Take All' algorithm [RZ86]. Each node receives the same input vector and compares this to its pattern of weights (which initially are random). The node with a pattern of weights closest to the input pattern is designated the winner. During training, each winning node alters its weight values so that these are closer to its inputs. After a period of training each node has specialised to represent a class of similar input vectors (those for which it 'won'). After training the nodes are labelled with the classes to which they correspond. The nodes can then be used to classify input vectors, the class of each vector being decided by the label of the winning node. The vectors we use are those produced at the 24 output nodes from the MLP first stage classifier. At present no lateral inhibition or Kohonen neighbourhoods [Koh84] are used, each winning node updating only its own weights. It may be necessary to introduce some form of refinement near class boundaries as it becomes clear how the subclasses lie in weight space.

The results of classifying misclassified chromosomes from the Edinburgh and Philadelphia data sets, using a competitive network are presented in Table 5.5. The Copenhagen data has not been used in this experiment as the MLP produces too few misclassifications.

The performance of this simple classifier is encouraging. It shows that, even when the highest value in the MLP output vector does not correspond to the true class, the entire vector contains information which allows classification to be made. However the classifier is not attempting to classify all chromosomes, only those misclassified by the MLP. It is possible to train other competitive nodes to classify chromosomes correctly classified by the MLP. The nodes classifying these may then be included with nodes classifying misclassified chromosomes. In combining 'correct' trained and 'error' trained competitive nodes in this manner, we have so far only managed to achieve a classification performance equivalent to selecting the highest MLP output as the correct class.

Data Set	Percentage of chromosomes correctly classified	
	Training data	Unseen data
Edinburgh	42.1%	30.4%
Philadelphia	43.4%	31.7%

Table 5.5 - Percentage of chromosomes misclassified on the basis of MLP output which are correctly classified by a competitive network trained on misclassified chromosomes.

Our experiments involving the application of context to the classification of chromosomes also make use of a competitive network. The contextual constraint is that a cell of 46 chromosomes will possess 2 chromosomes each of classes 1 to 22, then either one X and one Y chromosome or a pair of X chromosomes. Application of this constraint has been shown to effect an improvement in the performance of statistical classifiers [TG83, TKM91]. We are currently investigating methods of applying this constraint using a competitive network. One method currently under consideration is to classify all the chromosomes in a cell using a competitive network pre-trained to recognise MLP output vectors. A mechanism of penalising and rewarding competitive nodes according to how well they match the contextual constraints is applied in the winner take all competition. Nodes winning for too few chromosomes in classification should therefore receive more, while those receiving too many chromosomes should receive less.

5.4 DISCUSSION

Overall the application of trainable neural networks for chromosome classification has proved effective. The first stage of classification involving 2 MLPs outperforms a highly optimised statistical classifier working with the same data and splitting mechanisms [Pip91]. We have begun investigations into the use of competitive networks in a second classification stage, with emphasis on applying contextual constraints for classifying all the chromosomes in a cell. Results so far are equivocal.

However there still remain possibilities for further enhancement in the first stage of classification. The classification results we present in this chapter refer to one or two MLPs working on all of the data sampled at one sampling rate (15 samples along the chromosome length). Although in experiments conducted with variable sampling rates 15 samples was found to be near optimal, there is some evidence to suggest that oversampling of short chromosomes may be occurring, while longer chromosomes with more bands, may be undersampled. It is possible to construct 2 or more MLP classifiers with different sampling rates and on the basis of length (for instance), selectively classify a chromosome using the MLP best suited for the task. Work is being carried out to investigate this approach, alongside the work on the second stage of classification.

ACKNOWLEDGEMENTS

This work was greatly facilitated by the exchange of materials and ideas available within the Concerted Action of Automated Cytogenetics Groups supported by the European Community, Project No. II.1.1/13. We are grateful to Jim Piper of the MRC Human Genetics Unit, Edinburgh for permission to reproduce some of his results. This work is partially funded by the U.K. Science and Engineering Research Council (SERC).

REFERENCES

[Bau88]   Baum, E.B., On the Capabilities of Multilayer Perceptrons, *Journal of Complexity*, 4, 193-215, 1988.

[CW73]   Castleman, K.R. and Wall, R.J., Automated Systems for Chromosome Identification, *Nobel Symposium 23-Chromosome Identification*, Caspersson, T. (ed.), Academic Press, N.Y., 1973.

[CM76]   Castleman, K.R. and Melnyk, J., An Automated System for Chromosome Analysis: Final Report, *Internal Document No. 5040-30*, Jet Propulsion Laboratory, Pasedena, Texas, 1976.

[Den60]   Denver Conference, A Proposed Standard System of Nomenclature of Human Mitotic Chromosomes, *Lancet*, 1, 1063-65, 1960.

[Fah88]   Fahlman, S.E., Faster Learning Variations on Back-Propagation: an Empirical Study, in *Proceedings of the Connectionist Models Summer School*, 38-51, 1988.

[Gra73]   Granlund, G.H., The Use of Distribution Functions to Describe Integrated Density Profiles of Human Chromosomes, *Journal of Theoretical Biology*, 40, 573-89, 1973.

[Gra76]   Granlund, G.H., Identification of Human Chromosomes Using Integrated Density Profiles, *IEEE Trans. Biomed. Eng.*, BME-23, 183-92, 1976.

[Gra80]   Granum, E., Pattern Recognition Aspects of Chromosome Analysis, Computerised and Visual Interpretation of Banded Human Chromosomes, PhD Thesis, Technical University of Denmark, 1980.

[Gra82]   Granum, E., Application of Statistical and Syntactical Methods of Analysis to Classification of Chromosome Data, *Pattern Recognition Theory and Application*, Kittler, J., Fu, K.S., Pau, L.F., (eds.), 373-98, NATO ASI (Oxford) 1982.

[Gra87]   Graham. J., Automation of Routine Clinical Chromosome Analysis I: Karyotyping by Machine, *Analytical and Quantitative Cytology and Histology*, 9, 383-90, 1987.

[GP87]   Graham, J. and Pycock, D., Automation of Routine Clinical Chromosome Analysis II: Metaphase Finding, *Analytical and Quantitative Cytology and Histology*, 9, 391-7, 1987.

[GTK89]   Groen, F.C.A., Ten Kate, T.K., Smeulders, A.W.M. and Young, I.T., Human Chromosome Classification Based on Local Band Descriptors, *Pattern Recognition Letters*, 9, 211-22, 1989.

[HH91]   Huang, S.C. and Huang, Y.F., Bounds on Number of Hidden Neurons in Multilayer Perceptrons, *IEEE Transactions on Neural Networks*, 2, 47-55, 1991.

[Jen90]   Jennings, A.M., Chromosome Classification Using Neural Nets, MSc Thesis, University of Manchester, U.K., 1990.

[Koh84]   Kohonen, T., Self-Organisation and Associative Memory, *Series in Information Sciences*, Vol. 8, Springer-Verlag, Berlin-New York-Tokyo, 1984, 1988 (2nd edition).

[LIL80]   Ledley, R.S., Ing, P.S. and Lubs, H.A., Human Chromosome Classification Using Discriminant Analysis and Bayesian Probability, *Comput. Biol. Med.*, 10, 209-18, 1980.

[LLG76]   Lundsteen, C., Lind, A.M. and Granum, E., Visual Classification of Banded Chromosomes I: Karyotyping Compared with Classification of Isolated Chromosomes, *Clin. Genet. Lond.*, 40, 87-97, 1976.

[LGG81]   Lundsteen, C., Gredes, T., Granum, E., and Philip, J., Automatic Chromosome Analysis II: Karyotyping of Banded Human Chromosomes Using Band Transition Sequences, *Clin. Genet.*, 19, 26-36, 1981.

[LGM86]   Lundsteen, C., Gerdes, T. and Maahr, J., Automatic Classification of Chromosomes as Part of a Routine System for Clinical Analysis, *Cytometry*, 7, 1-7, 1986.

[LPG80]   Lundsteen, C., Philip, J. and Granum, E., Quantitative Analysis of 6985 Digitised Trypsin G-banded Human Metaphase Chromosomes, *Clin. Genet.*, 18, 335-70, 1980.

[NNW66]   Neurath, P.W., Nablouzian, B. Warms, T., Serbagl, R. and Falek, A., Human Chromosome Analysis by Computer: An Optical Pattern Recognition Problem, *Ann. N.Y. Acad. Sci.*, 128, 1013-28, 1966.

[NGH75]   Neurath, P.W., Gallus, G., Horton, J.B. and Selles, W., Automatic Karyotyping: Progress, Perspectives and Economics, in *Proceedings of the Asilomar Workshop: Automation of Cytogenetics*, Pacific Grove, California, 17-26, National Technical Information Services, Springfield, VA, 1975.

[Par71]   Paris Conference (1971), Standardization in Human Cytogenetics, *Original Article Series*, 8(7), The National Foundation, New York, 1972.

[PNM82]   Piper, J., Nickolls, P., McLaren, W., Rutovitz, D., Chisholm, A., and Johnstone, I., The Effect of Digital Image Filtering on The Performance of an Automatic Chromosome Classifier, *Signal Processing*, 4, 361-73, 1982.

[PG89]   Piper, J. and Granum, E., On Fully Automatic Feature Measurement for Banded Chromosome Classification, *Cytometry*, 10, 242-55, 1989.

[Pip91]   Piper, J., Aspects of Chromosome Class Size Classification Constraint, *CAACG Interlab Meeting and Topical Workshop on High-level Classification and Karyotyping, Approaches and Tests*, University of Aalborg, 13-14 March 1991.

[RRK90]   Ruck, D.W., Roggers, S.K., Kabrisky, M., Oxley, M.E. and Suter, B.W., The Multilayer Perceptron as an Approximation to a Bayes Optimal Discriminant Function, *IEEE Trans Neural Networks*, 1, 296-7, 1990.

[RHW86]   Rumelhart, D.E., Hinton, G.E. and Williams, R.J., Learning Internal Representations by Error Propagation., in *Parallel Distributed Processing: Explorations in the Microstructures of Cognition: Foundations, Vol. 1*, Rumelhart, D.E., McCelland J.L., (eds.), 318-62, MIT Press, Cambridge, MA, 1986.

[RZ86]   Rumelhart, D.E. and Zipser, D., Feature Discovery by Competitive Learning, in *Parallel Distributed Processing: Explorations in the Microstructures of Cognition: Foundations, Vol. 1*, Rumelhart D.E., McCelland J.L. (eds.), 151-93, MIT Press, Cambridge, MA, 1986.

[SA91]   Sartori, M.A. and Antsaklis, P.J., A Simple Method to Derive Bounds on the Size and to Train Multilayer Neural Networks, *IEEE Transactions on Neural Networks*, 2, 467-71, 1991.

[TG83]   Tso, M.K.S. and Graham, J., The Transportation Algorithm as an Aid to Chromosome Classification, *Pattern Recognition Letters*, 1, 489-96, 1983.

[TG86]   Thomason, M.G. and Granum, E., Dynamically Programmed Inference of Markov Networks from Finite Sets of Sample Strings, *IEEE Trans. PAMI*, 8, 491-501, 1986.

[TKM91] Tso, M.K.S., Kleinschmidt, P., Mitterreiter, I. and Graham, J., An Efficient Transportation Algorithm for Automatic Chromosome Karyotyping, *Pattern Recognition Letters*, 12, 117-26, 1991.

[Wan90] Wan, E.A., Neural Network Classification: A Bayesian Interpretation, *IEEE Trans Neural Networks*, 1, 303-4, 1990.

[ZJA86] Zimmerman, S.O., Johnston, D.A., Arrighi, F.E. and Rupp, M.E., Automated Homologue Matching of Human G-Banded Chromosomes, *Comput. Biol. Med.*, 16, 223-33, 1986.

Chapter 6

Applications of Artificial Neural Networks to Fetal Monitoring During Labour

Emmanuel C. Ifeachor [1], Shailesh R. Patel [1], Jennifer Westgate [2], John S. Curnow [2] and Keith R. Greene [2]

Plymouth Perinatal Research Group, University of Plymouth [1] and Plymouth Postgraduate Medical School [2], U.K.

Overview

This chapter presents two applications of artificial neural networks in fetal monitoring.

During human labour, the condition of the fetus is often inferred from the continuous recording of fetal heart rate and uterine activity, which together comprise the cardiotocogram (CTG). This involves subjective recognition of important patterns within the CTG and an assessment of the significance of changes in these patterns. Misinterpretation of the CTG may lead to incidents of unnecessary medical intervention, fetal injury or loss at birth. We have been developing an intelligent system, known as the INFANT (INtelligent Fetal AssessmeNT), to assist in the interpretation of the CTG and to allow for a more accurate assessment of the condition of the fetus during labour. Key features from the CTG are extracted and classified using conventional signal processing and neural network algorithms. This information, together with pertinent patient-specific information is passed on to the intelligent system for interpretation. The CTG contains 5 key features. It has been found that it is necessary to use separate neural networks to detect and classify each feature into its subtypes, if a performance comparable to that of human experts is desired. Pre-processing of the CTG to extract meaningful parameters before using the neural network is important. An overall performance of over 96%, compared to human experts, is achievable with such neural networks.

We have also developed neural network algorithms for accurate measurement of fetal heart beats from noisy data to ensure the information passed on to the INFANT is suitable for interpretation. For good quality data the detection performance of the neural network algorithms is 99.8%, falling to about 93% for very poor quality data. As in the case of the CTG, pre-processing of the data before it is applied to the neural network is necessary to achieve a good detection performance. This involves filtering the data to minimise the influence of sources of signal degradation, such as mains noise and baseline shifts, and then thresholding it so that only possible QRS complexes (see Section 6.1.2) are passed to the neural network for detection. The performance drops by up to 10% if a threshold is not applied. The dependence of the performance of the neural networks on thresholding is a drawback because of the difficulty of selecting a suitable threshold level. A simple but effective solution is suggested.

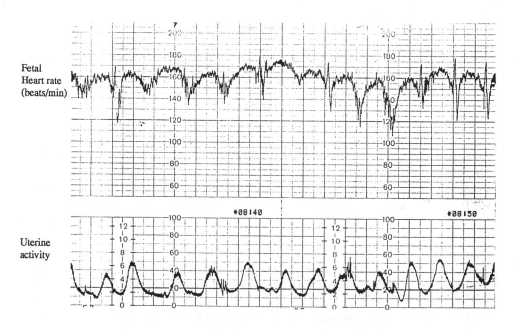

Fig. 6.1 - An example of a cardiotocogram (CTG).

6.1   INTRODUCTION

In many areas of biomedicine, physiological signals are used to aid diagnosis and for patient monitoring which often involves a great deal of pattern recognition. Artificial neural networks are essentially pattern recognition systems and, potentially, this makes them useful in biomedicine. The main attraction of neural networks in this field is their ability to learn to recognise patterns from examples, which could aid clinicians to recognise important patterns within the data more accurately and consistently. In this paper, we present two specific applications of neural networks in fetal monitoring during labour.

6.1.1 The Cardiotocogram

During human labour, the condition of the fetus is often inferred from the continuous recording of fetal heart rate and uterine activity, which together comprise the cardiotocogram (CTG), see Fig. 6.1.

The key features in the CTG thought to reflect fetal condition [Hon63, HQ67, Ame72] are

1. *baseline* heart rate, which can be thought of as the "modal heart rate" in the absence of accelerations or decelerations in heart rate (see Fig. 6.2). The instantaneous heart rate fluctuates about the baseline.
2. *variability* in heart rate, which are rapid perturbations superimposed on the baseline. Variability is described as absent, reduced, normal or increased
3. *accelerations* in heart rate; transient increases in heart rate from the baseline, which are said to be either absent or present.
4. *decelerations* in heart rate; transient decreases in heart rate from baseline, classified according to their size and time of occurrence relative to the peaks in uterine contractions.
5. the magnitude and frequency of uterine *contractions*.

Much of the art of CTG interpretation involves the recognition of important patterns within the CTG and the assessment of the significance of changes in these patterns. During labour, it is difficult for clinicians to achieve a consistent and accurate interpretation of the CTG [BJM90]. Misinterpretation of the CTG may lead to incidents of unnecessary medical intervention, fetal injury or loss at birth. Over the past four years, we have been developing an intelligent computer-based system, the INFANT (INtelligent Fetal AssessmeNT), to provide clinicians at all levels of experience with an advisory tool to assist in the management of labour and to enhance decision making. Of the 5 CTG features, heart rate variability and decelerations cause the most difficulty for clinicians to interpret.

A critical issue in computerised CTG interpretation is the need to extract and classify key features from the CTG in a similar way and at the same level of performance as the expert. Previous systems [Mae90, Kra90], employed rules and numerical algorithms, which require the expert knowledge to be quantified. An elegant and perhaps more natural approach is to teach artificial neural networks (neural networks) to recognise and classify patterns within the data, and to pass this information, together with pertinent patient-specific data to an expert system for interpretation [IKW91]. This approach allows us to mimic the methods employed by

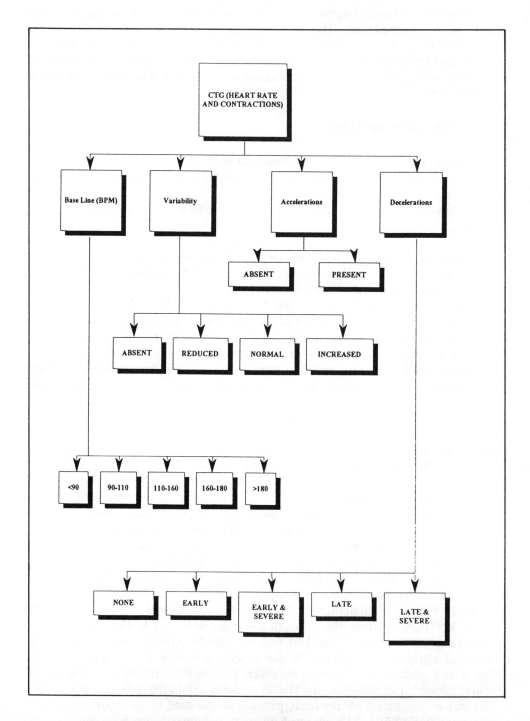

Fig. 6.2 - Classification of the CTG into subtypes of key features.

clinicians when they analyse the CTG. The INFANT uses this approach. A simple classification of the CTG in a form suitable for a neural network to learn is given in Fig. 6.2.

6.1.2 Detection of Fetal Heart Beats

The fetal heart beats are routinely detected during labour from the electrocardiogram (ECG), the electrical activity of the heart (see Fig. 6.3) or ultrasound. Like the adult ECG, normal fetal ECG is characterised by five prominent peaks and valleys labelled with successive letters of the alphabet P, Q, R, S, T [Gre87]. The most prominent part of the ECG, labelled QRS, is often referred to as the QRS complex. The reciprocal of the heart period in seconds, i.e. the time interval between the R-to-R peaks, multiplied by 60 gives the instantaneous heart rate in beats per minute. The fetal heart rate (FHR) pattern in the upper half of Fig. 6.1 is a plot of successive instantaneous heart rates (scale 1cm/min).

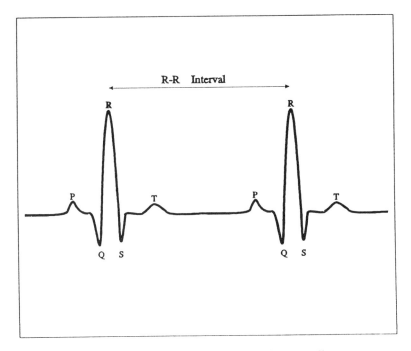

Fig. 6.3 - An illustration of the fetal electrocardiogram.

A fundamental problem in CTG-based fetal monitoring is how to detect fetal heart beats reliably, especially during the second stage of labour. Signal degradation due for example, to baseline wander, mains interference, uterine contractions, ADC (Analogue-to-Digital Converter) saturation, and movements of the baby or mother may lead to false or missed detection of heart beats. To ensure that the data the

APPLICATIONS OF ARTIFICIAL NEURAL NETWORKS TO FETAL MONITORING

INFANT receives is of adequate quality for interpretation, it is necessary to develop robust algorithms for detecting fetal heart beats.

In practice, to detect fetal heart beats a suitable digital signal processing (DSP) algorithm is employed to detect, in hardware or software, successive QRS complexes and from these calculate the R-to-R intervals and the corresponding FHR. Most QRS detection methods assume that the shape of the QRS complex is known a priori, but that its time of occurrence is unknown. This assumption is reasonable, although not always valid as the shape of the QRS complex may change from patient to patient and indeed within the same patient [AL80, QHT92]. Thus by comparing the ECG signal against a known, representative QRS template the locations of the QRS complexes in the ECG can be determined based on some measure of similarity, e.g. a high value of cross correlation. The problem of QRS (i.e. heart beat) detection can be viewed as one of pattern recognition and as such may be solved using neural networks. The use of neural networks for QRS detection has recently been reported [QHT92], although this was for adult ECG and the techniques used were somewhat involved. We present a simpler approach for the fetal ECG.

6.2 NEURAL NETWORK CLASSIFICATION OF THE CTG

6.2.1 Methods

Our first attempt was to classify nearly all the key features in the CTG using a single neural network. A back-propagation network with 136 input nodes, 20 hidden nodes, and 11 output nodes (136x20x11) was used to classify 5-minute segments of CTGs into baseline, accelerations, decelerations and their subtypes (see Fig. 6.2). The 136 inputs to the neural network were derived, for each 5-minute segment of the CTG, by averaging FHR and contraction data at 4.444 seconds intervals. Using a library of 50,000 CTG segments, constructed by an expert, the training software ran 24 hours a day for 2 months on a 486 PC, and after 100 million presentations, only partial learning was achieved. It appeared this approach was unsuccessful because the single neural network was attempting to do too much, and so the task was scaled down. The approach is clearly impractical and represents anecdotal evidence on how not to use a neural network.

A 136x15x5 neural network was used to classify just decelerations in heart rate into 5 subtypes, in relation to contractions, (see Fig. 6.2). The training set for this network contained 1300, 5-minute examples, and learning was completed in 24 hours (i.e. until the average root mean square error between the desired and actual outputs of the network was less than 1% for 90% of the examples). The performance of the neural network was assessed by reviewing, with an expert, digitised CTGs stored on optical disc media. This neural network was successful but only if the heart rate and contraction data were both present and of good quality. In the absence of the contraction data the neural network was of little use.

The task was scaled down even further by pre-processing possible decelerations in heart rate and then using a single, smaller neural network to classify them into one of three categories: not decelerations, mild decelerations and severe decelerations. First, a training set of 3000 examples of decelerations was pre-processed by robust algorithms to generate, for each example, the four variables that characterise decelerations: minimum below the baseline heart rate, duration below baseline, the dip area, and heart rate variability. The variables were used as inputs to a 4x10x3 fully connected, feedforward back-propagation network, which converged in an hour. This was subsequently optimised to give a 4x5x3 network. The performance of the neural network was compared to an expert using 511 'unseen' possible decelerations.

6.2.2   Results

Table 6.1 summarises the results for the last case. There was a 97.8% agreement between the expert and the neural network classifications for not decelerations, 94.2% agreement for mild decelerations, and 87.1% for severe decelerations, with an overall agreement of 96.1%. Severe decelerations were never wrongly classified, but there was a tendency for the neural network to classify incorrectly some decelerations as severe when in fact they were mild, according to the expert.

Expert

		Not	Deceleration	Severe
Neural Network	Not	318	7	0
	Deceleration	9	146	0
	Severe	0	4	27

Number of examples = 511

Table 6.1 - Summary of classification of decelerations with a small neural network.

6.3   NEURAL NETWORK DETECTION OF THE QRS COMPLEX

6.3.1   Methods

The fetal ECG data used in this study was taken from our fetal research database. The ECGs were analogue bandpass filtered (passband 0.05 - 100 Hz), and digitised at 500 samples/s to a resolution of 8-bits. Three hundred segments of fetal ECGs from thirteen patients were subjectively divided into three grades based on the severity of mains interference, baseline shifts, ADC saturation, etc., grade 1 (good quality), grade 2 (average), and grade 3 (poor quality). Examples of the three grades of ECG are shown in Fig. 6.4. In the top figure (grade 1) the spikes indicate the R-waves of the QRS complexes. These spikes are progressively masked by noise and baseline shifts in the middle figure (grade 2) and the bottom figure (grade 3).

For reliable QRS detection, it is necessary to pre-process the raw ECG to minimize the influence of the various sources of signal degradation (mains noise and baseline shifts, etc). An optimal linear phase Finite Impulse Response (FIR) bandpass digital filter was used to pre-process the raw ECG before QRS detection. The use of a linear phase FIR filter ensures that the delay through the filter is known precisely, and so the exact locations of the R-waves in the raw ECG can be determined. The filter used has the following characteristics (at the sampling frequency of 500 samples/s)

filter length	99
stopbands	0 - 1 Hz, 47 - 250Hz (40 dB attenuation)
passband	9 - 39 Hz (0.5 dB ripple)

The filter characteristics were determined from a study of the spectrum of the sources of signal degradation, and from a consideration of the bandwidth necessary to extract the QRS.

Four sets of training data, each containing 30 examples of QRS complexes and 30 examples of non-QRS complexes, were generated for three neural networks (30x10x1, 20x6x1, 10x6x1). The first training set contained examples of QRS complexes from grade 1 ECGs, the second set contained examples of QRS complexes from grade 2 data, the third set contained examples of QRS complexes from grade 3 data, and the fourth set examples of QRS complexes from an equal proportion of the three grades of ECGs.

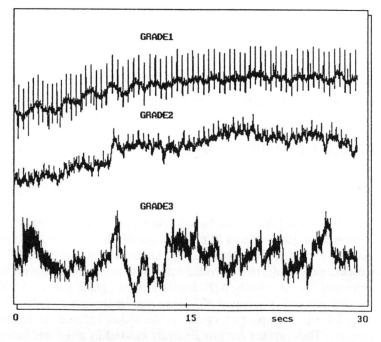

Fig. 6.4 - Examples of grades of ECGs.

The QRS complexes in the training sets were manually extracted from the filtered ECGs (with data points normalised to lie in the range ± 1), after visual inspection. For each QRS, the largest peak (representing the R-wave) is first identified, and then the data points on either side of the R-wave as well as the R-wave itself were extracted.   For the 30x10x1 neural network, 29 data samples plus the sample representing the peak are taken, 15 samples before the peak and 14 samples after the peak, see Fig. 6.5. For convenience, the data points for each QRS for this neural network architecture is represented as a sequence, $x_{30}(nT))$ with $-15T \le nT \le 14T$ where T is the sampling interval, and the suffix indicates the number of data samples representing the QRS which is also the number of input nodes for the neural network.

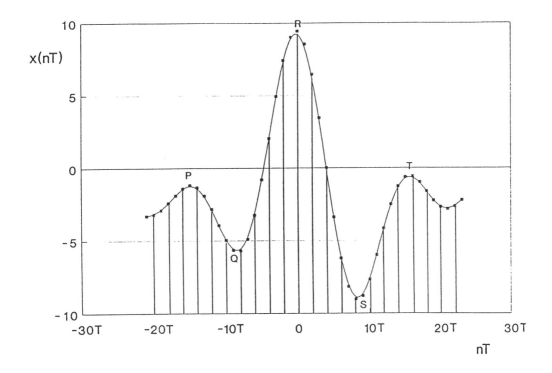

Fig. 6.5 - Representation of a QRS complex by a sequence of data values.

The QRS complexes in the training set for the 10x6x1 neural network were derived from those of the 30x10x1, by taking every other data sample on either side of the R-wave as follows

$$x_{10}(nT) = x_{30}(2nT) \qquad\qquad -5T \le nT \le 4T.$$

Similarly, for the 20x6x1 neural network, the QRS complexes in the training set were derived as

$$x_{20}(nT) = x_{30}(nT) \qquad\qquad -10T \le nT \le 9T.$$

For all three neural networks, the data value representing the R-wave is at nT=0, i.e. it is located near the middle, and during training this is the format the data sequence for each QRS is presented to the neural network. For all the neural networks, learning was completed in less than 5 minutes (convergence to 2% error) for all four types of training sets.

To test each neural network, filtered ECGs were thresholded to detect possible QRS complexes. For each possible QRS, the largest peak (assumed to be an R-wave) above a specified threshold was first found by a peak detection algorithm. The appropriate number of data points either side of the largest peak, depending on the number of input nodes, are extracted and then applied to the neural network to determine if the possible QRS complex was "genuine" or not. A QRS was assumed to have occurred if the output of the neural network exceeded a threshold level of 0.97.

We investigated the effects on the performance of the neural networks of varying the number of hidden nodes, training the neural networks with grades 1, 2, or 3 data only or a mixture of all grades. Assessment of the effectiveness of the neural networks in detecting the QRS was based on the following measure of performance

$$\frac{\text{(Total no of heart beats - no of misses - no of false detections) x 100\%}}{\text{Total no of heart beats}}$$

This performance measure attains a value of 100% only if all the QRS complexes in the record are correctly detected, i.e. no misses and no false detections. The number of misses or false detections were determined by comparing, visually, the outputs of the neural networks and the filtered ECG.

6.3.2   Results

Table 6.2 compares the performance of the three basic neural networks (10x6x1), (20x6x1), (30x10x1) for various grades of test data and training examples using a limited number of QRS complexes. Variations in the number of hidden nodes had little effect on the performance of the neural networks. The neural networks also appear to be insensitive to the type of training examples used.

The results suggest that the neural network, with architecture 20x6x1, was marginally the best. A more extensive test was carried using this neural network. The performance of the neural network for various grades of data are summarised in Table 6.3. The results were obtained with a learning rate of 0.3 and a momentum term of 0.8. Examples of the use of the neural network to detect QRS complexes from grades 1 and 3 ECGs are shown in Figs. 6.6 and 6.7, respectively. These examples illustrate the type of misses or false detections indicated in Table 6.3. To reduce the number

TEST DATA	Grade1 training set			Grade2 training set		
	NN_{10}	NN_{20}	NN_{30}	NN_{10}	NN_{20}	NN_{30}
GRADE1	99.69	99.69	99.54	99.69	99.69	99.69
GRADE2	98.56	98.71	98.39	98.71	98.71	98.71
GRADE3	93.75	93.89	93.72	93.89	93.89	93.89

TEST DATA	Grade3 training set			Equal mixture of grades 1, 2, and 3 in one training set		
	NN_{10}	NN_{20}	NN_{30}	NN_{10}	NN_{20}	NN_{30}
GRADE1	99.69	99.69	99.69	99.69	99.69	99.69
GRADE2	98.71	98.71	98.71	98.71	98.71	98.71
GRADE3	93.89	93.89	93.89	93.89	93.89	93.89

Table 6.2 - Comparison of the performance of the three neural networks for different grades of training sets (No of grades 1, 2, and 3 QRS complexes: 631, 587, and 559).

of missed or false detections, the neural network was complemented by a conventional algorithm based on cross correlation techniques. As a further check the so-called 28-beat rule, used by clinicians, was incorporated into the detection algorithm. In the rule, successive instantaneous heart rates are compared. If the current instantaneous heart rate is greater than the previous one by more than 28 beats per minute then the current R-R interval is too short and a false QRS detection is assumed to have occurred. On the other hand, if the current instantaneous heart rate is less than the previous one by -28 beats per minute, then a QRS is assumed to have been missed. This rule is based on the reasonable assumption that there is a limit to how fast the heart rate can change in humans.

TEST DATA	TOTAL NUMBER OF DETECTION BY NN	TOTAL NUMBER OF MISSED BEATS	TOTAL NUMBER OF FALSE DETECTIONS	PERFORMANCE OF NN_{20} (%)
GRADE 1	1,268	0	2	99.8
GRADE 2	1,153	10	14	97.9
GRADE 3	1,147	31	49	93.4

Table 6.3 - The performance of the neural network with architecture 20x6x1.

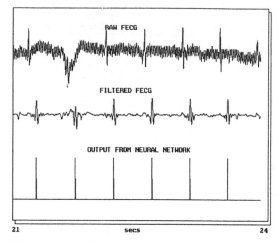

Fig. 6.6 - An example of QRS detection for grade 1 ECG.

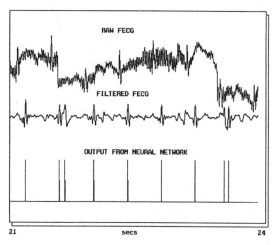

Fig. 6.7 - An example of QRS detection for grade 3 ECG.

6.4   DISCUSSION AND CONCLUSIONS

The results presented here indicate that the use of neural networks to classify CTGs can be successful provided they are used for small and well defined subtasks, such as decelerations and accelerations in heart rate. In each case, pre-processing of the data to extract basic features before the data is applied to the neural network is important to reduce the size of the input nodes and to feed the neural network with only meaningful data. Classification of the entire CTG with a single neural network is impractical, especially if raw data is used, as there are too many variables to classify and because a large number of training examples will be necessary to ensure the examples are representative of the whole range of possible CTG patterns.

Classification of decelerations in relation to contractions was successful only if the heart rate and contraction data were both present and of good quality. In practice, the loss of contraction data is not infrequent and so this approach is of limited use.

Although we have only successfully developed the neural network for deceleration, the approach is applicable to other features in the CTG: accelerations, baseline heart rate, variability and contraction timing. At the present, the latter features of the CTG are performed in the INFANT by conventional algorithms, but plans are underway to extend the neural network technique to accelerations and variability.

The neural networks seemed suited to the pattern recognition tasks involved in CTG classification and could be trained to operate in a similar way and close in performance to experienced clinicians. An important question that remains is how to reconcile the differences of opinion that may exist between clinicians in classifying the features of the CTG, notably decelerations and variability, into their subtypes. The results reported here were based on only one expert. In a recent study, we compared the performance of the neural network to 5 clinicians (3 CTG experts - 2 experienced Senior Registrars and 1 experienced Midwife, with current daily experience in the labour ward; 1 Sister and 1 Consultant Gynaecologist with previous experience in CTG interpretation) and to a conventional algorithm used in a commercial antenatal monitor (System 8000, Sonicaid). There was a high degree of agreement between the three CTG experts, and between them and the neural network. The neural network agreed the most with one of the experts, the one that provided the train examples! There were small but significant disagreement between the experts themselves, and between them and the neural network.   There were larger and significant disagreements between the three CTG experts and the neural network on the one hand, and the Sister and the Gynaecologist on the other. The results highlight the need, in this application, to choose the expert who provides the examples very carefully, and possibly to use a consensus of expertise. These issues are being investigated as part of the clinical validation of the INFANT system. The results of the further work will be published in due course. The performance of the neural network far exceeded that of the conventional algorithm used in the System 8000.

In our first attempt at QRS detection we applied the filtered ECG data directly to the neural networks, and this produced a poor performance compared to a good conventional method. For each genuine QRS the output of the neural network reached the threshold level as many as 5 times. The neural network was also unable to cope with noisy data. The performance only improved by retraining the neural network for each piece of ECG data, and was sensitive to the number of hidden nodes.

By thresholding the data, it was possible to improve the performance of the neural network without the need to retrain it. The threshold level depends on the grade of data and on the amplitudes of potential QRS complexes. An important problem with thresholding is deciding on a suitable level. We investigated the choice of threshold levels and found that a simple method that gives a good result is to detect, by a peak detection algorithm, 5 successive R-waves with the threshold level set at a high level. A new threshold is then set at about 50% of the average of the R-wave amplitudes. In a real-time system this may have to be adjusted adaptively, with appropriate checks for outliers.

ACKNOWLEDGEMENTS

The Authors gratefully acknowledge the financial support for this work from the South West Regional Health Authority, the PCFC, and the Northcott Devon Medical Foundation. The contributions of the final year students (1991/92) in the School of Electronic, Communication and Electrical Engineering, University of Plymouth in the initial investigation in QRS detection is acknowledged. We are grateful to Mr. R. Keith for his comments and contributions to both the CTG and QRS detection work. The results of the CTG were first presented at a conference in Alaska [KWI92]. We thank Mr. N. Outram for drawing some of the diagrams in this paper.

REFERENCES

[AL80]   Azevedo, S. and Longini, R.L., Abdominal-Lead Fetal Electrocardiographic R-Wave Enhancement for Heart Rate Determination, *IEEE Trans. Biomed. Eng.*, BME-27(5), 255-60, 1980.

[Ame72]   American College of Obstetrics and Gynaecologists, Guidelines for Monitoring, Terminology and Instrumentation, *Technical Bulletin*, 32, Harper and Row, Hagerstown PA, 1972.

[BJM90]   Barrett, J.F.R., Jarvis, G.J., MacDonald, H.N., Buchan, P.C., Tyrell, S.N. and Lilford, R.J., Inconsistencies in Clinical Decisions in Obstetrics, *Lancet*, 336, 549-51, 1990.

[Gre87]   Greene, K.R., The ECG Waveform, in *Balliere's Clinical Obstetrics and Gynaecology*, Vol. 1, Whittle, M. (ed.), 131-55, London, 1987.

[Hon63]   Hon, E.H., The Classification of Fetal Heart Rate I: A Working Classification, *Obstet and Gynaecol.*, 22, 137-46, 1963.

[HQ67]   Hon, E.H. and Quiligan, E.J., The Classification of Fetal Heart Rate II: A Revised Working Classification, *Conn. Med. J.*, 31, 779-84, 1967.

[IKW91]   Ifeachor, E.C., Keith, R.D.F., Westgate, J. and Greene K.R., An Expert System to Assist in the Management of Labour, in *World Congress on Expert Systems*, Vol. 4, Liebowitz, J. (ed.) 2615-22, Pergamon Press, 1991.

[KWI92]   Keith, R.D.F., Westgate, J., Ifeachor, E.C., and Greene, K.R., Investigation Using Artificial Neural Networks for Feature Extraction from the Cardiotocogram during Labour (Abstract), in *Proceedings of the 3rd World Symposium Comp. in Obstet., Gynaecol. and Neonatology*, Anchorage, Alaska, USA, 6-10 June, 1992.

[Kra90]   Krause, W., Natalie by Niess. A Computer-Aided Monitoring System for Supervision of Labour, in *Computers and Perinatal Medicine*, Maeda, K. et al (eds.) 103-11, Elsevier Science Publishers, B.V. Amsterdam, 1990.

[Mae90]   Maeda, K., Computerised Analysis of Cardiotocograms and Fetal Movements, in *Balliere's Clinical Obstetrics and Gynaecology London*, Vol. 4, Lilford, R. (ed.), 797-81, 1990.

[QHT92]   Qiuzhen, X., Hu, Y.H. and Tompkins, W.J.,   Neural-Network-Based Matched Filtering for QRS Detection, *IEEE Trans. Biomed. Eng.*, 39(4), 317-29, 1992.

Chapter 7

Managing Exchange Rate Prediction Strategies with Neural Networks

A.N. Refenes and A. Zaidi

Department of Computer Science, University College London, U.K.

Overview

This chapter describes a hybrid system for managing exchange rate trading strategies. The system is based on a neural network back-end controller which uses the predictions of a portfolio of strategies, and also contextual information, in order to switch between trading strategies. The key idea is to predict (on the basis of past performance) which of the strategies is likely to perform best/worse in the current context, and thus minimise losses.

The network is trained on daily currency exchange data from 1984 through to 1986, and is tested "out-of-sample" from 1986 through to February 1992. Its annual returns outperform the best classical techniques by an average of 6 percentage points on a $1m position (including transaction costs).

7.1   INTRODUCTION

Commonly used techniques for exchange rate prediction and trading include the moving averages, oscillators, mean-value, etc.   Each of these techniques has complementary advantages. For example, the moving average technique performs quite well when the market is in a trend but performs rather poorly around turning points and/or oscillations. Likewise, oscillator techniques tend to perform well on oscillations but poorly on trends. Currently there is no decision rule for dynamically selecting strategies in order to avoid losses.

This chapter describes a neural network back-end system which uses the predictions of a portfolio of strategies, and also contextual information, in order to switch between trading strategies. The key idea is to predict (on the basis of past performance) which of the strategies is likely to perform best/worse in the current context, and thus minimise losses.

The network is trained on daily currency exchange data from 1984 through to 1986, and is tested "out-of-sample" from 1986 through to February 1992. Its annual returns outperform the best classical techniques by an average of 6 percentage points on a $1m position (including transaction costs). In Section 7.2, we give a brief overview of the techniques which are commonly used for currency exchange rate prediction (e.g. moving averages, oscillators, etc). In Section 7.3, we describe the experimental set-up and network architecture and in Sections 7.4 and 7.5 we discuss the results.

7.2   COMPUTER TRADING STRATEGIES

Several computer trading strategies have been developed over time, and are routinely used in the capital markets. Amongst them, moving averages and mean-value based strategies are well known [Bro63, Men89].

7.2.1   Moving Averages

The moving averages strategy is quite simple. Given a time-series on k points $(v_0, .., v_k)$ the system computes two moving averages for the $k+1^{\text{th}}$ point. The Long Moving Average (LMA) is given by

$$LMA_{k+1} = \frac{1}{n} \sum_{i=1}^{n} v_i \qquad (7.1)$$

Likewise, the Short Moving Average (SMA) is given by

$$SMA_{k+1} = \frac{1}{m} \sum_{i=1}^{m} v_i \qquad (7.2)$$

with $m < n < k$. Depending on the relative lengths of the two moving averages (n and m), LMA gives a much smoother curve than SMA. The decision rule for taking a position in the market is straightforward, and is based on the characteristics of the lines drawn from v_k to $v_{LMA_{k+1}}$, and $v_{SMA_{k+1}}$.

Positions are taken if the two lines intersect (see Fig. 7.1).   If the LMA line is intersected from below the system takes a *long* position (cf. buy the asset at the current price). Conversely, if the LMA line is intersected from above the system takes a *short* position (cf. sell at the current price).

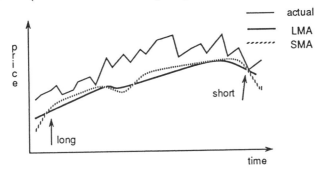

Fig. 7.1 - Trading with Simple Moving Averages.

The moving averages technique performs quite well when the market is in a state of trend but performs rather poorly around turning points and/or oscillations, because it receives delayed signals of the abrupt changes.

7.2.2 Mean-Value

The mean-value strategy, however, has some significant differences. The idea is to build a profile of the market along two axes; the horizontal axis plotting prices, and the vertical axis plotting frequency of transactions at the corresponding price (see Fig. 7.2).

   The key idea is that the commodity trades around a mean-value, with occasional (standard) deviations. If the hypothesis is true, the distribution of the time-series over a fixed time period will be normal. The decision rule for taking a position in the market is straightforward. If the price of the commodity takes a value higher than the mean-value (μ), the system takes a *short* position and vice-versa.

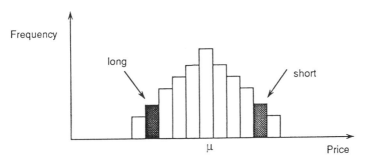

Fig. 7.2 - Trading with Simple Mean-Value (market profiling).

The mean-value strategy performs quite well when the market is in an oscillatory state.

When the market enters a trend, the histogram is rather flat and the strategy breaks down. Similarly, it is not possible to construct a normal distribution near turning points.

It is clear from the above that the two techniques have complementary advantages. Although both strategies perform badly around turning points, it is possible to avoid some of the losses by alternating strategies as the market changes from a trendy into an oscillatory behaviour and vice versa.

In this chapter we describe a neural network system which uses the predictions of these techniques plus contextual information, in order to make use of the (perceived) best strategy. The key idea is to predict (on the basis of past performance) which of the strategies is likely to perform best/worse in the current context, and thus minimise losses.

7.3   EXPERIMENTAL SET UP

7.3.1   System Architecture

The neural system described uses the following indicators as inputs. The first and second input are the recommendations (prediction) of the two techniques at time t (see Fig. 7.3). Each of these can be 0 or 1 denoting a *short* or *long* position respectively. The two indicators may be in agreement or they may give conflicting signals.

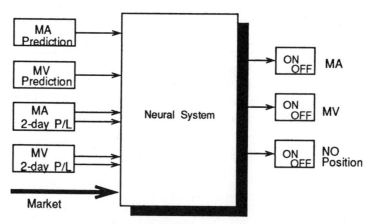

Fig. 7.3 - System Architecture.

The second and third indicators are related to the performance (i.e. the profit or loss) of the two strategies over the past two days. Each indicator gives two inputs.

The final indicator is directly related to the market, i.e. the rate of change over the past n days; this is implemented as n separate inputs to the network (for the results reported here $n=3$).

The output of the system gives three options for trading at time $t+1$. Namely,

MA   use the recommendation of the moving averages strategy,

MV   use the recommendation of the mean-value strategy, and

NP   take no position.

These are implemented as three different signals (outputs). Each signal can take values in the range [0,..,1] which is interpreted as the relative level of confidence. If both MA and MV are ON (i.e. greater than 0.5 plus a small user controlled bias δ) the largest of the two signals is chosen. If the NP signal is ON all others are ignored.

7.3.2 Training and Test Sets

The network is trained on daily data from 1984 through to 1986. We used several architecture configurations and learning algorithms including standard error Back-propagation networks [Wei90] and the Constructive Learning Procedure [RV91, Ref92]. With both procedures, the best results were obtained with networks of two layers of hidden units. Networks with no hidden units could not converge to sufficiently low levels of RMS. Networks with a single layer of hidden units produced solutions similar to two-layer networks but the consistency of the results varied significantly with the values of the control parameters (e.g. choice of learning rates, initial conditions and topology). The results with the Error Back-propagation network (9-12-6-3) are given in the following section.

7.4 RESULTS

Fig. 7.4 shows the cumulative profits on a daily basis from 1986 through to 1992 for the moving averages and mean-value strategies respectively. On an annual basis the returns are an average of 12.3% and 13.1% for the simple moving averages and mean value respectively.

Fig. 7.5 shows the cumulative profits for the back-propagation network; clearly the network outperforms both strategies. Its total cumulative return is $1.45m compared to $0.98 and $1.19m for the moving average and mean-value strategies respectively. On an annual basis the network gives an average return of 18%, on an $1 million position compared to 12.3% and 13.1% of the moving average and mean-value strategies respectively.

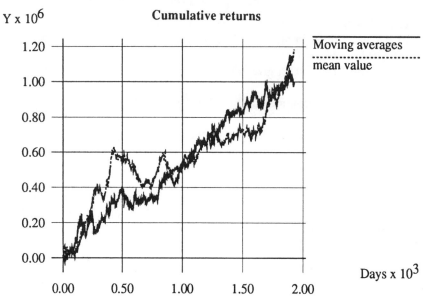

*Fig. 7.4 - Cumulative returns for the moving average
and mean value strategies.*

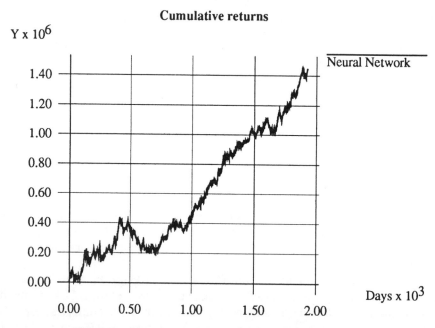

Fig. 7.5 - Cumulative returns for the neural network.

The network is an multi-layer perceptron (9-12-6-3). It was trained on daily data from 1984 through to 1986 for 2000 epochs. The standard deviation from this performance (with training times varying between 1000, and 5000 epochs) is 0.24.

The decision rule is to select the strongest signal from the three network outputs, as explained in the previous section. Alternative options (i.e. bias towards either strategy if the signal strength differs within small $\delta = 0.1$) were also examined and although they give similar results on average, the profile of the rolling returns is substantially different.

7.5 DISCUSSION

One of the major disadvantages of neural systems, at this stage of development, is the inability to explain their reasoning. This is very important for safety-critical or risk-aversive systems. To obtain an explicit understanding of the system's behaviour we analysed the attractor points in the network dynamics. Weight sensitivity analysis was used similar to [GS88]. This provided the basis for an explicit formulation of the "rules" that the network has learned about the market, and the trading strategies. The idea here is to see if these explicit rules make sense and if so to replace the network with the analytical model.

To simplify the problem we ignored the market contextual input to the network (i.e. the rate of change over the past n days). The resulting model was quite simple.

At any time t we are using either the moving average (MA state) or the mean-value (MV state) indicators. The decision rule is as follows

In the MA state
If you lost at t-1 and the indicators at t (for $t+1$) agree switch to the mean-value strategy.

In the MV state
If you lost at t-1 and t-2 and the indicators at t (for $t+1$) disagree then switch to moving averages.

To evaluate this heuristic rule discovered by the network, we computed the P/Ls for the moving average, mean-value, and the heuristic from 1984 to 1992. The heuristic rule gives a 3 percentage points gain on the mean-value strategy and a 3.2 percentage points gain on the moving average indicator.

7.6 CONCLUSION

We presented a hybrid for managing trading strategies in the foreign exchange markets. The results obtained for the US$/DM are superior to classical techniques such as moving averages and mean-value. We believe that the system is applicable both to managing a larger number of trading strategies, and also to other currencies and markets.

REFERENCES

[Bro63]   Brown, R.G., *Smoothing, Forecasting and Prediction of Discrete Time Series*, Prentice-Hall International, 1963.

[GS88]   Gorman, R.P. and Sejnowski, T.P., Analysis of Hidden Units in a Layered Network Trained to Classify Sonar Targets, *Neural Networks*, 1, 75-89, 1988.

[Men89]   Mendenhall, W. et al, *Statistics for Management and Economics*, PWS-KENT Publishing Co., Boston, USA, 1989.

[Ref92]   Refenes, A.N., Constructive Learning and its Application to Currency Exchange Rate Prediction, in *Neural Network Applications in Investment and Finance Services*, Turban, E., Trippi, R. (eds.), Chapter 27, Probus Publishing, USA, 1992.

[RV91]   Refenes, A.N. and Vithlani, S., Constructive Learning by Specialisation, in *Proceedings of ICANN '91*, Kohonen, T. (ed.), 923-29, Elsevier Science Publishers (North Holland), 1991.

[Wei90]   Weigend, A.S., Huberman, B.A. and Rumelhart, D.E., Predicting the Future: A Connectionist Approach, in *Non-Linear Modelling and Forecasting*, Casdagli, M., Eubank, S. (eds.), Proc. Vol. of the Santa-Fe Institute of Complexity, New Mexico, 1990.

Chapter 8

Trend Analysis of Remote Standby Generating Sets Using Parameter-Estimation Neural Networks

Scott D. Strudwick [1] and Roy Perryman [2]

Power Group International Limited [1], University of Greenwich [2], U.K.

Overview

This chapter outlines the techniques used in the analysis of long-term trends in standby diesel generators. These generating sets are installed to provide electrical power in the event of a mains supply failure, and as such are vitally important to many businesses and industries, especially those with large computer installations. A system currently exists that remotely monitors and controls generating sets throughout the country, recording run-time data, such as oil pressure, coolant temperature and vibration levels. Using this logged data, a neural network based expert system has been developed to identify and explain trends in generator performance over many months of operation. This is accomplished by training a back-propagation neural network to model the performance of eight fundamental parameters of a generating set. By using training data taken from generators running under different external influences such as temperature, electrical loading and run duration, accurate estimations of the monitored parameters are possible. The operational performance of the neural model can subsequently be compared to a sequence of actual generator runs, with deviations between real and model being recorded. Persistent or increasing deviations are then quantified and fed to a knowledge based system, which using the knowledge of expert engineers, endeavours to explain the highlighted trends and suggests suitable remedial action.

8.1 INTRODUCTION

8.1.1 In Search of Power

The use of standby power systems has never been as widespread as it is today, due primarily to the increased reliance of business and industry on computer-based equipment. Traditional customers such as hospitals, have been rapidly overtaken by the demands of banks, trading-houses and even supermarkets. As power systems become more complex, there is an increasing requirement for the response and reliability of standby equipment to be improved [Sma89]. Diesel powered standby generating sets comprise of a diesel engine coupled directly to an alternator, which in turn is connected to a customer's electrical load. The electronic controller is situated locally to the generator and waits for a mains-failure before initiating the start sequence and placing the generator on-load. These systems are traditionally operated for short periods and at infrequent intervals, decreasing the reliability of the equipment and the confidence that can be placed in it. Generating sets are unfortunately viewed by many users as unwelcome necessities, absorbing much-needed space, personnel and finance, and as such, they are often neglected until an emergency arises by which time it is too late.

8.1.2 Remote Condition Monitoring

To combat the indifference towards generating set maintenance, a system for remotely monitoring and controlling generators has been developed using automotive-specification micro-controllers. The system is able to remotely start, stop, and test suitably equipped generating sets located anywhere in the country. In addition to this, operating procedures allow a generating set (running or stationary) to communicate across the public telephone network and report to a central control station if any monitored variables exceed pre-defined limits, deemed necessary for correct operation. The remote monitoring system is shown in Fig. 8.1. On the left of the diagram is the generating set and the locally mounted microcontroller units which undertake the mains-failure detection, transducer monitoring, and communication tasks [RPL90]. These micro-controller units are designed around the Intel 80C196 micro-controller, communicating with each other over the Controller Area Network (CAN) bus, and with the outside world via an RS 422 link and modem. On the right of the diagram is the telecommunications link to the modem connected to an Apollo computer network situated at the national monitoring and control centre.

Whenever a generating set runs, on-board computers monitor and record vital operational parameters pertaining to the electrical and mechanical performance of the system, and when the set shuts down, it is able to communicate with the control station and down-load the data to the main computers. These computers provide the facility to either inspect the past operational performance of a generating set, or to monitor the performance in real-time by viewing dynamic bar-charts.

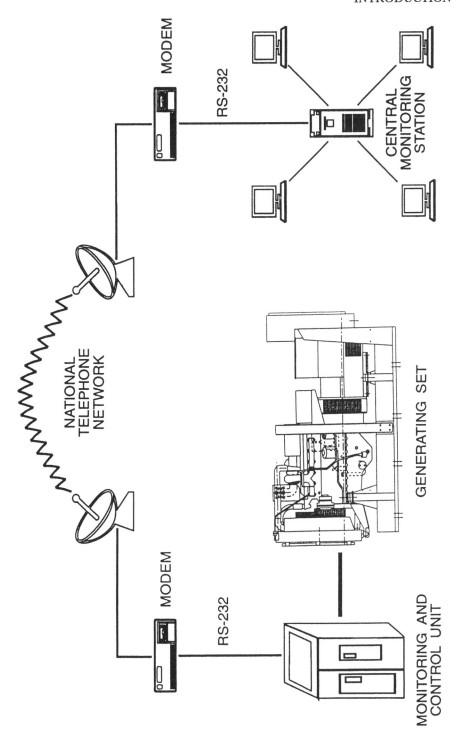

Fig. 8.1 - A Remote Condition Monitoring System for Standby Diesel Generators.

The constant monitoring of generating sets ensures that in the event of a parameter going out of pre-defined operational limits, an automatic warning is given. For example, if the starter battery became disconnected, discharged or simply stolen (a surprisingly common occurrence), since the battery voltage is a monitored parameter the situation would be identified and remedial action instigated before the generating set is again called upon to supply power. The same is true for a burst fuel-pipe or if the coolant thermostat becomes jammed. All these problems occur relatively rapidly, and often within the duration of a single run, however there are many problems that manifest themselves much more gradually. Oil pressure or engine vibration may increase over the course of five runs, with perhaps a month separating each run. Subtle variations in performance are altogether more difficult for an engineer to identify. It is these more gradual changes that can be used to detect component degradation which introduces the concept of "Condition-Based Maintenance" (CBM).

8.1.3   Condition Based Maintenance

CBM holds a great fascination for many branches of industry, but particularly to those who are involved in the selling and servicing of any type of machinery. The advantages of CBM are primarily those of savings in time and cost [Hen88], where instead of sending an engineer on a regular monthly service visit, with CBM it is only necessary to visit the installation when a problem is foreseen. As well as labour costs decreasing, component costs are also reduced since the precaution of regularly replacing parts is no longer necessary.

CBM is not, however, the great industrial panacea it first seems, due to the fact that it is very difficult to actually isolate and then quantify changes that are occurring. With diesel generating sets, the main complication is that any one particular run of a set will usually be under different operating conditions to those of previous runs. The different conditions can be identified as a) ambient temperature, b) electrical load, and c) run duration. These combine to produce a unique 'environment' for each run sequence, making it virtually meaningless to directly compare the operating performance of consecutive multiple runs. The technique of data-normalisation with respect to these three external influences is therefore necessary to enable the realistic and accurate comparison of operating data.

Fig. 8.2 shows how these two tasks can be carried out sequentially. Sampled information has firstly to be conditioned so that it is in the correct format for the data-normalisation unit (DNU). This unit consists of a group of Artificial Neural Networks (ANNs) which output performance data for an ideal generating set subjected to the same environmental conditions experienced by the real system. Both the model run-data and the actual run-data are then passed to an Error Calculation Unit (ECU), which calculates the mean deviations of the actual readings from those of the model. These deviations are in turn sent to a Trend Assimilation Unit (TAU), which uses deviation information from previous runs to create a schedule of performance trends that currently affect the generating set. This schedule provides the facts used by a Knowledge-Based System (KBS) that understands such trends as component degradation patterns.

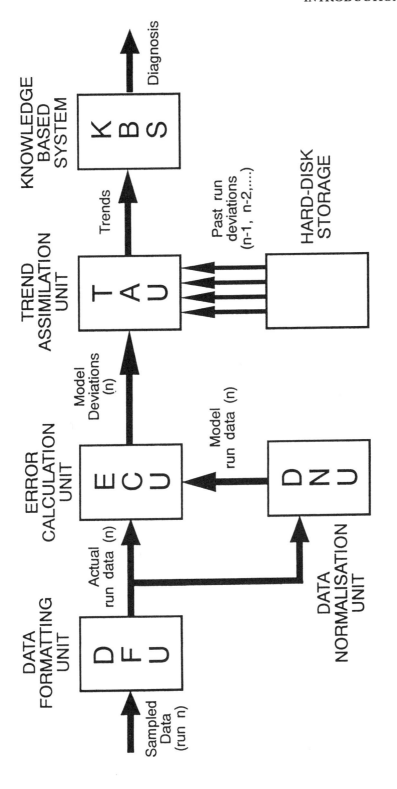

Fig. 8.2 - A Trend Analysis Expert System for use in the Predictive Maintenance of Standby Generators.

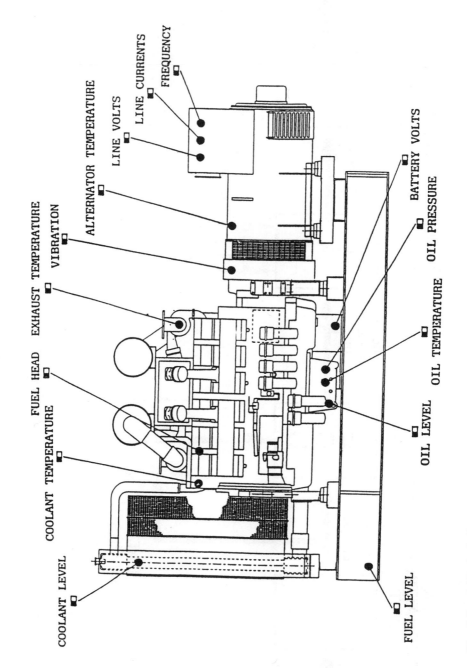

Fig. 8.3 - A Typical Generating Set Illustrating the Major Operational Parameters that are Monitored.

8.2 DATA ACQUISITION

Fig. 8.3 shows a typical generating set configuration, illustrating the positions of all the major sensors and the parameters they measure. Of these parameters, there are eight that portray the physical condition of the generating set and indicate whether the engine or alternator are operating abnormally. These eight fundamental parameters are starter battery voltage; alternator temperature; coolant temperature; oil temperature; oil pressure; vibration level; exhaust-bank 1 temperature; and exhaust-bank 2 temperature. All these parameters (with the possible exception of the starter-battery voltage) are influenced to a greater or lesser extent by the three environmental parameters, and can be termed the "dependent parameters" of the generating set.

All the analogue parameters monitored on the generating set are measured and recorded into the system memory by their dedicated on-board computers. The sampling continues at variable frequencies throughout the run cycle which comprises of starting the generator, applying load to the generator, taking the generator off-load, entering a cooling-run, and finally stopping the generator. The manner in which the sensor readings are sampled is reconfigurable, but at present the most efficient method (due to limited memory capacity) is as follows

A)   once every second for the first minute after the generating set starts up,

B)   once every minute for the next hour,

C)   once every hour until the generator goes off-load and enters a cooling-run,

D)   once every minute for up to 30 minutes during the cooling-run,

E)   once every second for the first minute after the generating set shuts down,

F)   once every minute for the next 30 minutes.

Any run sequence can therefore be broken-down into a maximum of 6 consecutive periods. Period A is important in that it captures the rapid changes in the battery-voltage, oil pressure, and vibration that occur during the engine starting. Period B is important in recording the temperature increases of the oil, coolant, alternator, and exhausts. During period C few changes occur since all parameters should have reached a steady-state condition, hence the infrequent sampling. Period D is of particular relevance to the exhaust temperature profile since the cooling-run is included specifically to disperse heat from the exhaust turbo-chargers. When the generating set has shut down in period E, the same parameters are of interest as in period A, hence the rapid sampling rate. In period F the cooling gradients of the oil, coolant, alternator, and exhausts are of importance.

After the on-board computer has recorded the final data packet, it communicates with the central monitoring station and down-loads all the information. This data is stored on the Apollo workstations and can be plotted graphically on the screen, as represented in Fig. 8.4. It is this information that can be used in conjunction with previous data to train a group of ANNs, enabling a model of the generating set to be formulated.

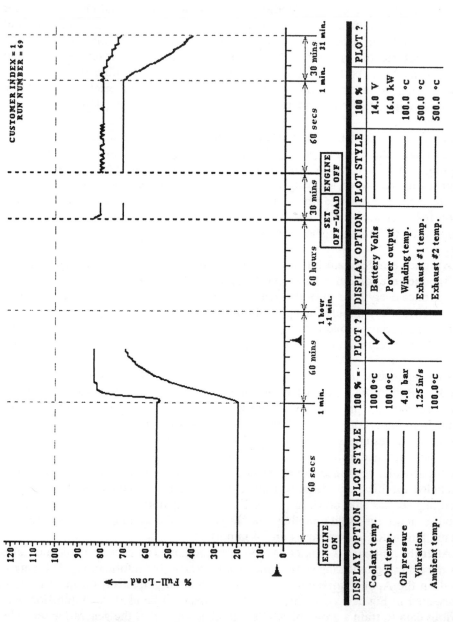

Fig. 8.4 - Oil and Coolant Temperature Performance Figures as illustrated on the Central Monitoring Computers.

8.3 DATA-NORMALISATION USING NEURAL NETWORKS

8.3.1 Parameter Estimation Using Back-Propagation

The fundamental requirement of the Data Normalisation Unit (DNU) is that it knows how an ideal generating set would perform given it's environmental conditions. Therefore, using data on ambient temperature and electrical loading, the DNU can estimate the value of a measured parameter at any time during a generator's run, creating a virtual model of that generator. This requirement is difficult to attain though since basic statistical analysis shows that the generator's parameters act in an extremely non-linear fashion.

It has been shown [LF87] that for "chaotic" time series predictions, neural networks can exceed conventional linear and polynomial predictive methods by orders of magnitude. The primary network used for parameter prediction and estimation is called a feedforward network, which uses a number of non-linear processing elements (PEs). There are many ways to train such a network, but most of them are related to the back-propagation algorithm [Was89]. A thorough description of how back-propagation works, together with some example networks is given in chapter 8 of [RM86] but in simple terms, back-propagation is a very powerful technique for constructing non-linear transfer functions between several continuously valued inputs and one or more continuously valued outputs.

A typical back-propagation network has an input layer, an output layer and at least one hidden layer. There is no theoretical limit on the number of hidden layers, but typically there will be one or two, each layer being fully connected to the succeeding layer. Back-propagation networks assume that all PEs and connections are somewhat to blame for erroneous output responses. Responsibility for the error is affixed by propagating the output error backward through the connections to the previous layer, until the input layer is reached. The name "back-propagation" derives from this method of distributing the blame for errors. The aim of the learning phase is to update the network's connection weights so as to minimise the global error of the system.

The mathematical formulae involved in back propagating the local error and minimising the global error are not detailed in this chapter, but there are a few concepts relating to the learning process that need to be dealt with briefly. The first of these is the "learning coefficient", which is used when modifying the weights within a network. Given a current connection weight, we need to determine how to increment or decrement it in order to decrease the global network error. This can be done by using a gradient descent rule which changes each weight according to the size and direction of negative gradient on the error surface.

The second concept to understand is that of "momentum". One of the problems with the gradient descent algorithm is that of setting an appropriate learning rate. The algorithm as it stands assumes that the error surface is locally linear, where "locally" is defined by the size of the learning coefficient. However, at points of high curvature this linearity assumption does not hold true, possibly resulting in divergent behaviour. Hence, it is important to keep the learning coefficient low so as to avoid this problem. On the other hand, a small learning coefficient invariably leads to very slow learning, presenting us with a dilemma. To resolve this problem, a momentum term can be used which introduces a proportion of the previous weight change into the calculation of the current weight change. This acts almost as a low-pass filter on the weight calculations, where general trends are reinforced and oscillatory behaviour cancels itself out, thus allowing a low learning coefficient but faster learning.

The learning cycle (consisting of input presentation, error calculation, and weight alteration) is iterated using a set of different input/output examples until the network's global root-mean-square (rms) error reaches an acceptably low level. The weights throughout the ANN are then frozen and the network is deemed ready for testing.

8.3.2 Implementing the Parameter Estimation Neural Network

The neural network used for estimating generator performance is illustrated in Fig. 8.5 and is a three-layer back-propagation network, with four PEs in the input layer, eight PEs in the output layer, and six PEs in the hidden layer. There is also a single Bias PE that maintains an output of 1 and is connected to all PEs in the hidden and output layers.

Before training of the network(s) can commence, the data has to be formulated such that learning can be as fast and efficient as possible (i.e. the global rms error must be as small as possible, and reached in as shorter time as possible). It was previously stated that any one run can be split-up into a maximum of six periods, each period having it's own particular set of parameter time responses. Thus any run can be divided into "episodes", allowing each episode to be treated separately in the data-normalisation process. This technique proved to be vitally important since the six specialised and independent ANNs learnt the generating set model much more accurately than did one general-purpose ANN. Once all the episodes of a run have been independently normalised, they can be compared directly with corresponding episodes from previous runs. There are consequently six identically constructed ANNs, each ready to be trained in modelling a generating set's performance during one particular episode. The following statements regarding the formulation of the training data, and the methods of training employed are true for all six of the networks.

In the estimation networks, there are four input PEs necessary to define the generating set's external environment at any one particular moment. The first input (PE #2) is perhaps the most abstract piece of information, and takes an integer value between 0 and 5 to represent the initial 5 samples of an episode. It is included so that the rapid changes that often occur at the beginning of an episode can be replicated by the network. For example, for the first sample in episode A, the PE #2 input will have a value of 5, the second sample a value of 4, the third a value of 3, and so on, but the sixth and subsequent samples will all have values of zero. Experiments were carried out on ANNs with and without this input parameter and the accuracy of the network with this "inverse-start-up" counter was notably better.

The second input (PE #3) takes an integer value between 0 and 60, and represents the position of the sample within the episode. For example, in episode F, the 15th sample will have a PE #3 value of 15.   This input gives the ANN an indication of how far through the episode the current data is, giving the network some notion of time.   This is especially important for battery and vibration monitoring.

The third input (PE #4) takes a real value and represents the total amount of electrical power that the generator has produced during the run up to that sample. For example, in episode B, the PE #4 value may be 2.13 kWh for the 8th sample and 2.40 kWh for the 9th sample. It should be noted that during regions D, E, and F, the value will not increase because the generating set is no longer subjected to electrical loading.

The fourth and final input (PE #5) also takes a real value and represents the current ambient air temperature at that sampling point. For example, in episode D, the PE #5 value for sample 6 may be 18.70 degrees Celsius. This input obviously has more influence in the modelling of operating temperatures such as alternator and oil temperatures.

The eight output PEs (PE #12 - PE #19) take real values and represent the eight fundamental parameters that are to be estimated, as detailed in section 8.2.   When presenting the networks with any kind of input data it is imperative that the values must be scaled-down so as to lie between -1 and 1.   This is because the transfer function that is used in the PEs can only operate on values less than +/-1. Similarly, the output values of the network should be scaled back up again in order to give the estimated parameters meaningful units. The hidden layer (PE #6 - PE #11) operates quite transparently to the user, each PE acting as a "feature-detection" unit, looking for a certain combination of input conditions before asserting it's output.   The pertinent features in a problem are determined solely through the network being trained and require no human-user intervention. Indeed, by careful interpretation the hidden layer's weights can reveal interesting and previously unknown properties within the process being modelled.

Having determined the network's general architecture and data format, the process of "tuning" the network's performance can begin.   First is the selection of a PE transfer function which is a typically non-linear function acting to transfer the internally generated PE sum to an output value. The choice is realistically between a sigmoid and a hyperbolic tangent (TanH).   Following a number of tests, the sigmoidal transfer function was found to give output values of up to 12 times better accuracy than equivalent TanH based networks. The sigmoid is a popular function, especially when used in conjunction with back-propagation, and it gives a continuous monotonic mapping of the input into an output value between zero and one.

The next decision to be made was which learning rule to use, the options being the Generalised Delta rule, the Cumulative Delta rule, and the Normalised Cumulative Delta rule. An in-depth discussion of these rules is given in [Neu91], but after further comparative tests, the more basic Generalised Delta rule proved itself over it's variants, possibly due to it's preference for well formulated and randomised training data.

The final group of training parameters to set can be called the network's "Learning Schedule". This schedule specifies the learning coefficients and momentum terms used by the hidden and output layers at different stages in the training process. When formulating a learning schedule, there are two points to be remembered.

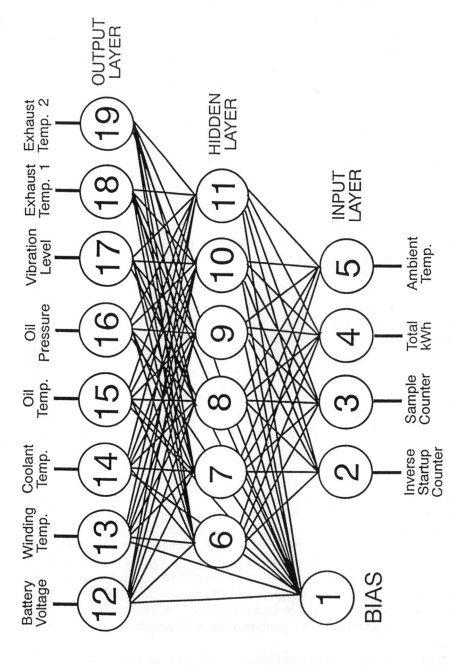

Fig. 8.5 - The Back-Propagation Neural Network used to Model the Performance of a Diesel Generator during a Specific Time "Episode".

Firstly, as training proceeds and convergence increases, both the learning coefficient and momentum terms should be reduced to aid convergence and to avoid performance oscillation. Secondly, it has been shown that different learning rates for different layers also helps convergence. In these tests, the learning coefficients in the output layer were set lower than those in the hidden layer. This is especially important for applications where the data does not derive from a strong underlying model. The learning schedule used for this application was as follows

	Number of iterations		
	up to 15000	up to 3000	up to 40000
Output layer, learn coeff	0.4	0.2	0.1
Output layer, momentum	0.8	0.4	0.2
Hidden layer, learn coeff	0.7	0.35	0.175
Hidden layer, momentum	0.8	0.4	0.2

The data sets used for training were anything from 139 to 793 lines in length, each line being an example of the input/output conditions required from the network during that particular episode. The examples were taken from 10 previous runs of the generating set, and a portion of one such file is shown below

5	0	0.00	19.7	13.0	10.4	52.9	7.7	0.3	0.00	18.5	19.2
4	1	0.00	19.7	13.0	10.4	52.9	7.7	0.3	0.00	18.5	24.0
3	2	0.00	19.7	13.0	10.4	52.9	7.7	0.3	0.00	18.5	19.2
2	3	0.00	19.7	10.8	10.4	52.9	7.7	0.8	1.16	18.5	19.2
1	4	0.00	19.7	12.5	10.4	52.9	7.7	2.8	1.86	18.5	24.0
0	5	0.00	19.7	14.1	10.4	52.9	7.7	4.0	1.33	18.5	19.2
0	6	0.00	19.7	14.1	10.4	52.9	7.7	4.0	0.83	18.5	24.0
0	7	0.00	19.7	14.1	10.4	52.9	7.7	4.0	0.66	18.5	24.0

This shows the beginning of a training set for episode A's network. The first four columns of the data represent the input PE values and the last eight columns represent the corresponding output PE values.

The data set used to train the network contained 728 examples and was randomly presented 50 times to the network, by the end of which, the rms error had fallen to 0.06. Similar performance levels were obtained from the other networks.

8.3.3   Neural Model Testing

Having trained the array of neural networks, the task of testing the model's estimating accuracy can be undertaken. This necessitates presenting all six networks with previously unseen data taken from new generating set runs. This was done for three test runs, conducted under different environmental conditions. When the model tests were completed, the following results were obtained

Network	% estimation error
A	8.5
B	2.5
C	insufficient data
D	3.1
E	3.2
F	1.9

Fig. 8.6 illustrates the accuracy of the neural network modelling technique by plotting both the actual and the estimated values of oil temperature during the entirety of a generating set run. Five networks were used to produce this profile (there was no episode C because the set ran on-load for less than 2 hours) and the four vertical lines on the graph illustrate where the estimation task passed from one episode's network to the next.

8.3.4 Measuring Errors in the Neural Model

Having shown that it is possible to estimate the operational parameters of a generating set given it's environmental conditions, it is a simple task to compare the neural model's performance with that of the real thing. Deviations in actual generating set performance can therefore be identified from that which would be considered normal operation. Referring to Fig. 8.2, this task is carried out by the Error Calculation Unit (ECU), which calculates the mean error (i.e. actual values minus model values) for each parameter in each episode. For example, from figure 8.6, the oil temperature in episode A had a mean error of +13.6 %, and in episode E it had an error of +2.2 %.

As long as a run's actual data is sufficiently close to that of the neural model, then all is well, but if significant errors occur then these need further attention. More importantly, if these deviations continue over consecutive generator runs, something within the system is deteriorating. It is at this point that CBM becomes viable, but only if the trends can be explained in a logical fashion. Currently, the only methods of doing this is to either show the trends to an experienced engineer, or present them to a KBS that encapsulates the expertise of such an engineer.

8.4 A KNOWLEDGE-BASED SYSTEM

A detailed description of the KBS is not feasible within the scope of this chapter, but a brief description of it's tasks and uses in conjunction with the neural networks will prove valuable.

The task of the Trend Assimilation Unit (TAU) is to take the deviations calculated by the ECU for the current generating set run, and those produced from previous generator runs, and to produce a list of factual statements. These statements

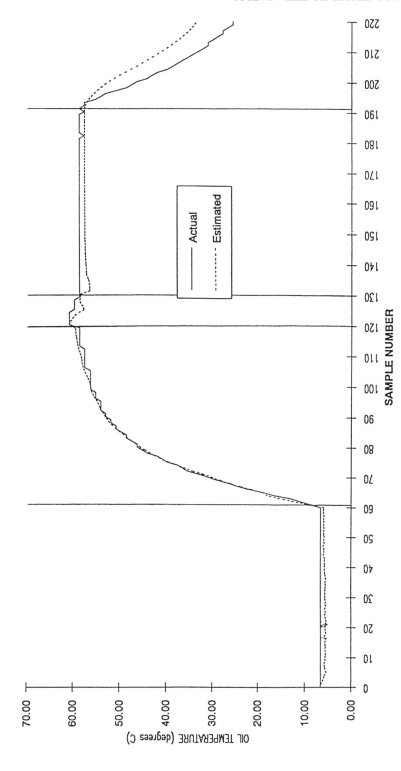

Fig. 8.6 - A graph illustrating the accuracy of the neural network model's estimate for oil temperature.

describe the duration and severity of the various parameters' trends, if there are any present. For example, suppose the ECU had produced the following facts about oil temperature during episode B for three consecutive runs

run 56 : mean error from model = -3.4%
run 57 : mean error from model = -0.3%
run 58 : mean error from model = +2.2%

Between runs 56 and 57, the oil temperature became 3.1% hotter, and between runs 57 and 58, it was 2.5% hotter. An increase in oil temperature is therefore identified during episode B of 5.6% over 2 runs, and this would be reported by the TAU as a trend.

It should be noted that trends between runs are not deemed significant if they are less than twice the ANN's estimation accuracy. In the above example, the accuracy of the oil temperature model is known to be +/- 0.8% in episode B, and since the run-on-run trend is greater than 1.6%, it is significant and beyond the realms of experimental error.

The TAU produces a database file that contains all the significant trend information necessary by the KBS. The KBS program is implemented in Prolog, primarily due to it's flexibility and ability to rapidly prototype a problem, enabling the expert appraisal/rule modification cycle to be undertaken both earlier and faster. This helps in maintaining the interest of the relevant domain expert.

The structure of the program is simple in that it checks that every part of the generating set is operating satisfactorily. If some part of the system indicates cause for concern, then a report of the problem is made, and advice is given as to which particular components on the generating set may need attention. The KBS program prints out a list of findings and corresponding diagnostic advice relating to the run currently being examined. The following is an example of just such a report

REPORT: **The set battery generated 9.9% less back-emf during the first minute of running, than it did 2 run(s) ago.**

ADVICE: **Internal resistance of the set battery appears excessive. Check the battery for signs of plate sulphurisation or low electrolyte level.**

8.5 CONCLUSIONS

In the past, there have been a number of studies applying ESs to diesel engines [Ric88, Bon82], but by and large they have been implemented on computers situated locally to the engine, accepting real-time performance data as input. These systems are thus adding intelligence to the areas of dynamic monitoring and control, whereby the system ensures that while the machine is running it is free from faults. In the case of standby generators, however, this does not provide sufficient assurance because the massive financial implications of start-up failures require a more comprehensive monitoring scheme.

The established remote condition monitoring system acts as the main source of information because it is able to control, monitor, and record everything that happens to a generating set. At this stage of the programme, a relatively small number of generating sets are on-line, enabling the existing control-centre staff to process the data and detect operational deviations.   However, as the system expands and generating set configurations become more complex, the amount of data being stored rapidly exceeds the ability of engineers to analyse it.

Once the Neural-Network/KBS is fully integrated and linked into the Apollo computers, it is proposed that a run synopsis be produced within 30 seconds of a generating set down-loading it's data. The entire system automatically accesses the generating sets' archive files on the Apollo network. Operator intervention is therefore limited to viewing the runs' synopses either on screen, or from a printer. The only other requirement is that for every additional generator configuration, a new model has to be created by training the ANN array in the data normalisation unit. No other part of the system need be updated since the rules in the KBS are sufficiently generic to be effective whatever the size of generator. To ensure that important trends are not over-looked, the rule-activation thresholds within the KBS are quite wide. This results in an extended run synopsis but as more tests are carried out and more confidence is placed in the system it is envisaged that these thresholds will tighten, effectively filtering out less certain recommendations.

ACKNOWLEDGMENTS

The authors gratefully acknowledge the support and advice given by Power Group International Limited and the University of Greenwich in the preparation of this chapter.

REFERENCES

[Bon82]   Bonissone, P.P., Outline of the Design and Implementation of a Diesel Electric Engine Trouble-Shooting Aid, in *Proceedings of the IEE Conference on Expert Systems '82: Theory and Practice of Knowledge-Based Systems*, 68-72, Brunel University, 1982.

[Hen88]   Henry, T.A., The Economics of Condition Based Maintenance, *IMechE Seminar on Condition Based Maintenance of Engines*, London, 1988.

[LF87]   Lapedes, A. and Farber, R., Non-Linear Signal Processing Using Neural Networks: Prediction and System Modelling, *Los Alamos National Laboratory Report*, LA-UR-87-2662, 1987.

[Neu91]   Neural Computing and NeuralWorks Reference Guide, NeuralWare Inc., Technical Publications Group, Pittsburgh, USA, 1991.

[Ric88]   Richards, R.A., Expert Systems for Condition Monitoring of Diesel Engines, in *Proceedings of the Institute of Marine Engineers International Conference: Maritime Communications and Control,* 1988.

[RM86]   Rumelhart, D.E. and McClelland, J.L., *Parallel Distributed Processing,* MIT Press, 1986.

[RPL90]   Reynolds, M.C., Perryman, R. and Lidgate, D., A Microcomputer Based Generating Set Controller, in *Proceedings of the University Power Engineering Conference,* Vol. 2, Robert Gordon Institute of Technology, Aberdeen, 1990.

[Sma89]   Smart, P.W., The Uninterruptable Power Supply Concept, *IEE/CIBSE Lecture,* London, 1989.

[Was89]   Wassermanm, P.D., *Neural Computing: Theory and Practice,* Van Nostrand Reinhold, 1989.

Chapter 9

Neural Network Based Electronic Nose Using Constructive Algorithms

Evor L. Hines, Claire C. Gianna and Julian W. Gardner

Department of Engineering, University of Warwick, U.K.

Overview

The human sense of smell is the faculty upon which many industries rely to monitor items such as beverages, food and perfumes. Previous work has been carried out to construct an instrument that mimics the remarkable capabilities of the human olfactory system. The instrument, or electronic nose consists of a computer-controlled multi-sensor array which exhibits a differential response to a range of vapours and odours. Elsewhere, we have reported on the application of Artificial Neural Networks (ANNs) to the processing of data gathered from the electronic nose [GHW90, GHT92]. In this chapter, we will describe aspects of our current work which are concerned with the design of a suitable network topology using automatic neural network construction techniques. Specifically, we will consider the relative merits of three algorithms, RCE, Alpaydin and RV [RCE82, Alp90, RV91]. All three models add neurons incrementally during training in order to minimize the network topology for the problem in hand. Our current results suggest that Alpaydin's model is the most efficient of the three techniques in terms of learning speed, the number of hidden units, and it compares well with other methods (for example, the back-propagation algorithm) in terms of generalisation performance.

9.1 INTRODUCTION

The human nose contains approximately 50-100 million olfactory neurons in the olfactory epithelium that act as primary receptors to odorants. There are about 10,000 glomeruli nodes associated with these primary receptors that synaptively link into about 100,000 mitral cells which in turn feeds the olfactory cortex of the brain [PD82]. This parallel architecture suggests an arrangement that could lead to an analogous instrument capable of mimicking the biological system. Fig. 9.1 shows the schematic representation of a biological nose and an electronic analogue that has been investigated at Warwick University [SGC89].

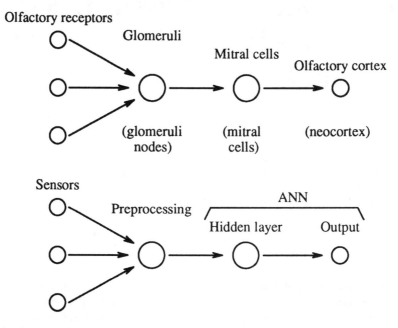

Fig. 9.1 - Schematic representation of a biological nose and our electronic analogue.

The olfactory receptor neurons in the biological nose have been replaced by an array of sensors (e.g. metal oxide films) that respond to a broad range of chemical vapours or odours. The response, characterised by a fractional change in electrical conductance, is processed at the secondary level by an analogue-to-digital converter (ADC) and is finally fed into a microcomputer for processing/analysis.

Previous work has been concerned with the analysis of data generated by an array of twelve commercial tin oxide gas sensors (Figaro Engineering Inc.) when exposed to various chemical species including alcohols [GH88, GHW90, GHT92]. To perform the analysis, the ANN approach was selected because it possesses several advantages over conventional methods in terms of adaptability (learning, self-organisation, generalisation and training), noise tolerance, fault tolerance, distributed associated memory, inherent parallelism generating a high speed of operation subsequent to training, and additionally, ANNs are amenable to VLSI implementation [RM86]. Due to its widespread applicability and the fact that it allows for the direct input of continuous data [Lip87], the multi-layer perceptron (MLP) was selected. The back-propagation technique was used to find the features of the network topology for recognising the different species of alcohols.

Disadvantages of the MLP network include the fact that training time increases with the size of the network and it is difficult to understand the resultant encoded data [DG89]. Moreover, the learning process sometimes converges to a local minimum. Besides which, no realistic *a priori* estimation can be made of the number of hidden units required to perform a particular task. For good generalisation, the network must be sufficiently large to learn the problem, but also necessarily small to generalise well. Therefore, many trials must be made before finding the optimum configuration of the network.

In this chapter, we will describe aspects of our current work which is concerned with the design of suitable network topologies using Automatic Neural Network Construction techniques. The network architecture is very important, and each application requires its own architecture. It is therefore desirable to find algorithms that not only optimise the weights for a given architecture (as the MLP does), but also optimise the architecture itself. This means, in particular, optimising both the number of layers and the number of units per layer. Approaches in which we construct or modify an architecture to suit a particular task look promising. There are two such ways to achieve the objective of having as few units as possible: start with too many and take some away (pruning algorithms) or start with too few and add some more (growing algorithms) [Wyn91]. The problem associated with pruning techniques is that they still require an estimate of the optimum size, additionally an initially large network can take a long time to train. An ideal algorithm for determining network architecture might combine growing and pruning techniques [CH91]. During the last few years, there have been several attempts to construct a network starting with a small one and gradually growing to one of the appropriate size; they include the RCE model [RCE82], Tiling algorithm [MN89], Upstart algorithm [Fre89], Neural Decision Tree [Gal86], Cascade Correlation [FL90], Alpaydin's model [Alp90], RV algorithm [RV91]. For our application, we chose to consider the relative merits of three algorithms (RCE, Alpaydin, RV) as our starting point. They all add units in the hidden layer of a three-layer network until the network performs the desired task. That is they try to automate the process of network design. Simulation results suggest that the Alpaydin technique is the most efficient of the three models, in terms of learning speed, the number of hidden units, and it compares well with other methods (for example the back-propagation algorithm) in terms of generalisation performance.

9.2 THE RCE MODEL

This model [RCE82] is dedicated to the classification of vectors $X^{(n)}$ associated to their class (supervised learning).

9.2.1 Topology of the Network

The network is composed of three layers

  - the input layer F,
  - the hidden layer G,
  - the output layer H (which gives the classification result).

Before learning, the network only contains input neurons. There are as many input neurons as there are parameters in each of the input vectors. During learning, the growing strategy adds the G and H neurons as necessary (Fig. 9.2).

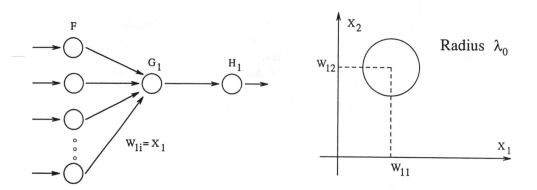

Fig. 9.2 - Presentation of the first pattern.

9.2.2 Training

A sample of the first class, the feature vector $X^{(1)}$ is presented to the network. The first hidden neuron G_1 and output neuron H_1 must then be created. If there are p input neurons, we must have p connections between these neurons and G_1. These connections are allocated the following weights

$$W_{1i} = X_i^{(1)} \tag{9.1}$$

If we, in general, enter a new vector $X^{(n)}$ ($n \neq 1$), the output of G_1 equals

$$\begin{cases} 1 \text{ if } \sum_i (X_i^{(n)} - W_{1i})^2 \leq \lambda_0 \\ 0 \text{ if greater} \end{cases} \tag{9.2}$$

where λ_0 is the influence radius of G_1.

H_1, which represents the first class, is directly connected to the output of G_1 with a weight of 1. In general, the output of H_1 equals

$$\begin{cases} 1 \text{ if } \sum(\text{inputs of } H_1) \geq 1 \\ 0 \text{ if lower} \end{cases} \qquad (9.3)$$

If the output is 1, the vector presented to the network corresponds to class 1.

Now, we study, in particular, a second vector $X^{(2)}$

1) if $X^{(2)}$ is a vector of class 1 and the output of H_1 equals 1, the network is not modified.
2) if $X^{(2)}$ is a vector of class 1 but the output of H_1 equals 0, this means that the new vector was misclassified. So, a new hidden unit G_2 must be added. The connections between G_2 and the input neurons have the following weights

$$W_{2i} = X_i^{(2)} \qquad (9.4)$$

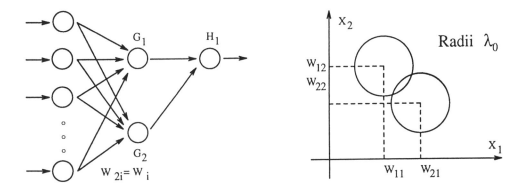

Fig. 9.3 - Creation of a new hidden neuron.

λ_0 is also the radius of G_2. The output of G_2 is connected to H_1 with a weight of 1.

3) if $X^{(2)}$ is a vector of class 2 and the output of H_1 equals 0, new units G_2 and H_2 must be created corresponding to this new class. The connection weights from G_2 to F are determined as follows

$$W_{2i} = X_i^{(2)} \qquad (9.5)$$

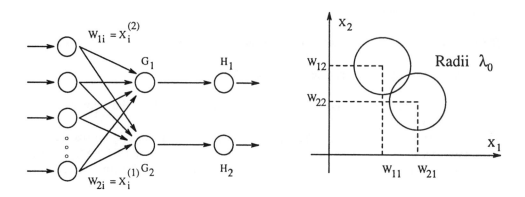

Fig. 9.4 - Creation of a new coding and output cells.

The influence radius of G_2 is λ_0 again. The output of G_2 is connected to G_1 through a unitary weight.

4)   if $X^{(2)}$ is an element of class 2 but is classified in class 1 (the output of H_1 equals 1), there is a mistake. As in the previous case, G_2 and H_2 must be created to represent the second class, but the influence radius λ_0 must be reduced to avoid future mistakes with the vector $X^{(2)}$.

Now, the new radius λ_1 for both G_1 and G_2 (the two cells leading to a mistake) is

$$\lambda_1 \leq \Sigma_i (W_{1i} - X_i^{(2)})^2. \tag{9.6}$$

This learning process continues for all the training data. The training data-base must be presented many times to the network until it produces no more modifications, that is no new neuron and no reduction of the different radii.

Several iterations are necessary due to the reduction of the radii when a misclassification occurs. Indeed, if a vector $X^{(k)}$ is inside the radius of a vector $X^{(j)}$ of its class, there is no network modification. If later, the radius of $X^{(j)}$ is reduced because of a confusion, the vector $X^{(k)}$ may be outside the new radius of $X^{(j)}$. So, a new hidden unit corresponding to the vector $X^{(k)}$ must be created. The number of iterations and the size of the learning data-base determines the algorithm's speed.

In our work, we added a pruning strategy to the RCE model. This technique is introduced in order to reduce the number of coding units G and to make this number as independent as possible of the presentation order of the training inputs.

The following procedure is employed to eliminate unnecessary coding cells. Each time we add a new unit to represent a class, we train the network again to obtain the correct size for the radius of this new unit. The network is then able to classify the training patterns which have been correctly used so far. So, we disconnect, one by one, each hidden neuron which belongs to the same class as the newly added neuron, and we train the network again. If no error occurs during this phase, the disconnected neuron is definitely removed, because we believe that the newly added neuron is a better representation of the class than the old hidden unit. Otherwise, we reconnect the temporarily disconnected neuron, because its removal would lead to misclassifications. This technique decreases the number of units in a network, but at the expense of further iterations.

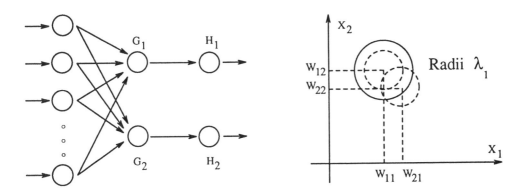

Fig. 9.5 - Creation of new coding and output cells and reduction of the radii.

9.3 ALPAYDIN'S MODEL

This algorithm [Alp90] is in some ways similar to that described in the previous model. The network is composed of an input layer F, a hidden layer G followed by a winner-takes-all structure and an output layer H. The activated neuron in the output layer determines membership of one of p classes.

The following comparisons can be made with the RCE model

- the neurons in the hidden and output layers are introduced during training,
- when a new unit G_j is created to represent a vector $X^{(j)}$, the following connection weights to the input layer are associated with it

$$W_{ji} = X_i^{(j)} \qquad (9.7)$$

In fact, the main difference is the "winner-takes-all" network. This structure selects the neuron G_i which minimizes the Euclidean distance metric $D(w_j, X)$

$$D(W_i, X) = Min [D(W_j, X)] = Min [\sum_k (W_{jk} - X_k)^2]$$ where X is the input vector.

The winner-takes-all structure guarantees that there will only be one activated output unit. The pruning strategy is the same as for the previous algorithm.

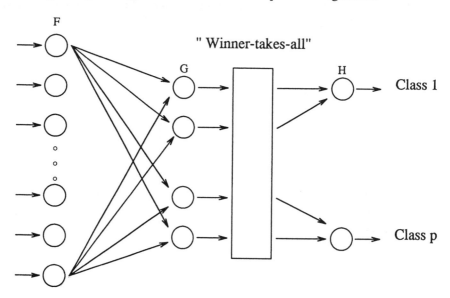

Fig. 9.6 - Network architecture for Alpaydin's algorithm.

9.4   THE RV ALGORITHM

9.4.1   Model

The RV procedure [RV91] is illustrated in Fig. 9.7. It begins with some N inputs and M outputs. The number of inputs and outputs is dictated by the problem and by the I/O representation.

Every input is connected to every unit in the hidden layer which is in turn connected to every unit in the output layer. The output units produce a linear thresholded sum of their weighted inputs. The hidden units are added to the network one by one.

The back-propagation algorithm is used to find the connection weights between the input and the hidden layer. In our implementation of the algorithm, the activation function used for the hidden unit is the sigmoid function: $1 / (1 + \exp(-x))$.

The hidden unit output weights are frozen at the time the unit is added to the network; only the input connections are trained repeatedly.

N Inputs

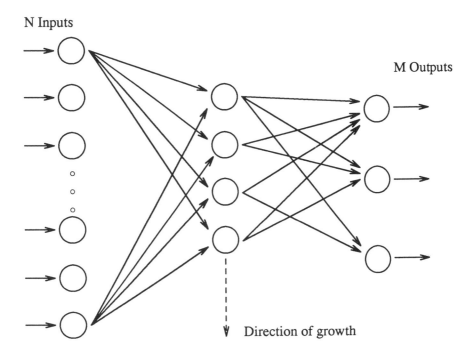

M Outputs

Direction of growth

Fig. 9.7 - Network architecture for the RV algorithm.

9.4.2   Steps Involved in the Algorithm

STEP 1: Feedforward test for training vector X_i. If any of the output units O_r makes an error then add a new unit H_k. Connect H_k to each output unit that is in error with a connection strength that corrects the error.

If the output unit O_r is wrongly ON then the connection strength, W_{kr} must have an inhibitory effect, i.e. must be negative.

Likewise, if the output unit is wrongly OFF, the connection strength must have an excitatory effect, i.e. must be positive.

STEP 2: Connect the newly added unit H_k to all the input units. The connection strengths must be such that the unit recognises the current vector X_i and none of the previous vectors, $X_0, X_1, ... X_{i-1}$, so that the previous properties of the network are not disturbed. This is achieved by perceptron learning.

It is possible that patterns appearing after the current pattern in the training set may activate the current unit. This is done to increase the generalisation capabilities of the network.

The procedure now moves to the next pattern in the training set. Exactly the same procedure that is used for training pattern X_i is used to train pattern X_{i+1}.

This carries on until the algorithm has been through all the training patterns in the training set.

9.5   RESULTS AND COMMENTS

9.5.1   Data-bases Used to Train the Network

To test our algorithms, we used a data-base provided by an Electronic Olfactory system [GH88]. The system, or Electronic Nose, consists of a computer-controlled multi-sensor array which exhibits a differential response to a range of vapours and odours. The response of twelve sensors to five different alcohols was measured with the Warwick electronic nose.   An alcohol series of methanol, ethanol, 1-butanol, propanol and 2-methyl-1-butanol was studied. Measurements were made by injecting 0.4 µl of each alcohol into a 20 l flask of air and recording the sensor outputs after 180 s. The process was repeated after first purging the glass vessel with clean air for 3 minutes and then allowing a 45 minute settling period.

The data were collected for each sensor in response to a particular measurand and the fractional change in conductances were normalised over the array to produce values between 0 and 1.

Fig. 9.8 indicates the ideal output states for the alcohol data-base. Eight sets of data were taken for the five alcohols. The networks were first trained and tested on the eight sets. Then, seven of the eight samples were used to train the network and the eighth data-set was used to test it. This is essentially the "v-fold" validation procedure [WK91].

Chemical species	Target outputs				
	Output 1	Output 2	Output 3	Output 4	Output 5
Methanol	1	0	0	0	0
Butan-1-ol	0	1	0	0	0
Propan-2-ol	0	0	1	0	0
2-Methyl-1-butanol	0	0	0	1	0
Ethanol	0	0	0	0	1

Fig. 9.8 - Ideal output states of processing units.

9.5.2   Previous Experiments Performed Using a 3-layer Back-Propagation Network (One Hidden Layer)

The input layer of this network [GHW90, GHT92] consists of twelve processing elements corresponding to the olfactory receptors in the artificial nose. The hidden layer contains four processing elements. The output layer has five output elements corresponding to the number of odours which are to be classified.

The back-propagation technique was used to train the network. The learning rate of the process was set to a value of 0.9 and the momentum coefficient to a value of 0.6.

Table 1 : Data-set 1 used for testing

Chemical species	Actual outputs				
	Output 1	Output 2	Output 3	Output 4	Output 5
Methanol	0.996	0.018	0.000	0.000	0.045
Butan-1-ol	0.003	0.994	0.000	0.000	0.003
Propan-2-ol	0.000	0.033	0.916	0.001	0.025
2-Methyl-1-butanol	0.000	0.008	0.063	0.977	0.000
Ethanol	0.005	0.012	0.021	0.000	0.695

Table 2 : Data-set 2 used for testing

Chemical species	Actual outputs				
	Output 1	Output 2	Output 3	Output 4	Output 5
	0.993	0.026	0.000	0.000	0.039
	0.003	0.995	0.000	0.000	0.004
	0.000	0.024	0.918	0.001	0.027
	0.000	0.006	0.055	0.981	0.000
	0.024	0.018	0.001	0.000	0.844

Table 3 : Data-set 3 used for testing

Chemical species	Actual outputs				
	Output 1	Output 2	Output 3	Output 4	Output 5
Methanol	0.996	0.032	0.000	0.000	0.063
Butan-1-ol	0.035	0.931	0.000	0.000	0.007
Propan-2-ol	0.000	0.054	0.857	0.001	0.027
2-Methyl-1-butanol	0.000	0.028	0.090	0.981	0.000
Ethanol	0.003	0.007	0.012	0.000	0.671

Table 4 : Data-set 4 used for testing

Chemical species	Actual outputs				
	Output 1	Output 2	Output 3	Output 4	Output 5
	0.990	0.023	0.000	0.000	0.020
	0.001	0.906	0.002	0.000	0.153
	0.000	0.011	0.931	0.000	0.071
	0.000	0.001	0.102	0.949	0.000
	0.002	0.009	0.475	0.000	0.907

Table 5 : Data-set 5 used for testing

Chemical species	Actual outputs				
	Output 1	Output 2	Output 3	Output 4	Output 5
Methanol	0.984	0.034	0.000	0.000	0.046
Butan-1-ol	0.001	0.974	0.000	0.000	0.061
Propan-2-ol	0.000	0.014	0.957	0.000	0.051
2-Methyl-1-butanol	0.000	0.001	0.079	0.968	0.000
Ethanol	0.027	0.113	0.000	0.000	0.782

Table 6 : Data-set 6 used for testing

Chemical species	Actual outputs				
	Output 1	Output 2	Output 3	Output 4	Output 5
	0.900	0.002	0.000	0.000	0.157
	0.003	0.986	0.000	0.000	0.031
	0.000	0.002	0.842	0.080	0.000
	0.000	0.012	0.052	0.936	0.000
	0.018	0.009	0.003	0.000	0.943

Table 7 : Data-set 7 used for testing

Chemical species	Actual outputs				
	Output 1	Output 2	Output 3	Output 4	Output 5
Methanol	0.909	0.016	0.000	0.000	0.036
Butan-1-ol	0.005	0.996	0.000	0.000	0.002
Propan-2-ol	0.000	0.004	0.544	0.123	0.000
2-Methyl-1-butanol	0.000	0.074	0.046	0.987	0.000
Ethanol	0.022	0.021	0.000	0.000	0.720

Table 8 : Data-set 8 used for testing

Chemical species	Actual outputs				
	Output 1	Output 2	Output 3	Output 4	Output 5
	0.992	0.008	0.000	0.000	0.087
	0.008	0.994	0.000	0.000	0.011
	0.000	0.002	0.870	0.039	0.000
	0.000	0.016	0.052	0.986	0.000
	0.034	0.007	0.003	0.000	0.953

Fig. 9.9 - Results obtained with the back-propagation algorithm.

Fig. 9.9 shows the results of the test. Data-set i means that the ith set of data was not used to train the network, but was used for testing. It should be noted that the lowest output values was 0.544 (Table 7) for an expected value of one, but was significantly higher than the corresponding 0 output of 0.123 in the particular data-set. Additionally, the largest 0 output was 0.475 (Table 4) but this was significantly smaller than the corresponding 1.0 output which was 0.907.

9.5.3   Results Obtained with the RCE Algorithm

Five networks were trained for each of the eight training files containing 35 patterns and for the one containing all 40 patterns, but each time, a different order (randomly selected) of the presentation of the training inputs was used.

1)   Number of Neurons Created.

The experiments show that the configuration of the trained network is dependent on the presentation order. In these experiments, between 5 and 7 hidden neurons were generated. Five is the smallest value that can be obtained by this algorithm, because there should be at least as many hidden neurons as there are classes.

2)   Number of Error During Testing.

	Alcohol	Alcohol 1	Alcohol 2	Alcohol 3	Alcohol 4	Alcohol 5	Alcohol 6	Alcohol 7	Alcohol 8
Small net	0	1	0	1	2	1	1	0	1
Large net	0	1	1	1	1	1	1	0	2

Fig. 9.10 - Number of errors during testing.

For each training file, only the smallest and the largest of the five networks obtained were tested. Fig. 9.10 shows the results of the test.

As expected, there is no error when the network was trained with the complete data-base (alcohol): the RCE algorithm always converges on the training file, because it adds a new cell when necessary.

Of the eight small networks that were not trained with the complete data-base (alcohol 1 to alcohol 8), only two networks make no misclassification. The maximum number of errors is two which corresponds to an error rate of 40% on the patterns not used during training.

We can see that the large network does not perform any better than the small one during testing.

Table 1 : Data-set 1 used for testing

Chemical species	Outputs of the coding cells before the comparson				
	Output 1	Output 2	Output 3	Output 4	Output 5
Methanol	0.0001	0.0191	0.0357	0.1575	0.0095
Butan-1-ol	0.0139	0.0124	0.0261	0.1360	0.0084
Propan-2-ol	0.0291	0.0292	0.0007	0.0597	0.0081
2-Methyl-1-butanol	0.1178	0.1045	0.0278	0.0046	0.0770
Ethanol	0.0121	0.0193	0.0078	0.0934	0.0017

Value of the radius of the hidden neurons :
cell 1 : 0.0081   cell 2 : 0.0163   cell.3 : 0.0081   cell 4 : 0.0291   cell 5 : 0.0055

Table 2 : Data-set 2 used for testing

Output 1	Output 2	Output 3	Output 4	Output 5
0.0001	0.0179	0.0352	0.1541	0.0092
0.0152	0.0123	0.0259	0.1336	0.0084
0.0294	0.0289	0.0008	0.0594	0.0078
0.1281	0.1193	0.0321	0.0019	0.0837
0.0088	0.0169	0.0136	0.1112	0.0009

cell 1 : 0.0080   cell 2 : 0.0163   cell 3 : 0.0078
cell 4 : 0.0283   cell 5 : 0.0055

Table 3 : Data-set 3 used for testing

Chemical species	Output 1	Output 2	Output 3	Output 4	Output 5
Methanol	0.0001	0.0147	0.0340	0.1511	0.0082
Butan-1-ol	0.0191	0.0124	0.0338	0.1456	0.0157
Propan-2-ol	0.0285	0.0181	0.0010	0.0609	0.0083
2-Methyl-1-butanol	0.1279	0.1054	0.0315	0.0022	0.0863
Ethanol	0.0116	0.0104	0.0082	0.0935	0.0012

Value of the radius of the hidden neurons :
cell 1 : 0.0080   cell 2 : 0.0085   cell 3 : 0.0079   cell 4 : 0.0283   cell 5 : 0.0052

Table 4 : Data-set 4 used for testing

Output 1	Output 2	Output 3	Output 4	Output 5
0.0001	0.0174	0.0348	0.1509	0.0078
0.0138	0.0125	0.0215	0.1257	0.0052
0.0266	0.0174	0.0054	0.0698	0.0090
0.1160	0.1051	0.0244	0.0048	0.0744
0.0125	0.0163	0.0106	0.0999	0.0007

cell 1 : 0.0080   cell 2 : 0.0167   cell 3 : 0.0082
cell 4 : 0.0283   cell 5 : 0.0057

Table 5 : Data-set 5 used for testing

Chemical species	Output 1	Output 2	Output 3	Output 4	Output 5
Methanol	0.0002	0.0171	0.0339	0.1512	0.0091
Butan-1-ol	0.0148	0.0125	0.0231	0.1284	0.0069
Propan-2-ol	0.0299	0.0282	0.0014	0.0612	0.0067
2-Methyl-1-butanol	0.1182	0.1081	0.0261	0.0048	0.0700
Ethanol	0.0120	0.0167	0.0273	0.1400	0.0068

Value of the radius of the hidden neurons :
cell 1 : 0.0080   cell 2 : 0.0163   cell 3 : 0.0078   cell 4 : 0.0282   cell 5 : 0.0051

Table 6 : Data-set 6 used for testing

Output 1	Output 2	Output 3	Output 4	Output 5
0.0064	0.0231	0.0130	0.0903	0.0059
0.0152	0.0121	0.0212	0.1204	0.0076
0.0543	0.0546	0.0052	0.0227	0.0266
0.1785	0.1705	0.0707	0.0029	0.1201
0.0084	0.0167	0.0108	0.1005	0.0004

cell 1 : 0.0080   cell 2 : 0.0163   cell 3 : 0.0057
cell 4 : 0.0244   cell 5 : 0.0053

Table 7 : Data-set 7 used for testing

Chemical species	Output 1	Output 2	Output 3	Output 4	Output 5
Methanol	0.0073	0.0237	0.0121	0.0857	0.0064
Butan-1-ol	0.0169	0.0124	0.0206	0.1143	0.0083
Propan-2-ol	0.0514	0.0521	0.0045	0.0237	0.0258
2-Methyl-1-butanol	0.1893	0.1816	0.0781	0.0051	0.1415
Ethanol	0.0098	0.0183	0.0080	0.0893	0.0007

Value of the radius of the hidden neurons :
cell 1 : 0.0080   cell 2 : 0.0163   cell 3 : 0.0057   cell 4 : 0.0220   cell 5 : 0.0052

Table 8 : Data-set 8 used for testing

Output 1	Output 2	Output 3	Output 4	Output 5
0.0009	0.0186	0.0269	0.1312	0.0070
0.0168	0.0127	0.0289	0.1362	0.0107
0.0509	0.0516	0.0042	0.0247	0.0252
0.1850	0.1774	0.0751	0.0043	0.1378
0.0080	0.0169	0.0122	0.1034	0.0005

cell 1 : 0.0084   cell 2 : 0.0163   cell 3 : 0.0058
cell 4 : 0.0223   cell 5 : 0.0052

Fig. 9.11 - Results obtained with RCE algorithm.

3)   Value of the Coding Cells and of their Influence Radii.

To better understand the problem of misclassification, we need to know what happens in the hidden layer, in other words, the values of the hidden neuron before they are compared with the influence radius, and the value of these radii.

In the tables in Fig. 9.11, we present the results for the five patterns which were not used during training, these patterns being the only ones which may be misclassified.

An hidden neuron will be set to one if the Euclidean distance between its connection weights and the input parameters is smaller than its radius. From the tables, we can see that the errors have two origins.

In Table 1, Table 4, Table 6 and Table 8, the error is due to there being too large a value of the radius of at least one hidden neuron. In these cases, the differences between the distances and the radii are very small, but they are sufficient to produce an error. The maximum relative difference is for the data-set 4, where the radius of the fifth hidden neuron equals 0.0057 and the Euclidean distance is 0.0052.

This first kind of error is not surprising. Indeed, we chose to keep the maximum possible values of radii. This reduces the number of hidden neurons during training, but also reduces the aptitude for network generalisation.

The other errors occur when the radius is smaller than the Euclidean distance. This is what happened in the case of data-set 3 and 5. The maximum relative error is for data-set 3, where the radius of the second hidden neuron equals 0.0085 which is smaller than the corresponding Euclidean distance 0.0123. To correct for these errors, the algorithm should have created more hidden neurons. However, it is very difficult to predict which hidden neuron to add and correct possible misclassification of future input patterns.

9.5.4   Results Obtained with Alpaydin's Algorithm

We used the same testing and training files as for the RCE algorithm.

1)   Number of Hidden Neurons.

For each network and for each training file, we only obtained five hidden neurons, which is the same as for the previous algorithm, the lowest value that can be obtained. So, in the case of this algorithm, the presentation order of the input patterns seems to have no, or very little, influence.

2)   Error Rate.

No error occurs during testing.

The geometry of the coding cell influence area created by this algorithm is thus more suitably adapted than the one created by the RCE algorithm, for this data-base.

3)   Value of the Hidden Neurons.

In the tables of Fig. 9.12, we present the values of the hidden neurons. The hidden neuron with the smallest value will set its corresponding output to one. As we can see from the following table, for all the data-sets, a correct difference exists between the smallest coding cell and the next smallest one.

Table 1 : Data-set 1 used for testing

Chemical species	Outputs of the coding cells before the comparison				
	Output 1	Output 2	Output 3	Output 4	Output 5
Methanol	0.0748	0.3188	0.4738	0.8714	0.2758
Butan-1-ol	0.3166	0.0474	0.3244	0.6676	0.1956
Propan-2-ol	0.3712	0.2784	0.0614	0.4390	0.1874
2-Methyl-1-butanol	0.7358	0.5754	0.3332	0.1352	0.5608
Ethanol	0.2330	0.2338	0.2148	0.6004	0.0904

Table 2 : Data-set 2 used for testing

Outputs of the coding cells before the comparison				
Output 1	Output 2	Output 3	Output 4	Output 5
0.0652	0.3050	0.4648	0.8226	0.2676
0.3152	0.0474	0.3224	0.6682	0.1936
0.3700	0.2742	0.0644	0.4410	0.1844
0.7390	0.6048	0.3430	0.0928	0.5490
0.2200	0.2194	0.2592	0.6398	0.0724

Table 3 : Data-set 3 used for testing

Chemical species	Output 1	Output 2	Output 3	Output 4	Output 5
Methanol	0.0568	0.3252	0.4614	0.8476	0.2598
Butan-1-ol	0.3614	0.1990	0.3820	0.7398	0.2952
Propan-2-ol	0.3630	0.2494	0.0744	0.4490	0.1896
2-Methyl-1-butanol	0.7440	0.5908	0.3454	0.1004	0.5630
Ethanol	0.2254	0.2133	0.2128	0.5918	0.0772

Table 4 : Data-set 4 used for testing

Output 1	Output 2	Output 3	Output 4	Output 5
0.0582	0.3024	0.4624	0.8426	0.2536
0.3068	0.0714	0.2886	0.6452	0.1638
0.3946	0.2768	0.1228	0.4926	0.2380
0.7210	0.5892	0.3096	0.1414	0.5440
0.2522	0.2140	0.1908	0.5698	0.0696

Table 5 : Data-set 5 used for testing

Chemical species	Output 1	Output 2	Output 3	Output 4	Output 5
Methanol	0.0642	0.3024	0.4508	0.8378	0.2678
Butan-1-ol	0.3148	0.0586	0.3162	0.6560	0.1888
Propan-2-ol	0.3814	0.2860	0.0792	0.4498	0.1922
2-Methyl-1-butanol	0.7354	0.6032	0.3400	0.1290	0.5462
Ethanol	0.2764	0.2666	0.3294	0.6864	0.1856

Table 6 : Data-set 6 used for testing

Output 1	Output 2	Output 3	Output 4	Output 5
0.1174	0.3566	0.3034	0.6852	0.2102
0.3138	0.0422	0.2862	0.6224	0.1898
0.5068	0.4152	0.1424	0.2978	0.3048
0.8648	0.7268	0.4844	0.1086	0.6488
0.2408	0.2228	0.2304	0.6098	0.0368

Table 7 : Data-set 7 used for testing

Chemical species	Output 1	Output 2	Output 3	Output 4	Output 5
Methanol	0.1310	0.3682	0.2894	0.6686	0.2260
Butan-1-ol	0.3226	0.0658	0.2782	0.6038	0.1956
Propan-2-ol	0.4954	0.4102	0.1334	0.3102	0.2996
2-Methyl-1-butanol	0.8806	0.7582	0.5114	0.1350	0.6816
Ethanol	0.2502	0.2366	0.2094	0.5862	0.0584

Table 8 : Data-set 8 used for testing

Output 1	Output 2	Output 3	Output 4	Output 5
0.0672	0.3428	0.4010	0.7832	0.2382
0.3154	0.0818	0.3296	0.6598	0.2260
0.4916	0.4032	0.1254	0.3148	0.2946
0.8726	0.7482	0.5004	0.1274	0.6716
0.2412	0.2236	0.2410	0.6188	0.0438

Fig. 9.12 - Results obtained with Alpaydin's algorithm.

Smallest differences for each of these data-sets

Data-set 1 : 0.126 for a minimum value of 0.0614
Data-set 2 : 0.120 for a minimum value of 0.0644
Data-set 3 : 0.096 for a minimum value of 0.1990
Data-set 4 : 0.092 for a minimum value of 0.0714
Data-set 5 : 0.081 for a minimum value of 0.1856
Data-set 6 : 0.093 for a minimum value of 0.1174
Data-set 7 : 0.095 for a minimum value of 0.1310
Data-set 8 : 0.144 for a minimum value of 0.0818

The preceding results show that Alpaydin's algorithm is able to classify all the input patterns in the data-base and also generalises well.

9.5.5   Results Obtained with the RV Algorithm

Our version of this algorithm uses the back-propagation algorithm, so we have to choose values for the learning rate, the momentum coefficient, and the tolerance of the output neurons. In our experiments, we chose a momentum term of 0.6, a learning rate of 0.9, a tolerance of 0.2, and a maximum number of iterations for the back-propagation algorithm of 20,000 (several experiments suggested that these values were the most appropriate for our problem).

Just as in the case of previous algorithms, we are trying to find the minimum architecture required to give the best performance on the training file. So, we decided to consider an output greater than or equal to 0.5 to be equal to one and an output less than 0.5 to be equal to zero. With such thresholds, the output is always allocated to a class.

1)   Number of Hidden Neurons.

In the case of the files containing all 40 samples of the training data, the data being presented to the network in a different order each time, we obtained the following number of hidden neurons: 7, 11, 12, 11 and 9. These results show that this algorithm is very dependent on the order of presentation of the data in the training file.

With this algorithm, the best results are obtained when classes in the training file are cyclically ordered. So, in contrast to the method of testing used for the previous algorithms, we chose to train only one network for each of the files containing 35 patterns.

With the eight files containing 35 samples, we obtained the following number of neurons: 7, 7, 7, 6, 6, 7, 7 and 7.

2)   Error Rate.

One of the five networks trained with the 40-sample training files makes an error on the training data. There were no errors for the other networks. So, unlike the previous algorithms, the RV algorithm did not always find a network which correctly classified all the training data.   This is due to the use of the back-propagation algorithm which sets the weights between the input and the hidden layer. Indeed, the back-propagation algorithm sometimes gets stuck in a local minimum. In these cases, the tolerance threshold on the outputs is not reached, and the desired state of the hidden neuron (zero for all the trained patterns, except the last one) is not obtained.

For the files which only contain a part of the data-base, we obtained one error in the case of three of the networks, and no error for the others. The error always occurs in the case of data which was not used for training.

Table 1 : Data-set 1 used for testing

Chemical species	Outputs of the network				
	Output 1	Output 2	Output 3	Output 4	Output 5
Methanol	0.8272	0.0000	0.0000	0.0000	0.0000
Butan-1-ol	0.1767	0.7853	0.0000	0.0000	0.0000
Propan-2-ol	0.2392	0.1618	0.7703	0.0000	0.0000
2-Methyl-1-butanol	0.1167	0.1629	0.3332	0.6615	0.0000
Ethanol	0.4040	0.1485	0.5149	0.0000	0.4562

Table 2 : Data-set 2 used for testing

Chemical species	Outputs of the network				
	Output 1	Output 2	Output 3	Output 4	Output 5
Methanol	0.8243	0.0000	0.0000	0.0000	0.0000
Butan-1-ol	0.1546	0.8110	0.0000	0.0000	0.0000
Propan-2-ol	0.2195	0.1736	0.7646	0.0000	0.0000
2-Methyl-1-butanol	0.0938	0.1634	0.2747	0.7241	0.0000
Ethanol	0.4016	0.2288	-0.0232	0.0000	0.8203

Table 3 : Data-set 3 used for testing

Chemical species	Output 1	Output 2	Output 3	Output 4	Output 5
Methanol	0.8243	0.0000	0.0000	0.0000	0.0000
Butan-1-ol	0.2524	0.7057	0.0000	0.0000	0.0000
Propan-2-ol	0.2172	0.1861	0.7515	0.0000	0.0000
2-Methyl-1-butanol	0.0873	0.1708	0.2770	0.7217	0.0000
Ethanol	0.3810	0.1698	0.2399	0.0000	0.5197

Table 4 : Data-set 4 used for testing

Output 1	Output 2	Output 3	Output 4	Output 5
0.8243	0.0000	0.0000	0.0000	0.0000
0.1818	0.7811	0.0000	0.0000	0.0000
0.2770	0.1354	0.1354	0.7324	0.0000
0.0792	0.1810	0.3162	0.6782	0.0000
0.3253	0.2519	0.4728	0.0000	0.0000

Table 5 : Data-set 5 used for testing

Chemical species	Output 1	Output 2	Output 3	Output 4	Output 5
Methanol	0.8237	0.0000	0.0000	0.0000	0.0000
Butan-1-ol	0.1646	0.8008	0.0000	0.0000	0.0000
Propan-2-ol	0.2013	0.1951	0.7623	0.0000	0.0000
2-Methyl-1-butanol	0.0856	0.1719	0.3092	0.6870	0.0000
Ethanol	0.3494	0.5561	0.0000	0.0000	0.9924

Table 6 : Data-set 6 used for testing

Output 1	Output 2	Output 3	Output 4	Output 5
0.8267	-0.3131	0.4269	0.0000	0.0000
0.1542	0.8101	0.0000	0.0000	0.0000
0.2217	0.0624	0.5035	0.4200	0.0000
0.1004	0.1530	0.1629	0.8435	0.0000
0.4086	0.2194	0.0184	0.0000	1.0335

Table 7 : Data-set 7 used for testing

Chemical species	Output 1	Output 2	Output 3	Output 4	Output 5
Methanol	0.8260	-0.3333	0.4545	0.0000	0.0000
Butan-1-ol	0.1353	0.8312	0.0000	0.0000	0.0000
Propan-2-ol	0.2289	0.0604	0.5083	0.4049	0.0000
2-Methyl-1-butanol	0.1024	0.1520	0.1472	0.8601	0.0000
Ethanol	0.4100	0.1723	0.0959	0.0000	0.7031

Table 8 : Data-set 8 used for testing

Output 1	Output 2	Output 3	Output 4	Output 5
0.8209	0.0000	0.0000	0.0000	0.0000
0.1408	0.8232	0.0000	0.0000	0.0000
0.2283	0.0630	0.5116	0.4001	0.0000
0.1033	0.1508	0.1529	0.8540	0.0000
0.4234	0.2153	-0.0284	0.0000	1.1477

Fig. 9.13 - Results obtained with the RV algorithm.

3)   Value of the output neurons (Fig. 9.13).

First, it should be noted that it is possible to obtain small negative values or values slightly greater than 1 in the output layers. This is caused by the connections between the hidden and the output layers. Indeed, these connections are either positive or negative, so the results of the computation of the output neurons may be slightly negative.

In the case of data-set 1, input 5 produces three output values (for class 1, 3 and 5) of around 0.5. It is classified in class 3, because it is the only output greater than 0.5.

The fifth input of data-set 4 gives completely wrong results: the fifth output, corresponding to its class is equal to zero.

For data-set 5, the misclassification is due to the fact that there are two active output neurons. However, the value of the class 5 neuron (0.9924) is far greater than the value of the other active neuron (class 2, 0.5560).

9.6 CONCLUSION

The first drawback of the RCE algorithm is that the adjustments of the threshold requires a number of iterations, so it learns a little more slowly than Alpaydin's algorithm. However, it has the same advantage as Alpaydin's algorithm which is that it also does not use the back-propagation algorithm (only the RV model does and it is very time consuming). Alpaydin's algorithm trains one network with the entire data-base in 4 seconds, the RCE algorithm in 10 seconds and the RV algorithm in 2 minutes and using 45 seconds, on average using a Dell 386 personal computer with a maths co-processor.

To cover a certain region of the problem domain, the RCE algorithm needs more hidden neurons than Alpaydin's algorithm, and it generalises less effectively than Alpaydin's model. However, it would be interesting to try to improve the performance of this algorithm by trying to find the optimum value of both the influence radius and the centre of the domination areas.

The RV algorithm creates more neurons than the two previous algorithms, without an improvement on their performance. However, it would be interesting to try to change the decision criteria which associates an output to a class. For instance, instead of using a threshold to decide if the output is equal to zero or one, we could choose to set the largest value of the output cells to one. This idea has a drawback because at present the main interest in this algorithm is because of the fact that the outputs are continuous values.

So, this algorithm is not limited to classification applications. For instance, it may be possible to use it to indicate the proportion of each alcohol in a mixture of the five of them.

All three algorithms depend on the input presentation order. However, in the case of the RCE and Alpaydin's algorithms, it is possible to do some pruning during training. That is why they are less dependent on the order of presentation of the training data than the RV algorithm.

Our comparison of the three techniques, suggests that Alpaydin's algorithm is the best. This algorithm is easy to understand and to use: there is no requirement to search for an optimal parameter value (with the RV algorithm, the user must enter a value for the learning rate, the momentum term, the tolerance, and the number of iterations).

The problem associated with the network built by Alpaydin's algorithm is that the outputs are either 0 or 1. One does not have a continuous value which indicates to what extent the output is a member of a class, so it is difficult to determine the level of confidence one can have in the computed output. However, as far as this last point is concerned, there is the possibility of rejecting an output which should overcome this drawback. For instance, the algorithm can refuse to classify if the two closest hidden neurons to the input belong to different classes and if their respective values are closer than a threshold which depends on the application.

ACKNOWLEDGMENTS

The authors would like to thank Dr. H.V. Shurmer and other members of the Warwick Electronic Nose team for making this work possible.

REFERENCES

[Alp90]   Alpaydin, E., Neural Models of Incremental Supervised and Unsupervised Learning, PhD Thesis, Ecole Polytechnique Federale de Lausanne, Switzerland, 1990.

[CH91]   Chiu, W.C. and Hines, E.L., A Rule Based Dynamic Back-Propagation Network, in *Proceedings of the IEE Neural Net Conference, Bournemouth, UK,* 1991.

[DG89]   Debenham, R.M. and Garth, S.C., *IEE Coll. Digest No. 1989/83 18 May 6/1-6/3,* 1989.

[FL90]   Fahlman, S.E. and Lebiere, C., The Cascade-Correlation Learning Architecture, *Technical Report CMU-CS-90-100,* Carnegie Mellon University, USA, 1990.

[Fre89]   Frean, M.R., The Upstart Algorithm, a Method for Constructing and Training Feedforward Neural Networks, Department of Physics and Centre for Cognitive Science, Edinburgh University, UK, 1989.

[Gal86]   Gallant, S.I., Three Constructive Algorithms for Neural Learning, in *Proceedings of the 8th Annual Conference of Cognitive Science Society, Paris, France,* 1986.

[GH88]   Gardner, J.W. and Hines, E.L., Integrated Sensor Array Processing in an Electronic Nose, *IEE Colloquium*, 8-130, 1988.

[GHW90]   Gardner, J.W., Hines, E.L. and Wilkinson, M., Application of Artificial Neural Networks to an Electronic Olfactory System, *Meas. Sci. Technol.*, 1, 446-51, 1990.

[GHT92]   Gardner, J.W., Hines, E.L. and Tang, H.C., Detection of Vapours and Odours from a Multisensor Array Using Pattern Recognition Techniques, Part 2, *Artificial Neural Networks, Sensors and Actuators B*, 9, 9-15, 1992.

[Lip87]   Lippman, R.P., An Introduction to Computing with Neural Nets, *IEEE ASSP Magazine*, 4(2), 4-22, 1987.

[MN89]   Mezard, M. and Nadal, J.P., Learning in Feedforward Layered Network: The Tiling Algorithm, *Journal Physics A*, 22(12), 2191-203, 1989.

[PD82]   Persaud, K. and Dodd, G.H., Analysis of Discrimination Mechanisms in the Mammalian Olfactory System Using a Model Nose, *Nature*, 299, 352-5, 1982.

[RV91]   Refenes, A.N. and Vithlani, S., Constructive Learning by Specialisation, Technical Report, University College London, 1991.

[RCE82]   Reilly, D.L., Cooper, L.N. and Erlbaum, C., A Neural Model for Category Learning, *Biological Cybernetics*, 45, 35-41, 1982.

[RM86]   Rumelhart, D.E. and McClelland, J.L., *Parallel Distributed Processing*, MIT Press, 1986.

[SGC89]   Shurmer, H.V., Gardner, J.W. and Chan, H.T., The Application of Discrimination Techniques in Alcohols and Tobacco Using Tin Oxide Sensors, *Sensors and Actuators*, 18, 361-71, 1989.

[WK91]   Weiss, S.M. and Kulikowski, C.A., *Computer Systems that Learn*, Morgan Kaufmann, 1991.

[Wyn91]   Wynne-Jones, M., Constructive Algorithms and Pruning: Improving the Multilayer Perceptron, in *Proceedings of IMACS '91 Conference*, Vol. 2, 747-50, 1991.

Chapter 10

Detection and Identification of Potentiometric Flow Injection Analysis Peaks

Philip G. Barker [1] Dermot Diamond [2] Margaret Hartnett [2]

Interactive Systems Research Group, School of Computing and Mathematics
University of Teesside, U.K. [1]
School of Chemical Sciences, Dublin City University, Ireland [2]

Overview

In this chapter we discuss the application of back-propagation neural networks to the detection and identification of waveforms produced by the transient responses of electrodes selective to sodium, potassium and calcium ions injected into a flowing stream using a technique known as flow injection analysis (FIA).

The ability of the network to classify noisy data is studied by deliberately distorting the waveforms by a variety of mechanisms sometimes associated with potentiometric detection. In addition, an investigation of processes occurring within the network during training is performed by studying the variation of the lengths of the weight vectors and the angles which they make to the standard unit vector.

10.1   INTRODUCTION

In this section we provide the context for this chapter by discussing the previous applications of neural networks in analytical chemistry. We also discuss some of the basic principles of FIA and also the use of potentiometric detection.

10.1.1   Applications of Neural Network Technology to Analytical Chemistry

In recent years neural network technology has been successfully applied to a broad spectrum of problems from disciplines as diverse as commerce and engineering. Unfortunately, the same cannot be said for analytical chemistry where the number of applications of neural network technology have been relatively small. This is partially due to the predominantly algorithmic and statistical approaches normally used for problem solving in this discipline. However, most would agree that analytical chemistry is often employed under conditions of imprecise knowledge or uncertainty about the physical, chemical and/or biological processes underlying a particular technique and its application, and also with respect to the interpretation of the results of a particular analysis or group of analyses.

One of the most successful forms of artificial intelligence to be applied to analytical chemistry has been the expert system, which uses rules for the control of inference based on predicate calculus, which are specific to a particular problem domain. Expert systems have found several applications including those in high performance liquid chromatography (HPLC) method development [LBV90], chemical structure elucidation based on mass spectrometry data [HE90], and advice on sample pretreatment for elemental analysis [SDK89]. However, expert systems have their own associated problems. Perhaps the most troublesome problem is the acquisition and coding of the expert knowledge, as an expert may not be able to express the rules that are used to solve a problem in a coherent fashion, or groups of experts may interpret data in different ways. In addition to these problems, the system designer has to build in rules to cope with as many situations as possible. A limitation of expert systems is also seen when they move outside their areas of expertise in the problem domain, where their performance tends to drop.

Some of the advantages of neural network technology which may help to alleviate these problems include the ability of neural networks to generalise data which has not been presented to it in the training set, the ability of neural nets to recognise patterns from incomplete or distorted data, and finally the relationship between a problem and its solution does not have to be explicitly encoded by the designer.

While there are a number of different types of networks which can be used to solve various kinds of problems, the back-propagation net has been the most commonly used for analytical applications. Some examples of this approach are described below.

Bos et al [BBV90] applied a back-propagation net for the simultaneous determination of calcium and copper(II) ions in binary mixtures of copper(II) nitrate and calcium chloride, and also for the simultaneous determination of potassium, calcium, nitrate and chloride ions in mixtures of potassium chloride, calcium chloride and ammonium nitrate using arrays of ion-selective electrodes.

Robb and Munks [RM90] applied a simple linear neural net (i.e. without a hidden layer) to the interpretation of the infra-red spectra of organic compounds in order to identify different functional groups present in the molecules. A detection level of 53.3% on a test set of 541 compounds with 24 functional groups was achieved, and of the detected groups, 91.5% were identified correctly. They later improved upon their linear model by adding a hidden layer [MMR91] and demonstrated an improvement in the identification of functional groups in the training set using a net with a hidden layer when compared with the linear net.

Wythoff, Levine and Tomellini [WLT90] used a fully connected three layer back-propagation net for the verification and recognition of infra-red spectral peaks of vapour phase species. The widths of some of the spectral features were of the order of the resolution with which the spectra were acquired, meaning that spectral peaks were sometimes represented by a single data point (which made the distinction between the spectral features and noise spikes rather difficult). It was found that the addition of a noise reference to the signals in the training set produced an improvement in the mean absolute difference between the desired identification of patterns in the test set and the actual output from the network from an original value of 0.357 to a value of 0.19.

Long, Gregoriou and Gemperline [LGG90] used a back-propagation net for nonlinear multivariate calibration. They then applied neural network techniques to the determination of protein in wheat from near infra-red (NIR) spectroscopic data and to the quantitation of the ingredients in two pharmaceutical products using UV-visible spectroscopic data. It was found that principal components regression (PCR) performed better than neural networks when using perfectly linear simulated data. This was attributed to model error produced from fitting a sigmoid function to linear data. In the case of the wheat, PCR only slightly outperformed the neural network approach. The spectral data from the pharmaceuticals displayed non-linearities due to stray light and interactions between the pharmaceutical components at high concentrations. It was found that the non-linear response was inadequately modelled by the PCR, and consequently the neural network calibration results were found to be slightly better than the PCR results.

Gardner, Hines and Wilkinson [GHW90] applied a back-propagation network to the pattern recognition of signals produced from an array of tin oxide gas sensors. It was found that vapour patterns of methanol, butan-1-ol, propan-2-ol, 2-methyl-1-butanol and ethanol could be recognised at the parts per million (ppm) level in all cases.

Chang et al [CIS91] used a back-propagation net for the recognition of patterns produced from an array of piezoelectric crystals coated with phosphatidylglycerol, phosphatidylethanolamine, phosphatidylserine and lipid A which responded to amyl acetate, acetoin, menthone, methanol, ethanol, propanol and butanol. It was found that odorants could be identified with 70% probability.

Sundgren, Winquist, Lukkari and Lundstrom [SWL91] applied a three layer neural net to the quantification of the individual components in two types of gas mixtures. The first gas mixture was comprised of hydrogen, ammonia, ethanol and ethylene in air and the second mixture contained hydrogen and acetone in air. The components of the mixtures were to be quantified based on the responses of six metal oxide semiconductor MOSFETs which were exposed to the mixtures.

It was found that both hydrogen and ammonia concentrations were predicted more accurately by the neural net than by partial least squares (PLS), and the same was found for the hydrogen and acetone in the two component mixture.

Meyer et al [MHN91], used a back-propagation net for the identification of one-dimensional ^{1}H-NMR spectra of oligosaccharides derived from xyloglucan (a plant cell wall hemicellulose). It was found that the spectra were identified correctly by the neural net even when the spectra were perturbed by slight variations to their chemical shifts.

Bos and Weber [BW91] carried out a comparison of the training of neural networks by backwards error propagation and genetic algorithms for quantitative x-ray fluorescence (XRF) spectrometry of iron, nickel and chromium samples. The backwards error propagation trained networks performed better than the genetic algorithm trained networks for these samples. However it was found that the two types of training procedures produced nets which performed equally well when trained on a larger data set composed of XRF spectra of thin iron and nickel layers on a substrate.

Long et al [LMH91] used a back-propagation net for pattern recognition of jet fuel chromatographic data obtained by gas chromatography (GC) and gas chromatography with mass spectroscopy (GC-MS). It was found that classification by neural nets was dramatically better than that by K nearest neighbour (KNN) and simple modelling of class analogy (SIMCA) for the water soluble fraction of the jet fuels.

Gemperline, Long and Gregoriou [GLG91] investigated the use of different multivariate techniques and neural networks for the detection and modelling of non-linear regions of spectral response in multivariate, multicomponent spectroscopic assays of pharmaceutical products. It was found that neural networks could be used to develop non-linear calibration models that performed better than PCR or PLS.

Peterson [Pet92] described the use of a counterpropagation net for the modelling and prediction of the Kovats retention indices of a set of substituted phenols using the nonempirical structural descriptors, molar refractivity and dipole moments, to describe the phenols. It was found that the neural network approach produced results which were significantly better than the results produced by linear regression.

The following references are recommended for more general reading on the theory and application of neural network technology: [Ale88, Bar91, Hec90, KS90, Pao89, Zup90].

10.1.2   Flow Injection Analysis

With increased public awareness and concern about health, food and environmental issues, there has been a concomitantly dramatic increase in the volume of routine analyses performed by laboratories. The problem of producing large volumes of accurate and precise data motivated the design and development of rapid and inexpensive automatic analytical systems, which are now employed in a diverse range of applications including the monitoring and control of industrial processes, diagnostic and screening clinical tests, environmental monitoring of a wide variety of species in the air, soil and water and quality control in the food processing and pharmaceutical industries.

Automated analytical instruments can be broadly classified as being either discrete or continuous, although instruments which are hybrids of the two classes also exist. Discrete or segmented flow instruments simulate the operations which would be carried out in the manual version of a particular analysis. Samples are retained in discrete vessels throughout the various analytical operations such as dilution, reagent addition and mixing, leading to the final measurement. In contrast, in a continuous flow instrument such as FIA which is depicted in Fig. 10.1, the sample becomes a plug in a flowing stream and is carried from the injection port to the detector and then to waste.

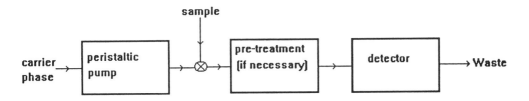

Fig. 10.1 - Schematic of flow injection analysis.

A wide variety of different detectors and operating conditions such as carrier phase composition, mixing reagents and flow rate have provided the means to analyse for a diverse range of species. Some applications include: spectrophotometric detection of phosphate and chloride in blood sera [RH76] and glycerol in water [BR76]; kinetic determination of glucose in blood sera [HRR77]; and potentiometric determination of chloride in tap and sewage water [IC85], fluoride in tap water, beverages and urine [FB86] and sodium, potassium and calcium in mineral water and plasma [FD92].

[Bor82] and [SH89] provide more background information relating to flow injection analysis.

10.1.3 Potentiometry

Electrochemical techniques can be broadly divided into voltammetric and potentiometric methods. Potentiometry is a technique which involves the measurement under zero current conditions of potentials generated by electrochemical cells. One half of the cell is an ion-selective electrode (ISE) which generates a potential related to the activity of the ion of interest (primary ion). Changes in the potential are measured against that of a reference electrode which is also in contact with the sample solution. Ideally the reference electrode potential is unaffected by changes in the sample composition. The basic apparatus used for a potentiometric measurement is depicted in Fig. 10.2.

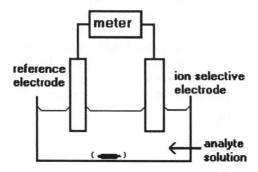

Fig. 10.2 - Basic potentiometric system.

Mathematically the potential measured between an ideal electrode and the reference electrode is described by the Nernst equation

$$E = E° + S\log_{10}a_i \qquad (10.1)$$

where E is the measured cell potential, E° is the standard cell potential, and S is the slope of the electrode, which has a value of 59.2 mV divided by the number of electrons per ion involved in the electrochemical process, when measurements are performed at 25°C. The variable a_i describes the activity of the primary ion which is a thermodynamic quantity related to the concentration of the ion.

Unfortunately, electrodes do not respond to the primary ion alone, i.e. the electrodes are selective but not specific. The additional effects of other ions present in the system are accounted for by the Nikolskii-Eisenmann expression.

$$E = E° + S\log_{10}\left(a_i + \sum_j k_{ij}^{pot} a_j^{z_i/z_j}\right) \qquad (10.2)$$

The variables E, $E°$, S and a_i are as before. k_{ij}^{pot} is a weighting factor or selectivity coefficient which refers to the selectivity of an electrode for its primary ion relative to the other ions present in the system.

Because potentiometry is a high impedance technique, it is particularly prone to the uptake of noise from its surroundings. Hence all the cables used in potentiometric experiments are generally shielded to reduce the effects of noise, but there can still be problems with inductive and RF noise and static. This technique is also characterised as having a floating earth, since the potential difference is measured relative to a reference electrode rather than to ground, which can sometimes produce problems associated with the shifting of the baseline potential through current leakage to ground.

[Mor81] and [WMD90] are recommended for further reading about the theory and application of potentiometric analysis.

10.1.4 Potentiometric Flow Injection Analysis

Fig. 10.3 depicts a typical trace obtained from FIA apparatus using three ion selective electrodes for the detection of sodium, potassium and calcium ions. The traces represent the potential differences measured between the different ion selective electrodes and the reference electrode over a period of time in which a sample containing these three ions is injected into the carrier phase and is swept past the electrodes by the carrier phase to waste.

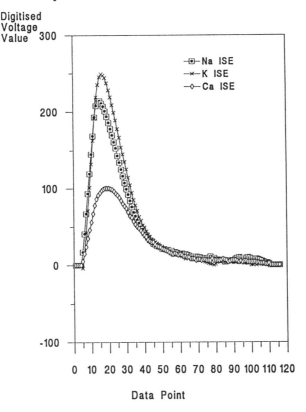

Fig. 10.3 - Typical potentiometric FIA traces.

The traces show a rapid rise as the sample reaches the electrodes and then a more gradual descent as the tail of the sample passes the electrodes on its way to waste. The duration of a particular peak is dependent on several variables, including how fast the pump is pumping the sample and carrier phase past the electrodes, but the typical duration of a peak would be 30 seconds or less. The potential difference measured between the reference and each ion selective electrode is acquired and digitised on separate channels of a data acquisition card fitted inside a computer. A voltage range can then be defined allowing the digitised values corresponding to the responses of the electrodes at different times during the analysis to be prescaled for further processing.

10.2 EXPERIMENTAL METHOD

The continuous flow system used for transient ion detection, which is shown schematically in Fig. 10.4, is as described by Forster and Diamond [FD92].

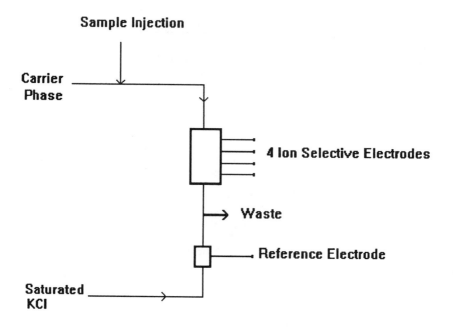

Fig. 10.4 - Computer controlled flow injection analysis system.

The electrodes used for the detection of sodium, potassium and calcium were based on three ionophores (p-t-butylcalix[4]methyl acetate [CDS89], valinomycin (Fluka) and ETH 129 (Fluka), respectively), each of which were immobilised within a plasticised PVC matrix (CDS89]. Membranes were cast from solutions of the ionophore, ion excluder, plasticiser and PVC in tetrahydrofuran (THF). The membranes were then mounted in the electrode block which was reconnected to the rest of the continuous flow system.

The experimental data were captured via an Analog Devices RTI-815 data acquisition card fitted inside an IBM 286 compatible PC. Data acquisition and processing software was written in Microsoft QuickBASIC.

Two types of neural network software were investigated namely, Neural Technologies Ltd. NT5000 running on an 80486 PC and NeuralWorks Professional II running on a SUN SPARC.

Data preparation for the neural networks and results analyses from the neural nets were performed using software written in Borland Turbo C and SUN C version 1.1.

10.3   RESULTS

In this section two sets of results are described and discussed. First, we present the results from the NT5000 software and then present the details of the results obtained from the experiments performed using the NeuralWorks software.

10.3.1   Using the NT5000 Software

There were seven possible combinations of the sodium, potassium and calcium ions on their own or with the other ions in the group. Data files composed of 80 data points per electrode (240 data points in total) were prepared and prescaled for the neural net. The initial training set was composed of the electrode response profiles to the 7 possible combinations of the cations and also contained a synthetic profile corresponding to the absence of any of the cations.

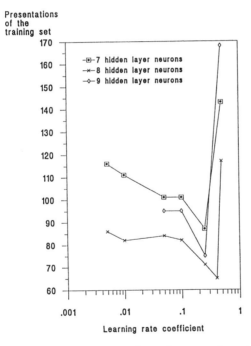

Fig. 10.5 - Convergence dependency on learning rate.

The number of iterations required for the maximum output error to converge to the predefined value of 0.03 was investigated with respect to the learning rate coefficient and momentum for different numbers of hidden layer neurons (where the output error is considered to be the difference between the desired output of a network and its actual output).

Fig. 10.5 shows how the number of presentations of the training set required for convergence varies with learning rate for neural networks with 7, 8 and 9 neurons in the hidden layer.

As can be seen from this figure at very low learning rates the nets converge slowly to a solution, and at very high learning rates the nets also converge slowly to a solution, but in this case it is due instability in the learning process produced by the large learning coefficient.

Fig. 10.6 shows how number of presentations of the training set required for convergence varies with momentum for neural networks with 7, 8 and 9 neurons in the hidden layer. As can be seen in this figure the number of iterations required for convergence decreases dramatically with increased momentum which acts to stabilise learning.

It was found that a momentum of 0.75 and a learning coefficient of 0.5 produced the shortest convergence time for the training process.

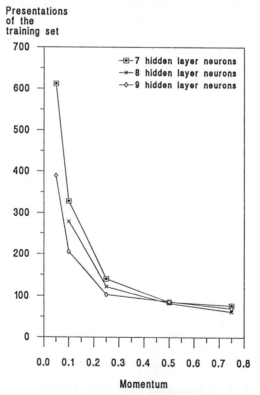

Fig. 10.6 - Convergence dependency on momentum.

Fig. 10.7 shows how the number of presentations of the training set required for convergence varies with respect to the number of neurons in the hidden layer; it shows a gradual decrease in the number of presentations of the training set required for convergence with increasing number of hidden layer neurons, until at 65 neurons the problem becomes more difficult to solve and the number of iterative cycles increases.

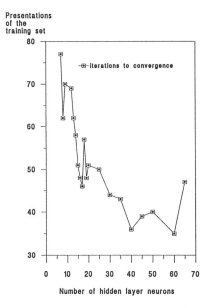

Fig. 10.7 - Convergence dependency on number of neurons in the hidden layer.

Test sets composed of distortions of response profiles in the training set were composed to study the ability of networks to deal with the distortions discussed in the introduction. A mean squared error (MSE) was used as a means of determining the performance of the networks, where the error is considered to be the difference between the desired output of a given output layer neuron (corresponding to a presence or absence of one of the three ions) and its actual output.

10.3.1.1 Variation of MSE with Noise Level and Number of Neurons in the Hidden Layer

An investigation was performed into how the MSE of a test set varied as a function of the noise composition of the test set and the number of neurons present in the hidden layer of a network. Noise was added at 10%, 25%, 50% and 75% of the maximum/minimum peak/trough height to the patterns in the training set. The results of this study are depicted graphically in Fig. 10.8.

As expected the smallest MSE is found at the lowest noise level and the MSE generally increases with increased noise level. It can also be seen from this figure that while the MSE decreases with increasing number of neurons in the hidden layer that the variance of the MSE around the different noise levels also increases.

This suggests that at low numbers of hidden layer neurons, the net has not been able to fully build a model representing a mapping of the response profiles to the ion identities, but while the nets with larger number of hidden layer neurons form a better model, the model itself is less robust, i.e. more sensitive to pattern distortion by noise addition.

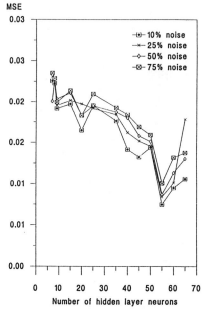

Fig. 10.8 - MSE dependency on added noise.

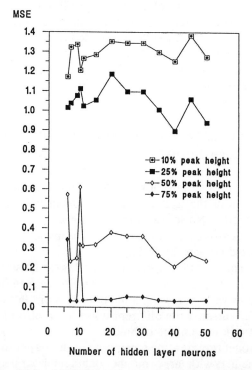

Fig. 10.9 - MSE dependency on relative peak height.

10.3.1.2   Variation of MSE with Peak Height and Number of Hidden Layer Neurons

An investigation was performed into how the MSE of a test set varied as a function of the amplitude alteration of the original patterns and the number of neurons in the hidden layer of the network.

The heights of the peaks were reduced to 75%, 50%, 25% and 10% of their original heights. The results of this study are shown in Fig. 10.9.

It can be seen from the units on this figure that the MSE shows a very great dependency on the relative peak heights, to a greater extent than to noise levels. The largest MSE is seen at very low peak heights where it is difficult to distinguish between a peak and its baseline.

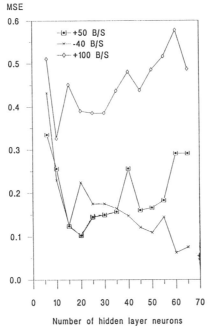

Fig. 10.10 - MSE dependence on peak displacement.

10.3.1.3   Variation of MSE with Baseline Shifting as a Function of the Number of Neurons in the Hidden Layer

An investigation was performed into how the MSE of a test set varied as a function of the displacement of the original peaks in the amplitude window, the results of which are depicted graphically in Fig. 10.10.

The baselines of the peaks were shifted by +50, +100 and -40 digitised units, which corresponds to approximately +20%,+40% and -16% of the original monovalent ion peak heights. It can be seen from Fig. 10.10 that for peaks shifted in the negative direction that the MSE decreases with increasing number of neurons in the hidden layer, whereas for peaks shifted in the positive direction that the opposite trend is generally true.

This suggests that as the number of hidden layer neurons increases that any features above a given level in the amplitude window are classified as being peaks and features below this level as not being peaks irrespective of the underlying shape of the feature.

10.3.1.4 Discussion of Results

It can be seen from the scales of the MSE axes in Figs. 10.8, 10.9 and 10.10 that variation of the peak heights had the most deleterious effect on the MSE followed by baseline shifting and noise addition. This suggests that the trained networks were sensitive to the position of the peak baseline in the predefined voltage range and the relative height of any feature above this baseline.

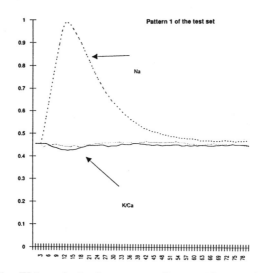

Fig. 10.11 - FIA peaks in the test set of a sample containing sodium.

10.3.1.5 Further Training

A training set composed of 70 random patterns representing different levels of baseline shift, peak variation and noise addition effects investigated earlier was designed and a testing set of 56 patterns was composed in a similar fashion.

For a net with 50 neurons in its hidden layer, 77% of the patterns in the testing set were classified correctly, based on the assumption that an output of greater than 0.9 indicated the presence of the species and an output of less than 0.1 indicated its absence.

Fig. 10.11 depicts the test pattern produced from an FIA trace of a sample containing sodium. The original trace was distorted by shifting its baseline by approximately 60% of the original peak height. The neural net with 50 neurons in its hidden layer produced a classification of the pattern as 1 (sodium present), 0.067 (potassium not present) and 0.017 (calcium not present).

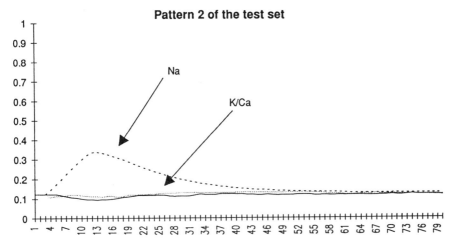

Fig. 10.12 - FIA peaks in the test set of a sample containing sodium.

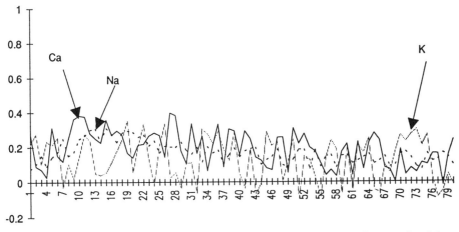

Fig. 10.13 - FIA peaks in the test set of a sample containing sodium and calcium.

Fig. 10.12 depicts the test pattern produced from the same FIA trace as Fig. 10.11. However, in this case the original trace was distorted by reducing the peak height to 40% of its original value. The neural net with 50 neurons in its hidden layer produced a classification of the pattern as 1.0 (sodium present), 0.011 (potassium not present) and 0.01 (calcium not present).

   Fig. 10.13 depicts the test pattern produced from an FIA trace of a sample containing sodium and calcium. The original trace was distorted by reducing the peak heights of the sodium and calcium peaks by 30% and 80% of their original values respectively. Noise at 40% of the maximum peak heights was also added to each peak. The neural net with 50 neurons in its hidden layer produced a classification of the pattern as 0.999 (sodium present), 0.003 (potassium not present) and 0.982 (calcium present).

Fig. 10.14 depicts the test pattern produced from an FIA trace of a sample containing potassium and calcium. The original trace was distorted by shifting its baseline by approximately 10% of the original maximum peak height, by reducing the peak heights of the potassium and calcium peaks to 40% and 60% of their original values respectively and by adding 60% maximum peak height noise onto the FIA peaks. The neural net with 50 neurons in its hidden layer produced a classification of the pattern as 0.001 (sodium not present), 0.998 (potassium present) and 0.998 (calcium present).

However when the MSE on the test set at convergence was investigated as a function of the number of neurons in the hidden layer a distinct oscillation was seen, and so further investigation of the learning process was performed using NeuralWorks Professional II.

Pattern 42 of the test set

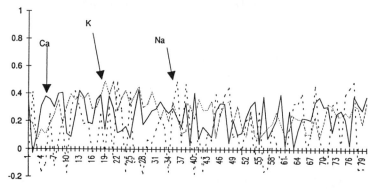

Fig. 10.14 - FIA peaks in the test set of a sample containing potassium and calcium.

10.3.2   Using NeuralWorks II

Using this software it was possible to study the MSE on the training and testing sets during the training period. It was also possible to save the connection weights at intervals during training.

It was decided to investigate some of the processes occurring in the neural nets during training by studying the lengths of the vectors represented by the connection weights between the input and hidden layers and hidden and output layers, and also to study the variation of the angle formed between these vectors and the unit vector during training.

If all the connection weights from one layer to another are treated as a single vector, then its length can be described by

$$||W|| = \sqrt{\sum_i \sum_j W_{ij}^2} \qquad (10.3)$$

$\sqrt{n}$, (n being the dimension of the weight vector).

From the definition of the dot product of two vectors

$$U.W = ||U|| \, ||W|| \cos\theta \qquad (10.4)$$

$$\cos\theta = \frac{U.W}{||u|| \, ||W||} = \frac{\sum_i \sum_j W_{ij}}{\sqrt{n} \sqrt{\sum_i \sum_j W_{ij}^2}} \qquad (10.5)$$

$$\theta = \cos^{-1}\left(\frac{\sum_i \sum_j w_{ij}}{\sqrt{n} \sqrt{\sum_i \sum_j W_{ij}^2}} \right) \qquad (10.6)$$

10.3.2.1 Comparison of Training and Testing Set Errors

Fig. 10.15 shows the variation of MSE values from the training and testing sets with the number of presentations of the training set for a back-propagation net with 20 neurons in its hidden layer.

Fig. 10.16 zooms in on the later stages of training of the net seen in Fig. 10.15 and demonstrates how the MSE of the training set can continue to decrease while the MSE of the test set can begin to increase. This effect is a feature of overtraining.

It was observed that overtraining or the potential for overtraining was a problem for all the neural nets studied. For some of the nets the overtraining was much more obvious and occurred before the convergence point defined in the NT5000 software, indicating the difficulties associated with the interpretation of the MSE of the test set as a function of the number of hidden layer neurons.

In addition to the overtraining problem there was some oscillation in the MSEs of the test set in the later stages of training which, while being very small relative to the error at the start of training, made direct comparison of the networks in terms of their MSEs after a fixed number of iterations difficult. However, it was observed that were differences between the variations and values of the MSEs between the NT5000 software and the NeuralWorks II software. This may be due to variations in the random values of the connection weights at the start of training.

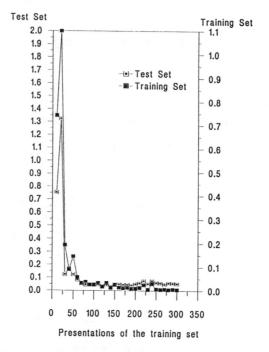

Fig. 10.15 - Variation of MSE during training.

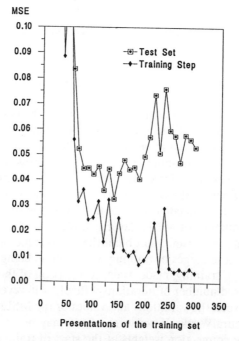

Fig. 10.16 - Overtraining effects.

10.3.2.2   Variation of Vector Length and Angle Formed with the Unit Vector During Training

Fig. 10.17 shows how the lengths of the vectors corresponding to the connection weights between the input and hidden layers and hidden and output layers varied during training for a back-propagation net with 25 neurons in the hidden layer.

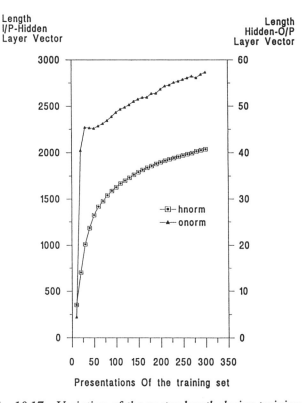

Length
I/P-Hidden
Layer Vector

Length
Hidden-O/P
Layer Vector

Presentations Of the training set

Fig. 10.17 - Variation of the vector length during training.

Fig. 10.18 shows how the angles between the unit vector and the vectors corresponding to the connection weights between the input and hidden layers and hidden and output layers varied during training for the back-propagation net in Fig. 10.17.

It can be seen in Fig. 10.17 that the length of the input to hidden layer vector was greater than the length of the hidden to output layer vector throughout the training process, which can be attributed to the greater dimensionality of the first vector. Similarly it can be seen in Fig. 10.18 that the hidden to output layer vector made a larger angle with the unit vector than did the input to hidden layer vector.

The initial rapid decrease in MSE during training is characterised by a rapid increase in the length of the hidden to output layer vector in Fig. 10.17, whereas the input to hidden layer vector length tends to display a smooth continuous trend throughout training. The angle that the input to hidden layer vector makes to the unit vector in Fig. 10.18 forms a spike during this period, while the hidden to output layer vector angle increases slowly.

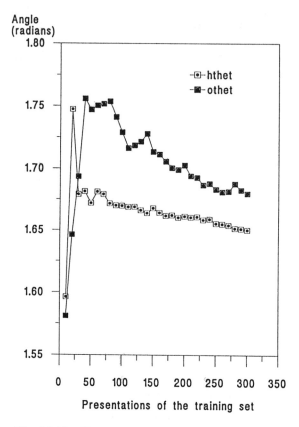

Fig. 10.18 - Variation of vector angle during training.

This suggests that during the initial stages of training that the input to hidden layer vector gradually increases in length but fluctuates in direction, whereas the input to hidden layer vector shows a rapid change in length and direction.

After this initial period of rapid change the length of the hidden to output layer vector continues to increase, but at a much slower rate than before and the input to hidden layer vector continues its smooth increase in length.

Those networks which displayed signs of overtraining also suggested some interesting properties of their vector lengths and angles. Fig. 10.19 shows how the angle formed between the unit vector and the vectors corresponding to the input to hidden layers and hidden to output layers vary during training for the network whose MSE change is shown in Fig. 10.15.

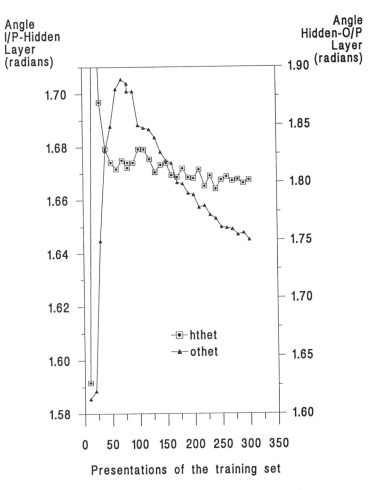

Fig. 10.19 - Variation of vector angle during training.

As can be seen in Fig. 10.16 a net with 20 neurons in its hidden layer was clearly overtraining after about 120 iterations. This period, in which the model for the training set was improved to the detriment of the test set, was associated with a rapid decrease in the angle that the hidden to output layer vector made with the unit vector compared to the rate of decrease of the angle formed by the hidden to output layer vector (Fig. 10.19).

Fig. 10.20 shows the variation of MSE of the training and testing sets during training for a back-propagation net with 45 neurons in the hidden layer. As can be seen from this figure the MSE on the training set is improving as the magnitude of the oscillations in the MSE of the test set are reducing during the later stages of training.

Fig. 10.21 shows how the lengths of the vectors corresponding to the connection weights between the input and hidden layers and hidden and output layers vary during training for the same net.

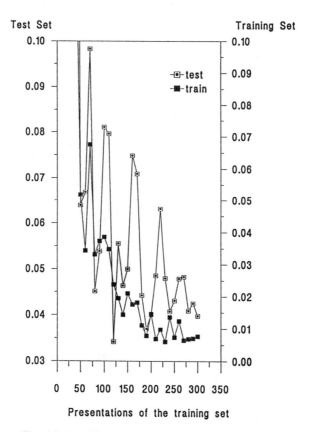

Fig. 10.20 - Variation of MSE during training.

As with the other networks studied, two distinct regions can be identified in the variation of the hidden to output layer vector length during training. It can be seen that the normal rapid increase in the vector length during the early stages of training is present, followed by a slower increase in the vector length while the network model of the training set is being more gradually improved, until about 130 presentations of the training set, at which point the vector length appears to be increasing more rapidly. This suggests the presence of another period of change in the vector length corresponding to the period in the training of the network in which the network model stabilises.

Fig. 10.22 shows how the angles formed between unit vector and the vectors corresponding to the connection weights between the input and hidden layers and hidden and output layers vary during training for this network.

The three regions already seen in Fig. 10.21 can also be seen in Fig. 10.22, which shows how the angles formed between unit vector and the vectors corresponding to the connection weights between the input and hidden layers and hidden and output layers vary during training for this network. A rapid increase in the angle is seen during the initial stage of training, followed by a more gradual increase corresponding to the second region in the variation of vector length plot and followed again by a region where the angle gradually decreases, corresponding to the stabilisation of the network model.

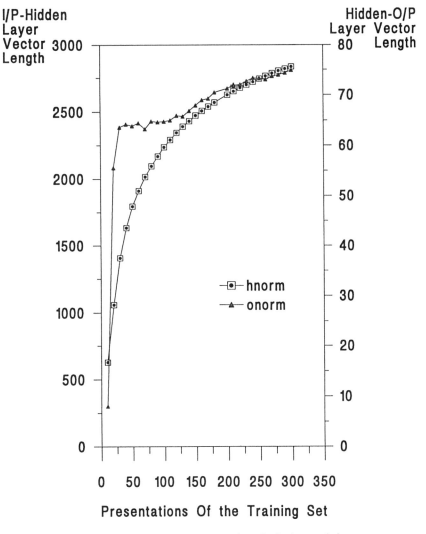

Fig. 10.21 - Variation of vector length during training.

10.4 CONCLUSION

Back-propagation networks have been investigated for the detection and identification of some metal ions in solution based on the transient response profiles of ion selective electrodes to these ions when they are injected into a flowing stream. The effects of distorting the patterns (in fashions similar to those found in practice) on the ability of the networks to perform their identification task was studied, and training and testing sets were devised to consider these deleterious effects. The networks performed well on the test sets even at distortion levels much higher than those normally found in real-life measurements.

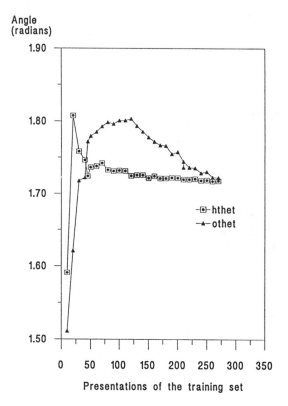

Fig. 10.22 - Variation of vector angle during training.

The same testing and training sets were used to investigate the training process further using a second type of neural network software. There were some variations between the results produced by the two pieces of software which was attributed to possible differences in the initial connection weights. The processes occurring within some networks during training were investigated by studying the variation of the lengths of the vectors representing the connection weights between the input and hidden layers and the hidden and output layers, and also by studying the variation of the angle formed between these vectors and the unit vector as training progressed.

It would be of interest to expand the use of neural network technology to FIA pattern recognition using other types of neural networks, such as the counter-propagation net, and also to investigate real time pattern recognition using spatio-temporal neural networks such as recurrent back-propagation nets.

ACKNOWLEDGEMENT

The FIA patterns used for this study were provided courtesy of Mr. Francisco Jose Saez De Viteri Alonso, from the School of Chemical Sciences, Dublin City University.

REFERENCES

[Ale88]   Aleksander, I., *An Introduction to Neural Computing,* TAB Books Inc., Blue Ridge Summit PA, 1988.

[Bar91]   Barker, P.G., Some Artificial Intelligence Techniques for the Interpretation of Experimental Data, *Anal. Proc.,* 28(4), 110-15, 1991.

[BBV90]   Bos, M., Bos, A. and van der Linden, W.E., Processing of Signals from an Ion Selective Electrode Array by a Neural Network, *Anal. Chim. Acta,* 233(1), 31-39, 1990.

[Bor82]   Borman, S.A. (ed.) *Instrumentation in Analytical Chemistry*, Vol. 2, American Chemical Society, Washington D.C., 1982.

[BR76]   Betteridge D. and Ruzicka J., The Determination of Glycerol in Water by Flow Injection Analysis: A Novel Way of Measuring Viscosity, *Talanta,* 23(5), 409-10, 1976.

[BW91]   Bos, M. and Weber, H.T., Comparison of the Training of Neural Networks for Quantitative X-Ray Fluorescence Spectrometry by a Genetic Algorithm and Backward Error Propagation, *Anal. Chim. Acta,* 247(1), 97-105, 1991.

[CDS89]   Cadogan, A.M., Diamond, D., Smyth, M.R., Deasy, M., McKervey, M.A. and Harris, S.J., Sodium-Selective Polymeric Membrane Electrodes Based on Calix[4]arene Ionophores, *Analyst,* 114(12), 1551-54, 1989.

[CIS91]   Chang, S.M., Iwasaki, Y., Suzuki, M., Tamiya, E. and Karube, I., Detection of Odorants Using an Array of Piezoelectric Crystals and Neural Network Pattern Recognition, *Anal. Chim. Acta,* 249(2), 323-29, 1991.

[FB86]   Frenzel, W. and Braetter, P., The Fluoride Ion Selective Electrode in Flow Injection Analysis, III: Applications, *Anal. Chim. Acta,* 188, 151-64, 1986.

[FD92]   Forster, R.J. and Diamond, D., Nonlinear Calibration of Ion Selective Arrays for Flow Injection Analysis, *Anal. Chem.*, 64(15), 1721-28, 1992.

[GHW90]   Gardner, J.W., Hines, E.L. and Wilkinson, M., Application of Artificial Neural Networks to an Electronic Olfactory System, *Meas. Sci. Technol.* 1, 446-51, 1990.

[GLG91]   Gemperline, P.J., Long, J.R. and Gregoriou, V.G., Nonlinear Multivariate Calibration Using Principal Components Regression and Artificial Neural Networks, *Anal. Chem.*, 63(20), 2313-23, 1991.

[HE90]   Hart, K.J. and Enke, C.G., An Automated Chemical Structure Elucidation System (ACES) for Mass Spectrometry/Mass Spectrometry Data, *Chemometrics and Intelligent Laboratory Systems*, 8(3), 293-302, 1990.

[Hec90]   Hecht-Nielsen, R., *Neurocomputing*, Addison-Wesley, Mass, USA, 1990.

[HRR77]   Hansen, E.H., Ruzicka, J. and Rietz, B., Flow Injection Analysis VIII: Determination of Glucose in Blood Serum with Glucose Dehydrogenase, *Anal. Chim. Acta*, 89(2), 241-54, 1977.

[IC85]   Ilcheva, L. and Cammann, K., Flow Injection Analysis of Chloride in Tap and Sewage Water Using Ion Selective Electrode Detection, *Fresenius 'Z, Anal. Chem.*, 322(3), 323-26, 1985.

[KS90]   Kateman, G. and Smits, J.R.M., Neural Networks in Analytical Chemistry, in *Proceedings of the Scientific Computing and Automation Conference (Europe)*, 151-60, 1990.

[LBV90]   van Leeuwen, J.A., Buydens, L.M.C., Vandeginste, B.G.M. and Kateman, G., Expert Systems in Chemical Analysis, *Trends in Analytical Chemistry*, 9(2), 49-54, 1990.

[LGG90]   Long, J.R., Gregoriou, V.G. and Gemperline, P.J., Spectroscopic Calibration and Quantitation Using Artificial Neural Networks, *Anal. Chem.*, 62(17), 1791-97, 1990.

[LMH91]   Long, J.R., Mayfield, H.T., Henley, M.V. and Kromann, P.R., Pattern Recognition of Jet Fuel Chromatographic Data by Artificial Neural Networks with Back-Propagation of Error, *Anal. Chem.*, 63(13), 1256-61, 1991.

[MHN91]   Meyer, B., Hansen, T., Nute, D., Albersheim, P., Darvill, A., York, W. and Sellers, J., Identification of the ^{1}H-NMR Spectra of Complex Oligosaccharides with Artificial Neural Networks, *Science*, 251, 542-44, 1991.

[MMR91]   Munk, M.E., Madison, M.S. and Robb, E.W., Neural Network Models for Infra-Red Spectrum Interpretation, *Mikrochim. Acta*, II, 505-14, 1991.

[Mor81]   Morf, W.E., *The Principles of Ion-Selective Electrodes and of Membrane Transport Studies in Analytical Chemistry*, Vol. 2, Elsevier, Amsterdam, 1981.

[Pao89]   Pao, Y.H., *Adaptive Pattern Recognition and Neural Networks*, Addison-Wesley, Mass, USA, 1989.

[Pet92]   Peterson, K.L., Counter-Propagation Neural Networks in the Modelling and Prediction of Kovats Indices for Substituted Phenols, *Anal. Chem.*, 64(4), 379-86, 1992.

[RH76]   Ruzicka, J. and Hansen, E.H., Flow Injection Analysis VI: The Determination of Phosphate and Chloride in Blood Serum by Dialysis and Sample Dilution, *Anal. Chim. Acta*, 87(2), 353-63, 1976.

[RM90]   Robb, E.W. and Munk, M.E., A Neural Network Approach to Infra-Red Spectrum Interpretation, *Mikrochim. Acta*, I (3-4), 131-55, 1990.

[SDK89]   Settle, Jr. F.A., Diamondstone, B.I., Kingstone, H.M. and Pleva, M.A., An Expert-Database System for Sample Preparation by Microwave Dissolution, I: Selection of Analytical Descriptors, *Journal of Chemical Information and Computer Sciences*, 29(1), 11-17, 1989.

[SH89]   Strobel, H.A. and Heineman, W.R., *Chemical Instrumentation: A Systematic Approach*, Wiley Interscience Publication, John Wiley and Son, New York, USA, 1989 (3rd edition).

[SWL91]   Sundgren, H., Winquist, F., Lukkari, I. and Lundstrom, I., Artificial Neural Networks and Gas Sensor Arrays: Quantification of Individual Components in a Gas Mixture, *Meas. Sci. Technol.*, 2(5), 464-69, 1991.

[WMD88]   Willard, H.H., Merritt, Jr. L.L., Dean, J.A. and Settle, Jr. F.A., *Instrumental Methods of Analysis*, Wadsworth Publishing Company, Belmont, California, 1988 (7th edition).

[WLT90]   Wythoff, B.J., Levine, S.P. and Tomellini, S.A., Spectral Peak Verification and Recognition Using a Multilayered Neural Network, *Anal. Chem.*, 62(24), 2702-9, 1990.

[Zup90]   Zupan, J., Can an Instrument Learn from Experiments Done By Itself?, *Anal. Chim. Acta*, 235(1), 53-63, 1990.

Chapter 11

Identification of Lighting Flicker Sources Using a Neural Network

P. Williams and A.W.G. Duller

School of Electronic Engineering and Computer Systems
University College of North Wales, Bangor, U.K.

Overview

A common problem found on the electricity supply to many homes and businesses is that of lighting flicker. This is usually an intermittent problem caused by the use of high current equipment in local industrial installations. E.A. Technology, formally the Electricity Research and Development Centre, has developed a P.C. based flickermeter for collecting data on these faults. The work reported here is a neural network system which allows the automatic identification of the flicker source from the collected data. Two popular paradigms are used; the Kohonen self organising feature map, performs vector quantization of the input patterns, while a multilayer perceptron is used for classification of the resulting binary vectors.

11.1 INTRODUCTION

Since the advent of the back-propagation [RHW86, Lip87] algorithm for multilayer perceptrons it has rapidly become the most popular adaptive neural network training algorithm in use today. It has been successfully applied to many pattern recognition and classification problems, examples of which include [GS88, MJD89, RMS89].

The first of these three applications involved the recognition of sonar returns from two objects, a metal cylinder and a rock of similar size (approximately 5ft in length).

The architecture used consisted of 60 input units and 2 output units. Experiments were run with a varying number of hidden units.

A total of 1200 returns were collected and 111 cylinder returns and 97 rock returns were used as training data. The raw data was preprocessed by filtering and spectral information was obtained and used as the input vectors.

Two types of experiment were performed; aspect angle independent and aspect angle dependent. Results of these experiments varied depending on the number of hidden units selected for the network. In general the average performance on the training and testing data sets varied from 77.1% to 99.8% correct classification on the aspect angle independent set; and between 73.1% and 100% correct classification on the aspect angle dependent set.

The second application used a neural network to diagnose system faults in an automotive control system. Experts in the automotive industry may use the inputs and outputs of an electronic engine control computer to diagnose faults in an engine. The data obtained is a mixture of high speed analogue and digital information which regulate the operation of the engine. An engineer can examine the complex data produced and determine whether the engine is operating normally, unfortunately most technicians would find the amount and structure of the data bewildering. The traditional approach to diagnostics is that a trained human expert formulates the rules by which the data can be analysed. However, the set of rules may be quite large. Also a heuristic approach generally fails to obtain sufficient information on the decision boundaries in the multidimensional space of the input vectors. It is true to say that the development of the heuristic rules in many problems of this sort are very time consuming, in that the engineer must first understand the system operation principles before production of the rules may begin.

[MJD89], thus experimented with neural classifiers to perform the recognition task. The data for training the network was obtained by introducing 26 different types of fault into the engine and observing engine performance. The training set consisted of 16 sets of data for each failure introduced, i.e. 16*26 data vectors with 52 elements in each vector (representing a single engine cycle). A test set of equal size was also obtained to test the network performance after training. The experimenters were satisfied that the network learned the classification in 24 hours.

The third and final example explored a neural network approach to optical character recognition of different fonts, sizes and even handwritten characters. Their approach was to obtain feature abstraction by preprocessing the input data. The character data was expanded in a set of orthogonal functions. Walsh functions were used for this purpose. They found that this method of feature abstraction reduces complexity without loss of relevant information. Firstly an intensity distribution function was obtained, which depended on the distribution of dark pixels in a character image. The Walsh functions were then obtained from this, forming a unique set of coefficients which form the feature vectors for that character.

The single hidden layer network used for this application consisted of 20 input units, corresponding to 10 features in the vertical direction and 10 features in the horizontal direction of the character's image, and the number of outputs was based on the number of characters in the standard alphanumeric character set; for numbers, letters and special characters this implied a 7 dimensional output vector if each symbol was to be represented by a 7 bit binary word. Therefore, the number of output units was 7. It was also determined (heuristically) that the number of hidden nodes must be the same as the number of input units, i.e. 20 nodes. Increasing the number of hidden units increases the convergence rate and also the recognition rate. The researchers produced a network that achieved a recognition rate between 97% and 99% for varying fonts and handwritten characters.

Two out of the above three examples used preprocessing of the data to obtain feature vectors for application to the network. Preprocessing of data is important since it can reduce the complexity of the classification task by reducing the input vector dimensionality and the amount of data necessary for inclusion in the data set. This process has far reaching effects when considering decreases in training time while maintaining the level of information contained in the training data set. The reduction of input vector size results in the reduction of the required number of hidden units required to successfully converge on the training problem. Indeed, the use of a neural network for pattern recognition reduces the need for a large database that would be required in an expert system. The recognition capability of the network lies in the connection weights between neurons and storage of data is merely a matter of changing a fixed size data structure.

In Section 11.2 we outline the flicker problem with an explanation of how the data is collected. In Section 11.3 we briefly describe the two paradigms used in this work. Section 11.4 explains the preprocessing of the data and the proposed network structure. Results and a discussion are presented in Section 11.5.

11.2 FLICKER PATTERNS AND DATA COLLECTION

11.2.1 Motivation

Fig. 11.1 outlines the basic principle of flicker generation. If a load impedance should suddenly draw more current, there would be a lowering of output voltage level, from the generator at the point of common coupling where other supplies, including domestic, are taken from. This voltage change manifests itself in domestic and business premises as flicker and is obviously most noticeable on the lighting supply.

E.A. Technology conducted experiments with human volunteers. Three categories of flicker disturbance were obtained; perception, awareness and severity. Tests were run on a human observer for each of these levels. A volunteer was placed in a room containing a 60W electric light fitting. Gradually the level of flicker applied to the bulb was increased until the observer just began to perceive it, this became the perception level. Another test provided the observer with a suitable distraction, e.g. a book. Again flicker was applied until the observer became aware of the flicker at which point he was distracted from his book; this then became the awareness level of flicker. The final category, that of severity, was obtained from the complaints collected from domestic users, at this level of flicker it is usually so annoying that local electricity boards had telephone calls from customers. It is necessary to have some way of recognising the causes of the phenomenon so that it may be tracked down to the offending installation and dealt with as soon as possible.

The P.C. based flickermeter, produced by E.A. Technology, was primarily designed for measuring the flicker produced by arc-furnaces, but has been used for gathering flicker data on other troublesome equipment. The instrument provides an output which classifies the flicker into the series of levels described above. A human expert is able to ascertain the cause of a flicker source by observing the data produced by the flickermeter. Since a wrong diagnosis can be costly, accuracy of diagnosis is important.

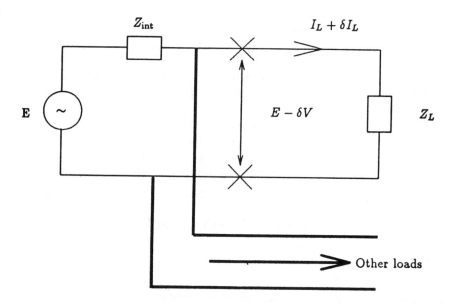

Fig. 11.1 - The Principle of Flicker Generation.

11.2.2 Derivation of Flicker Patterns

The flickermeter produces P.D.F.s (Probability Distribution Functions) by classifying the flicker into 200 classes. Each time the appropriate input flicker level value occurs, the counter of the corresponding class is incremented by one. In this way the frequency distribution function of the input sample is obtained. By choosing a scanning frequency sufficiently higher than the maximum flicker frequency, the final result at the end of the measuring interval represents the distribution of flicker level duration in each class. The P.D.F.s are 200 dimensional continuous valued vectors. Identification of the source of the flicker is possible by observing the "shape" of these vectors.

11.3 THE NEURAL NETWORK PARADIGMS

In the course of this work two neural network paradigms have been used. The theory behind these paradigms will not be developed in great detail, however, the basic concepts are outlined for completeness.

11.3.1 The Back-Propagation Algorithm

The back-propagation, algorithm for feedforward nets is a supervised learning paradigm that reduces the error between the desired output mapping and actual output mapping of the network by gradient descent. A typical 3 layer feed forward network is shown in Fig. 11.2. In supervised training the "teacher" supplies a desired output for the algorithm to ultimately reach.

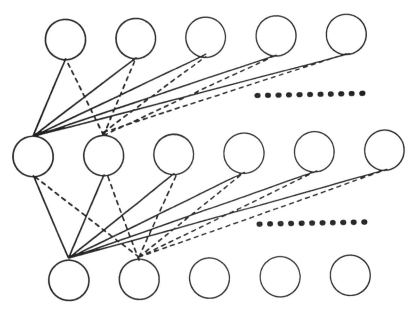

Fig. 11.2 - A three layer feed-forward network.

The activation of the jth unit for the pth training example a_{pj} is given by

$$a_{pj} = \sum_i w_{ji} o_{pi} + u_j \qquad (11.1)$$

where w_{ji} are the weights, u_j is a threshold and o_{pi} are the inputs to the neuron.

The error between the activation and its desired value, is used to determine the weight changes. The output of the jth node and pth input pattern is some function f_j of the activation a_{pj}

$$o_{pj} = f_j(a_{pj}). \qquad (11.2)$$

For the pth presentation of an input/output pair for training, the change for the weight which joins the jth unit to its ith incoming connection is proportional to some computed error for the jth unit. This is given by

$$\Delta_p w_{ji} = \beta \delta_{pj} o_{pi} \qquad (11.3)$$

where o_{pi} is the value of the ith incoming connection and is a constant which determines the rate of learning. δ_{pj} is the error for the jth neuron in the present layer for the pth training sample. For output units the error is calculated in a straightforward way based on knowledge of the desired target output value for the jth unit, t_{pj}. The error is given by

$$\delta_{pj} = (t_{pj} - o_{pj})f'(a_{pj}). \qquad (11.4)$$

It can be seen from the above equation that the output function of the back-propagation units must be differentiable. In the case of sigmoid functions the differential is such that it causes greater weight changes to take place for units where the output is less certain.

The error must be calculated differently if the units are in the hidden layer. If the unit is hidden, and its output is connected to K units, its error is defined as being proportional to the sum of the errors of all the K units modified by the weights connecting these units

$$\delta_{pj} = (\sum_{k}^{\infty} \delta_{pk} w_{kj})f'(a_{pj}). \qquad (11.5)$$

So the training implies two steps. Firstly a forward propagating step where an input vector is applied and propagated through the entire network, thus generating an output. From the output, the errors may be calculated and propagated back, layer by layer, through the network in order to update the weights. This process is then followed by another forward step which in turn is followed by another back propagating step and so on throughout the training data. The complete process is repeated until the overall error of the network reaches a preset value. An overall output error is defined as

$$E_p = \frac{1}{2}\sum_j (t_{pj} - o_{pj})^2. \qquad\qquad (11.6)$$

Using the above method it is quite possible for the training to become dependent on the order in which the data is presented to the network, thus increasing the chances of the training falling into a local minimum. It is quite usual for the weights to be updated only after a complete pass through the entire training set, i.e. batch mode training, and not after each input vector is presented. After each input vector is presented the 'weight update' is stored in an accumulator associated with each weight.   After each iteration the neurons update their weights by adding the accumulators to their weights and store the result as the new weight, the accumulators are then emptied ready for the next iteration.

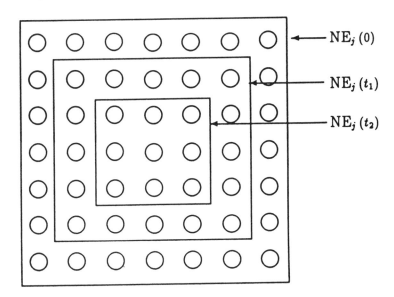

Fig. 11.3 - A feature map neighbourhood.

In order to improve convergence of the algorithm it is possible to add a momentum term to the weight update. This means that the present update not only depends on the errors but also on the last update of that weight. Each weight in the network then has a momentum value associated with the last update, thus

$$\Delta_p w_{ji}(t) = \beta \delta_{pj} o_{pi} + \alpha \Delta_p w_{ji}(t - 1) \qquad\qquad (11.7)$$

where α is the momentum factor and $\Delta_p w_{ji}(t - 1)$ is the last weight update. The momentum factor usually has a value between 0 and 1.

11.3.2 The Kohonen Self Organising Feature Map

Kohonen's algorithm [Koh89] creates a vector quantizer by adjusting weights from common input nodes to M output nodes arranged in a two dimensional grid as shown in Fig. 11.3.

Unlike back-propagation, the Self Organising Feature Map is an unsupervised learning paradigm, in that training examples are presented to the input layer without specifying the required output vector. After enough input examples have been presented, the weight vectors of the network are such that they form clusters that represent the probability density function of the input vectors. Also, topologically close output nodes are sensitive to inputs that are similar in structure. There is the ability to allocate reference vectors to the output nodes thus forming a powerful vector quantizer. The algorithm requires the formation of a neighbourhood around each output node, seen in Fig. 11.3. The neighbourhood slowly decreases as training continues. To train the network we first initialise the weights from N inputs to the M output nodes to small random values. We also set the initial size of the neighbourhood, preferably to a large value. A new input vector is presented to the network and the distance of the input to all nodes is computed as

$$d_j = \sum_{i=0}^{N-1} (x_i(t) - w_{ij}(t))^2 \tag{11.8}$$

where d_j = distance between the input and each output node j,
        $x_i(t)$ = input to node i at time t,
        $w_{ij}(t)$ = weight from input node i to output node j at time t.

Once these distances have been calculated we then need to select the output node, c, with the minimum $d_i = d_c$. The weights of node c and all nodes in the neighbourhood of c, defined by $NE_c(t)$ are updated. The new weights are then given by

$$w_{ij}(t + 1) = w_{ij}(t) + \eta(t)(x_i(t) - w_{ij}(t)) \tag{11.9}$$

for $j \in NE_c(t)$ $0 \le i \le N - 1$. The term $\eta(t)$ is a gain term $(0 < \eta(t) < 1)$ that decreases in time. The process repeats with the presentation of a new input.

11.4 METHOD

11.4.1 Preprocessing of Data

Fig. 11.4 shows two examples of PDFs. Large industrial motors, of the kind found in rock crushing plant, and arc-furnaces as used in the steel manufacturing industry. The raw data are sets of 200 dimensional continuous valued vectors.

In order to reduce the number of training examples and the input dimensionality of the data, the training set was applied to a Kohonen network. The network acts as a codebook [NF88] so that we obtain a given code depending on the particular output node activated by the input vector either by grouping nodes into regions and giving all nodes in that region the same code or individually coding each node. We believe the latter to be more useful, since it provides for a much higher decision resolution when considering quantization. It is known that convergence time in a back-propagation network scales with training set size [Tes87] so it may appear that a relatively small training set is preferable. However, for good generalisation it is necessary to have a reasonably large training set. It is therefore essential that a compromise is reached. For a lower training set size it may be necessary to increase the number of hidden layer units in order to improve generalisation.

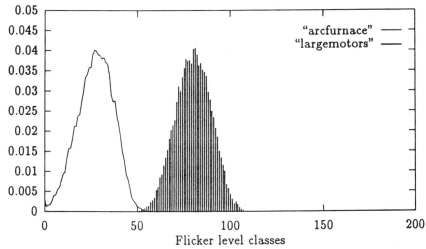

Fig. 11.4 - Examples of P.D.Fs for an arc-furnace and a large industrial motor.

The dimensionality of the input of a back-propagation network affects the optimum number of hidden units required for successful training. In general the higher the input dimensionality then the more hidden units are required for a given application. Also it has been suggested that the number of training examples, T, may have a bearing on the choice of number of hidden units, H, e.g. $H = T - 1$ or $H = log_2 T$.

Usually the selection of the number of hidden units is determined heuristically. Researchers train an application on a number of networks with a varying number of hidden units and find the network that provided the best performance, this can be a time consuming process. However, in some cases it is possible to determine the number of units required using mathematical means. One example of this is the N bit binary encoder problem. A three layer back-propagation network may be trained auto-associatively. In order to learn this mapping the network should have a number of hidden units equal to $log_2 N$. However, it has been shown recently that the N bit encoder may be solved using only 2 hidden units [Kru90]. Mirchandani [Mir89] has shown that the number of separable regions in the input space is a function of the number of hidden units and the input dimensionality. If we assume that a given output class reflects a certain separable region of input space, i.e. we have one region per class then we can determine the number of hidden units required from not only the input dimension but also the number of output classes. In d-dimensional space, the maximum number of regions that are linearly separable using H hidden units is given by

$$M(H,d) = \sum_{k=0}^{d} \binom{H}{k} \tag{11.10}$$

where

$$\binom{H}{k} = 0, \ H<k.$$

The benefits of input reduction are obvious; if our raw training examples are encoded in a suitable manner then we can speed up back-propagation training without much loss of information.

0100	0101	1101	1100
0110	0111	1111	1110
0010	0011	1011	1010
0000	0001	1001	1000

Fig. 11.5 - Kohonen Feature Map as a 'codebook' vector quantizer.

11.4.2 The Networks

In view of the advantages of reduction in the dimensionality of the input data a Kohonen Feature map has been used to reduce the 200 dimension raw data into a code which can then be used as the input to a back-propagation network.

Fig. 11.5 shows an 4 by 4 node Kohonen Feature map. This illustrates the type of coding used for individual nodes. The nodes are labelled such that the geometric distance is proportional to the Hamming distance between nodes. The neighbourhood is chosen using this metric.

A 4 by 4 map is shown for convenience, whereas in reality a 16 by 16 network was used with a corresponding 8 bit code. The same set of data was presented to the Feature Map as that presented to the back-propagation network, and a set of 8 bit vectors obtained. The learning rate for the Kohonen network was set to 0.1 with an initial neighbourhood of 15. A second back-propagation network was then trained using the resulting vectors and a comparison between the raw data trained back-propagation network and the 8 bit Kohonen code trained network was made.

11.5 RESULTS

The techniques described in the previous sections have been tested using a number of examples of flicker data. For comparison purposes the same data has been used for both the back-propagation network and the combination of the Kohonen network and back-propagation network.

The tests involved two training sets. One of 40 examples, 20 samples from arc-furnaces and 20 from heavy industrial motors with a test set of 16 examples in order to verify the performance. The other contains 58 samples, 20 samples from each of an arc-furnace and heavy industrial motors and 18 from a rolling mill.

Each of the networks were used to solve the above problems. Error plots for the 40 sample case are shown in Fig. 11.6. In each case the back-propagation networks used $\beta = 0.8$ and $\alpha = 0.3$. This is probably not the optimum value, but was kept constant in order to allow some form of comparison. In the future these results will be improved by finding the optimum settings for each problem and then performing the comparison. As can be seen from the results, with normal back-propagation increasing the number of hidden units reduces the number of iterations required but increases the work done per iteration. In both of these cases the input to the network was the "raw" flicker data containing 200 inputs. When the Kohonen network was used to reduce the input dimensionality, to 8 inputs, the convergence of the back-propagation increased dramatically as shown in the bottom plot of Fig. 11.6.

Currently, approximately 100 iterations through the complete sample set are used to produce the vectors from the Kohonen network. This requires considerable CPU time and if the combination of Kohonen and back-propagation is to be viable this number will have to be reduced. However, early results indicate that the ordering produced by using a very small number of iterations, 10-20, are good enough to be used as the input to the back-propagation network.

Similar tests were also performed using the 3 class, 58 sample problem. These results are shown in Fig. 11.7.

On the tests performed so far the generalisation properties of both network configurations appear to be similar. A few of the examples that we have obtained are wrongly categorised by all of our networks and it is possible that these have been wrongly attributed. This may be because in a sequence of samples that indicate a rolling mill, for example, there may be some which are taken when the rolling mill has been turned off. In terms of this application no difficulty arises since diagnosis will not be made using a single test sample. The source will only be determined after many samples have been collected.

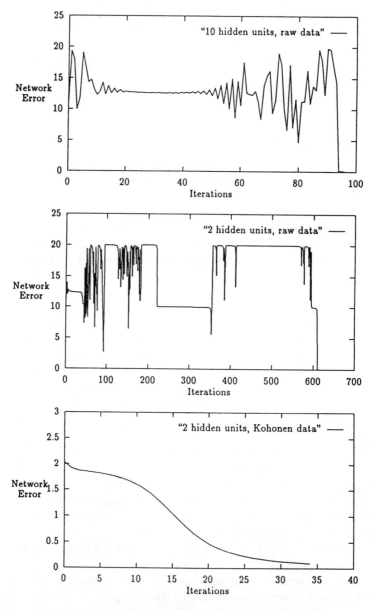

Fig. 11.6 - Error plots for 2 class, 40 sample data.

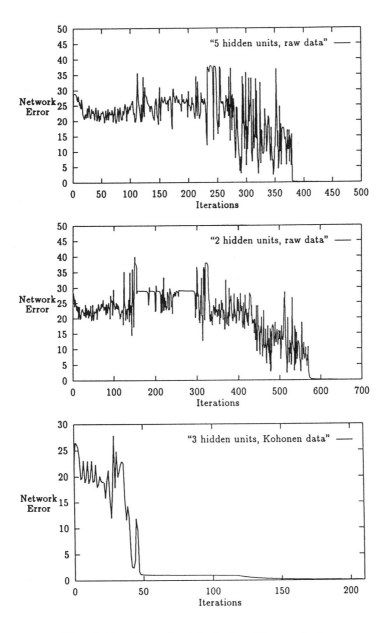

Fig. 11.7 - Error plots for 3 class, 58 sample data.

11.6 CONCLUSIONS

This work has shown that it is possible to recognise lighting flicker sources using neural network techniques. By extracting features from the raw input data we are able to both reduce input dimensionality and training set size.

It has been suggested that flicker sources also have a characteristic in the time domain and it is hoped that this time dependence can be added to the current networks to improve the recognition.

Future work includes expanding the size of the data sets with correspondingly larger numbers of output nodes. In order to properly test the generalisation, data is required for each type of fault from several completely different sources. In addition further investigation of the role of the Kohonen network may be required including the incorporation of extra parameters taken from the raw data.

ACKNOWLEDGMENTS

The authors wish to thank E.A. Technology for their support of this work through an SERC CASE award.

REFERENCES

[GS88]   Gorman, R.P. and Sejnowski, J., Analysis of Hidden Units in a Layered Network Trained to Classify Sonar Targets, *Neural Networks,* 1, 75-89, 1988.

[Koh89]   Kohonen, T., *Self-Organisation and Associative Memory,* Springer-Verlag, Berlin, Heidelberg, Germany, 1989 (3rd edition).

[Kru90]   Kruglyak, L., How to Solve the N-Bit Encoder Problem with Just Two Hidden Units, *Neural Computation,* 2, 399-401, 1990.

[Lip87]   Lippman, R.P., An Introduction to Computing with Neural Nets, *IEE ASSP Magazine,* 4-22, 1987.

[Mir89]   Mirchandani, G., On Hidden Nodes for Neural Networks, *IEEE Trans. Circuits and Systems,* 36(5), 661-64, 1989.

[MJD89]   Marko, K.A., James, J., Dosdall, J. and Murphy, J., Automative Control System Diagnostics Using Neural Nets for Rapid Pattern Classification of Large Data Sets, *IEEE International Joint Conference on Neural Networks,* 2, 13-16, 1989.

[NF88]   Nasrabadi, N.M. and Feng, Y.,   Vector Quantisation of Images Based Upon the Kohonen Self Organising Feature Maps, in *Proceedings of the IEEE International Conference on Neural Networks*, Vol. 1, 101-5, 1988.

[RHW86] Rumelhart, D.E., Hinton, G.E. and Williams, R.J.,   Learning Internal Representations by Error Propagation, in *Parallel Distributed Processing: Explorations in the Microstructure of Cognition, Vol. 1*, Rumelhart, D.E., McCelland, J.L. (eds.), 318-62, MIT Press, Cambridge, MA, 1986.

[RMS89] Rajavelu, A., Musavi, M.T. and Shirvaikar, M.V.,   A Neural Network Approach to Character Recognition, *Neural Networks*, 2, 387-93, 1989.

[Tes87]   Tesauro, G.,   Scaling Relationships in Back-Propagation Learning: Dependence on Training Set Size, *Complex Systems*, 1, 367-72, 1987.

Chapter 12

A Neural Net Controller for Navigation and Obstacle Avoidance for Non-Holonomic Mobile Robots Using Sensory Information

René Biewald

Control Systems Centre, University of Manchester Institute of Science and Technology, U.K.

Overview

A neural network technique for real-time navigation, obstacle avoidance, and control of non-holonomic vehicles based upon only constrained global world knowledge has been developed. Previous work on Back-Propagation Through Time (BPTT) has demonstrated the capability of a neural network to control the steering of a trailer truck backing to a loading dock, but without obstacles. In contrast, our neural network controller uses sensory data to incorporate obstacle avoidance into various local navigation strategies. Furthermore, a methodology is outlined, which merges this powerful neural network tool within a global Navigation System (NavS). Specifically, we assume a qualitative method for spatial world representation. The vehicle uses a symbolic route description to travel through an environment and employs another neural network to classify sensory data. Navigation actions are handled by different neural networks, just as in human visual guided navigation.

12.1   INTRODUCTION

This chapter is concerned with the evaluation of a neural network based real-time NavS for realistic, non-holonomic vehicle models (objects with kinematic constraints, i.e. they cannot turn-in-place), assuming that only constraint global world knowledge is available.

Modern flexible manufacturing requires fast and safe operating autonomous transport systems. The performance of existing autonomous Mobile Robots (MRs) in speed, safety and complexity is rather poor if compared with the human abilities to steer a vehicle. Applying neural networks can help to emulate many aspects of human behaviour in real-time. The aim of this chapter is to demonstrate how neural networks may be applied in this way.

12.1.1   Mobile Robot Navigation

Traditional robot navigation approaches, like potential fields [War90] and graph search methods [LT89, ZL91], are based on a detailed, accurate metric description of the environment. They are difficult to implement in real-time - especially if they take the kinematics constraints of the vehicle into account [Tou88, SG91]. On the other hand, fast obstacle avoidance algorithms employ idealised robot models (turn-in place vehicles) [BK91]. Since the conventional approaches represent the path (or at least the robot and target position) in terms of artificial coordinate systems, they are highly vulnerable to spatial inaccuracy in sensory devices and movement actuators [Elf89].

Nguyen and Widrow [NW90, NW89] proposed a neural controller that steers a trailer truck from almost any initial position to a loading dock using the truck position state to generate the next steering signal. The advantage of this approach is that it controls realistic vehicle models (highly nonlinear plants with kinematic constraints), but does not take into account the current environment. Plumer [Plu92] introduced a hybrid network architecture to permit the truck control in the presence of obstacles, implementing the conventional potential field method in a parallel processing system. Although this approach solves real-time path planning for non-holonomic MRs[1], some other drawbacks of the traditional approaches still remain. Employing a more qualitative (human like) world model, seems to have some promise to overcome the fragility of purely spatial methods.

---

[1]   However, the potential field method guarantees only a safe motion for a circular shape around a specified point of the vehicle, but does not take into account explicitly the kinematic constraints. Consequently, in unfavourable circumstances other parts of the vehicle may collide with obstacles.

12.1.2   Human Navigation Behaviour

Humans do not employ an accurate spatial environment model - at least not in terms of a coordinate system - to fulfil the navigation task. They use only some abstract, symbolic world knowledge (associative links between places and paths [Kui82]) to plan a route. This symbolic route description defines the necessary actions to be performed at selected, classifiable places in order to pilot a vehicle from a starting position to a destination. In addition, the steering and low-level navigation behaviour of humans, like obstacle avoidance, is based on experience and skills rather than high-level planning procedures (as used in common artificial intelligence robot NavS). Human travelling performance can be seen as a small set of basic visual guidance activities (like turning right, following a road) which are adapted to the current, specific environment configurations [Gib79].

Neural networks have been shown to be successful in emulating human (skilled) behaviour [Pom91, SM88]. Consequently, in our approach we suggest the implementation of these basic guidance activities into a set of neural network controllers, based on the powerful control learning architecture of [NW90]. In this connection, we used as the controller input sensory information rather than the position state of the vehicle. This enables the neural network controller to combine the local navigation strategy (abstract action) with obstacle avoidance.

12.2   THE NAVIGATION SYSTEM

12.2.1   Overall Structure of the System

Fig. 12.1 shows the structure of the overall NavS which fulfils the symbolic world description paradigm and covers all four major navigation activities: path control, obstacle avoidance (local navigation), localisation, and path planning (global navigation).

Global navigation is performed by a task and path planner that selects the most appropriate route (e.g. shortest, safest, etc., or weighted combinations of optimisation criteria) to complete the required task. A symbolic route is defined as a sequence of places and paths, and actions. An action describes how to get from one place to another. The decision maker, responsible for localisation, compares the route description with the current environment by a classification system using sensory information. As a result, an action corresponding to the route is chosen. Local navigation is performed by a control unit that generates the required steering signals to execute the abstract action in the specific environment configuration using sensory data. The steering commands cause a movement of the vehicle according to its kinematics and dynamics. In this way, by transforming the steering signal into corresponding low-level motor commands, the path control is realised. At the next position the MR's sensors repeat the scanning of the environment, producing the required input information for the localisation unit and local navigator.

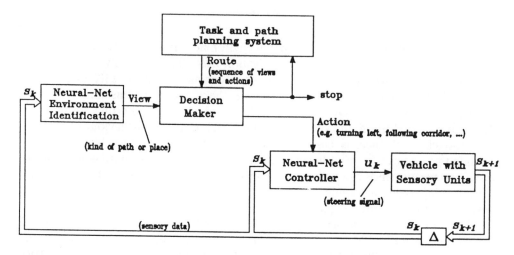

Fig. 12.1 - Block Diagram of the navigation system.

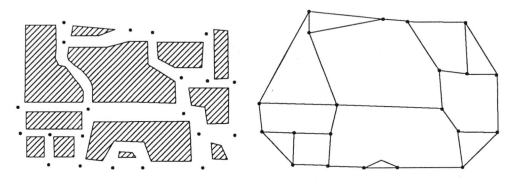

Fig. 12.2 - Typical man-made
environment (place are selected).

Fig. 12.3 - The corresponding
network of places and paths.

12.2.2   Symbolic World Description

Most man-made environments can be classified as simple semi-regular environments
as shown in Fig. 12.2. Fig. 12.3 represents the corresponding symbolic map, a network
of paths and places [Kui82]. The nodes represent the places and the connections are
the paths. This environment model has the advantage that it can describe relatively
complex (but structured) environments with a comparatively small number of various
places and paths.

The minimum set of places to describe such environments includes crossroads and
T-junctions as places, and corridors, left and right walls of various curvature as paths.

The corresponding set of actions must cover "turn left", "turn right", and "go ahead" at crossroads (see Fig. 12.4) as well as "follow corridor", "follow left wall", and "follow right wall". In a further development stage of this NavS the set may be extended. Various properties of the places or paths (metrical parameters, dangerous or safe, etc.) can be stored as attributes of the nodes or connections.

Navigation may also involve environment exploration and map building. Since the symbolic world model contains only high-level abstract spatial information, we assume that such a simple model can be built even by a human designer with a small effort. Nevertheless, automated exploration can be performed using the place and path classification system. An excellent discussion of such an exploration system that forms symbolic world models is found in [KB88]. (One may also see the navigation approach proposed here as enabling Kuipers and Byun's Qualitative Topological Mapping schema to cope with non-holonomic robot models).

12.2.3   Place and Path Classification

We have used in our work ultrasonic sensors, since they are fast, inexpensive and for many navigation tasks satisfactorily accurate. Normally, since up to a few tens of ultrasonic sensors are employed on MRs, it also appears reasonable to use one neural network input for each physical sensor. This simplifies the system architecture, avoids preprocessing, and combines fast environment sensing with fast parallel processing. However, this assumption does not put any restrictions on the general system architecture - any other kind of sensory data can be fed into the neural networks, but it might be necessary to find other input representations or to do some preprocessing.

A simple multi-layered perceptron trained by Back-Propagation (BP) is used for the place and path classification. The vector of distance values to the nearest obstacles obtained by the sensors is fed directly into the neural network. The binary network output vector represents the set of classifiable places and path.

12.2.4   Local Navigation and Obstacle Avoidance

For the local navigation and obstacle avoidance an extended version of Nguyen and Widrow's motion control architecture is used. The position state of the vehicle, used as the input of the neural controller, is replaced by the sensor signals. Consequently, the controller now learns to produce steering signals while avoiding nearby obstacles. The plant represents the vehicle kinematics (and dynamics) as well as the sensory units.

The local navigator combines two kinds of input information: the sensory signals and the action selected by the decision maker. This enables the controller to perform various navigation tasks at the same environment sample (Fig. 12.4). In our approach we trained separate neural controllers for each basic action rather than defining the action as an additional network input. This reduces significantly the complexity of the task(s) to be learned by one network and achieves a higher quality of control performance. [Pom91] also pointed out that it is more efficient to train several domain specific networks instead of training a single network for all situations.

In a hardware implementation the selecting function of the decision maker can be realised by loading various weight matrices into the parallel processing controller. However, it is crucial to define the right switching times since, when one controller takes over from another, instability of the system may occur. Hence, the decision maker has to make sure that at the switching moment the vehicle position is covered by the operational field of both controllers.

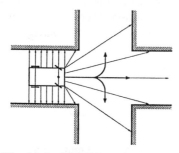

Fig. 12.4 - Possible motion directions on a crossroads.

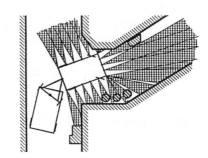

Fig. 12.5 - A mobile transporter in a factory environment.

12.3 LOCAL NAVIGATION USING BACK-PROPAGATION THROUGH TIME

The control aim of the local NavS is to generate a sequence of steering signals that applies abstract actions (extracted from a global navigation aim) to specific environment configurations. For instance, the mobile transporter, shown in Fig. 12.5, is only supplied with two items of information: a) the outputs of the ultrasonic sensors, and b) it has to turn right at the coming T-junction. Thus, based on the current position to the nearby obstacles, it generates the appropriate steering signals that will not cause a collision in the near future. In this way, the neural controller somehow defines an (sub)optimal trajectory for the action in a specific, but classifiable environment.

Although various controllers will be trained, the general control system structure and training procedure are the same for all of them. Training of neural controllers to perform various tasks is achieved by setting up corresponding desired responses.

12.3.1 Control System Structure

Fig. 12.6 shows the extended control system containing three two-layered feedforward nets - the neural network controller, and the emulator nets for the vehicle kinematics and sensory units. For training the neural network controller by supervised learning the error signal

$$\varepsilon_{u.k} = u_{k.desired} - u_{k.net} \qquad (12.1)$$

for all times k is needed. Since the sequence of steering signals $u_{k.desired}$ that makes the vehicle follow the desired trajectory is not known, the error signals of the desired trajectory $z_{k.desired}$

$$\varepsilon_{z.k}^{traj} = z_{k.desired} - z_{k.net} \qquad (12.2)$$

or of the desired distance values $s_{k.desired}$

$$\varepsilon_{s.k}^{traj} = s_{k.desired} - s_{k.net} \qquad (12.3)$$

are utilised. In order to generate the error signals at the controller output, BPTT [Wer90] is applied. In contrast to Nguyen and Widrow, the system was separated into two subsystems to simplify the plant modelling. Before training the neural network controller, two neural networks had to be trained to simulate the behaviour of the system using standard BP. This is in effect system identification.

The network architecture is similar to that described by Nguyen and Widrow. All nets contain an input buffer and two layers of net units - one hidden and one output layer. The sigmoid activation function $f(x) = \tanh(x)$ is used.

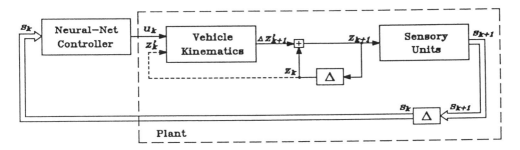

Fig. 12.6 - Plant details and neural controller.

12.3.2   The Vehicle Emulator Net

The position and orientation of the employed vehicle model is uniquely characterised by a state vector of three components $z_k = \{x_k, y_k, \theta_k\}$, where x_k, y_k are the centre coordinates of the front axle and θ_k is the orientation (angle) of the vehicle (Fig. 12.7). The steering signal u_k is proportional to the angle of the front wheels. Note that the position state z_k of the vehicle is only an internal representation of the system model. Once the neural controller has learned the required task, the system operates without any artificial coordinate system.

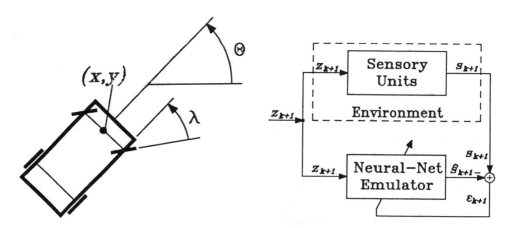

Fig. 12.7 - Vehicle model ($\lambda = \lambda_{max}u$).   Fig. 12.8 - Training of the vehicle emulator.

In contrast to Nguyen and Widrow, the emulator network (containing 20 hidden units) is trained to predict the change of the state Δz_{k+1}, rather than the new state z_{k+1}, in order to achieve a higher prediction accuracy [Bie92]. Furthermore, a specific representation of Δz_k is employed: $\Delta z'_k = \{p_k, o_k, \Delta\theta_k\}$, where p_k is the forward movement in the direction of θ_{k-1}, o_k is the sideward replacement, and $\Delta\theta_k$ is the orientation change. This allows training of the emulator net without feeding the current state into the network (Fig. 12.8). Training is achieved by presenting randomly chosen steering signals u_k to the network while the net learns to predict $\Delta z'_{k+1}$. Note that training such an emulator is not absolutely essential, since the sensitivity matrix for the error BP during controller training could be used.

12.3.3 The Environment Emulator Net

The emulator net for the sensory units is trained to predict the output values s_k of each sensor i for the position states z_k in the operational range of the MR (Fig. 12.9). The network emulates the environment scanned by sensors rather than the sensory units only. Therefore, for various sample environments, different emulators have to be trained. The neural network develops an internal representation of the surrounding obstacles and produces a modified output for each sensor.

The vehicle is equipped with $n = 25$ ultrasonic sensors (Fig. 12.10). We followed an approach similar to [Opi90] by using a logarithmic resolution of the sensory signals to enable accurate steering control near to the obstacles. Our environment emulator nets contained 20-40 hidden units in one layer - further layers and units did not improve the training result. Training of both emulator nets required approximately 12000-25000 trials. If we achieved for the vehicle emulator a root-mean-squared (rms) error of approximately 1% per output, then for the environment emulation only results of 4% to 10%, depending on the complexity of the environment sample, were reached. To decrease the rms error we kept the size of the environment samples as small as possible and restricted the possible vehicle orientations according to the action to be trained in this sample.

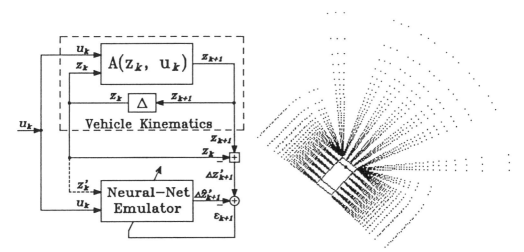

Fig. 12.9 - Training a neural net to store an environment.

Fig. 12.10 - Full range of the sensory units.

Despite the not very impressive training results, it is hoped that the achieved environment approximation is sufficiently accurate for the error BP during controller training, since for the forward pass the real environment data will be used. Once the emulator networks are trained, they can be used for the controller training.

12.3.4   Controller Training using Position States

The objective function for the training by position states is to follow a desired trajectory

$$J = E\left(\sum_{k=1}^{K} c_d (0 - d_k)^2 + c_\theta (\theta_{traj} - \theta_k)^2\right) \tag{12.4}$$

where d_k is the distance to the desired trajectory and θ_{traj} the tangential angle of the trajectory. The constants c_d and c_θ are chosen by the designer to weigh the importance of each error component.

The desired trajectory may not be feasible, since the motion of the vehicle is restricted by kinematic constraints. An appealing property of the BPTT is that it will find a trajectory which matches the desired one as closely as possible, according to the objective function J. Although the designer has to specify the desired trajectories that the vehicle may follow, the optimisation properties of the BPTT give the potential of approximate solutions.

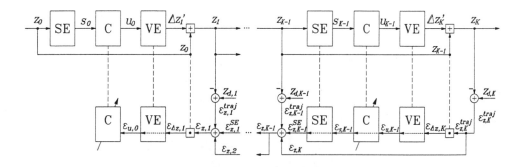

Fig 12.11 - Neural net controller training using position states
(C - controller, VE - vehicle emulator, SE - sensory emulator).

Fig. 12.11 illustrates the controller training in forward (recall) phase and in backward (learning) phase. The vehicle is positioned at a random state z_k that belongs to the set of possible initial positions. The sensors then scan the environment and deliver the required inputs s_k for the controller. The controller generates the appropriate steering signal u_k, which moves the vehicle to a new position z_{k+1}, and so on. The vehicle stops either when at least one sensor detects a collision, or when the maximum number of time steps K determined by the designer has been reached.

In the reverse sequence, the errors are back-propagated through all nets, while the weights are adjusted only in the controller net. The portion of the error generated by BP through the nets ($\varepsilon_{zk}^{SE} + \varepsilon_{z,k+1}$) can be seen as responsible for adjusting the steering commands that caused a deviation from the desired trajectory in the "near future" (trajectory optimisation). On the other hand, the error portion ε_{zk}^{traj} punishes the controller for immediate errors of tracking the reference trajectory. Note that during the forward pass the real plants are used and the emulator nets are only updated in parallel in order to reduce the error accumulation.

12.3.5   Controller Training Using Distance Values

One aim of the proposed NavS architecture is to reduce the designer's effort of determining the local trajectories. Learning by position state is used only for fast initial training. Training by distance values adapts and optimises motion trajectories to specific environment configurations and is more appropriate for the generalisation to unknown environments.

The designer determines a desired output value s_i (distance) for each sensor i that should be kept during task execution. In our work we defined an interval covering the smallest and the largest distance ($s_{i.\min}$ and $s_{i.\max}$ respectively) rather than a single distance. Thus, (Eqn. 12.3) becomes

$$\varepsilon_{s.ki}^{traj} = \begin{cases} (s_{i.\min} - s_{ki}), & \text{for } s_{ki} < s_{i.\min} \\ 0, & \text{for } s_{i.\min} < s_{ki} < s_{i.\max} \\ (s_{i.\max} - s_{ki}), & \text{for } s_{ki} > s_{i.\max} \end{cases} \qquad (12.5)$$

In the example shown in Fig. 12.12, the desired distance from the wall is only defined for the right side sensors (for the left side $s_{i.\max}$ is set to a value larger than the sensory scanning radius).

Controller training using the distance values is similar to the process shown in Fig. 12.11, while replacing the trajectory errors of z_k by those of s_k. The objective function becomes

$$J = E\left(\sum_{k=1}^{K} \sum_{i=1}^{n} c_i \, (\varepsilon_{s.ki}^{traj})^2 \right) \qquad (12.6)$$

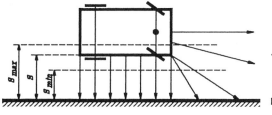
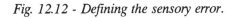

Fig. 12.12 - Defining the sensory error.   *Fig. 12.13 - Approaching and following a trajectory.*

12.4   NEURAL NET CONTROLLERS FOR LOCAL NAVIGATION

12.4.1   Learning to Keep Distance

The controller training is divided into several lessons. Firstly, the controller is trained to follow a trajectory parallel to a wall (keeping the vehicle at a safe distance, Fig. 12.13). On the basis of this common initial controller, several other neural controllers are trained to perform various tasks.

Since initially the steering signals of the controller are random, the motion sequence is stopped after $K=10$ time steps. The controller weights converged after approximately 100 training cycles. The controller net only contains 10 hidden units. Relatively small learning rates (0.001-0.0003) were employed to avoid unstable performance.

12.4.2   Learning to Follow a Wall

Training by the sensor distance values was employed on the next lesson. The vehicle (re)learns to follow the wall at various distances (Fig. 12.14). The weight matrix of the already trained controller was used for the weight initialisation and consequently, retraining was achieved very quickly after 20-30 training cycles. For retraining to follow the wall at small distances (1/10 of vehicle length), very small learning rates ($\approx$0.0001) have to be employed, otherwise the network shows a tendency to produce oscillating steering signals (alternately hard right and left).

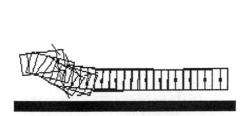

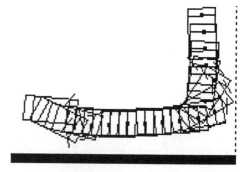

Fig. 12.14 - Approaching and following a trajectory at a small distance from the wall (1/5 to 1/3 of vehicle width).

Fig. 12.15 - Generalised wall following performance.

In order for the controller to turn the "steering wheel" to the left in time while approaching the wall, we introduce a second desired distance interval for the right front sensors. Good simulation results were achieved if $s_{i,min}$ was set to larger values than the ones needed from the geometrical viewpoint ($s_{i,min} \approx 1$ vehicle length). After further training, this is generalised to allow the finding of feasible motion trajectories at L-shaped wall configurations (Fig. 12.15).

12.4.3   Learning to Avoid Obstacles

Next, the neural network is taught to avoid obstacles while following a corridor. Fig. 12.16 shows the initial performance of the neural controller in the training environment. The weight matrix was initialised by using the weights of the "wall following" controller. For initial training, the "moving through obstacle" approach was applied, i.e. the vehicle does not stop when colliding with an obstacle. This is a kind of unrealistic training (at least for the training of systems implemented in hardware). On the other hand, it seems useful to teach the neural controller some initial knowledge through simulations, before doing the fine-tuning on real MRs.

After learning a "good" initial trajectory (Fig. 12.17), training was continued with vehicle-obstacle collision detection until the vehicle has learned to avoid all obstacles (Fig. 12.18).   Fig. 12.19 demonstrates the performance of the car driven by an controller with 25 hidden units (instead of 10). Here, training time was a little longer but smoothness and accuracy have been obviously improved.

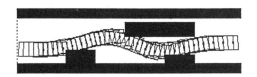

Fig. 12.16 - Controller performance before training, the "moving trough obstacle" approach is applied.

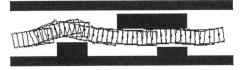

Fig. 12.17 - Performance after 50 training cycles, further training with collision detection.

Fig. 12.18 - After 100 additional cycles the task was learned (the supposed vehicle-obstacle contact appears due to the low screen resolution).

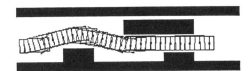

Fig. 12.19 - Performance of a neural net controller with 25 hidden units (instead of 10 used in the Figures before) after training.

12.4.4   Learning to Turn and Go Straight Ahead on Crossroads

Finally, different controllers were designed to perform the three standard tasks at crossroads. At first, the neural network is trained to steer the car around the right corner. Again the "moving through obstacles" approach is applied (Fig. 12.20).

The learning speed of this task is very impressive. As few as 5 training cycles were needed to achieve good "turning" performance (Figs. 12.21-12.22). The same training result can be achieved if the execution is stopped when the vehicle hits an obstacle, however over 100 training cycles were needed to achieve this performance.

A neural network may be trained to perform the "turning left" task by employing the same algorithm. However, it might be simpler to use the trained "turning right" controller, and generate the appropriate steering signals by spatially mirroring the sensory inputs of the neural network controller as well as changing the sign of the steering signal.

Fig. 12.23 illustrates the performance of a controller that has learned to steer a car straight ahead. This neural network was trained to follow a trajectory defined by the position states. By thorough observation of Fig. 12.23, one can notice that the car has some orientation problems at the centre of the crossroads, since the side sensors output an "infinite" distance to the nearest obstacles. At the crossing centre, the neural controller gets its only environment information from the few front sensors (compare with Fig. 12.4). Most probably, a more dense placement of front sensors will improve the "go straight ahead" performance.

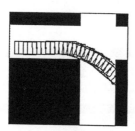

Fig. 12.20 - Performance before training.

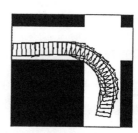

Fig. 12.21 - Performance after one training cycle.

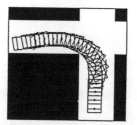

Fig. 12.22 - Performance after 5 training cycles.

Fig. 12.23 - Another neural net controller that has learned to go straight ahead.

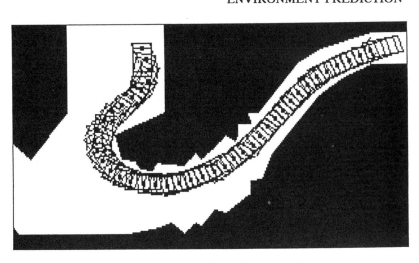

Fig. 12.24 - Performance in unknown environment.

12.4.5   Generalisation to Unknown Environments

Due to the generalisation capabilities of the neural networks, the controllers also perform well in environments which they have never seen before. No training took place in the environment shown in Fig. 12.24. The performance of the vehicle is especially impressive, since the employed controller was only trained on straight line walls. The car is able to follow curved walls and performs quite a smooth trajectory on highly irregular wall configurations.

12.5   ENVIRONMENT PREDICTION

Neural network controllers can learn to perform well in a wide range of environment configurations, although they were just trained in a constrained set of environment samples. However, training of emulator nets that have to learn to remember various environment samples is not satisfactory in terms of training time and rms error. To overcome this problem one might treat the environment in the same way as the vehicle kinematics: predicting the next environment view s_{k+1} (or more exactly the environment variation Δs_{k+1}) is based on the current view s_k, rather than to "store" the environment.

Employing the modified state change vector $\Delta z'_k = \{p_k, o_k, \Delta\theta_k\}$ has the advantage that it defines uniquely the vehicle motion (in contrast to $\Delta z_k = \{\Delta x_k, \Delta y_k, \Delta\theta_k\}$), according to the environment prediction. The corresponding control system architecture, shown in Fig. 12.25, illustrates that for the vehicle model employed the absolute state vector z_k may be completely excluded from the plant structure emulated by neural networks.

Note that the environment predictor net may be employed for the controller training in environments in which training of the emulator did not take place. Of course, the predictor net has to be trained initially with sufficient valid environment data.

Furthermore, we might even separate the environment prediction for the vehicle sides (Fig. 12.26), since the sensory information of one side is not needed to predict the view of the opposite side. In this manner, the complexity of the learning task is reduced and confusion from sensory data of the opposite side is excluded. This will give some benefit in the prediction quality. In addition, learning to estimate future views of the environment can be constrained to one vehicle side. By spatial mirroring of the net inputs and outputs on the vehicle centre line the same network can be employed to predict the environment on the opposite vehicle side.

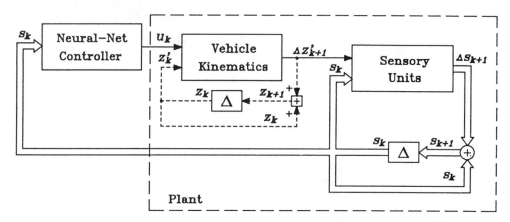

Fig. 12.25 - Plant details and controller for environment prediction system.

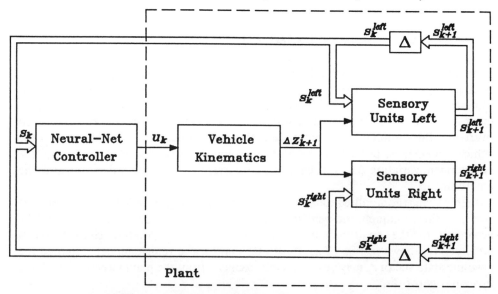

Fig. 12.26 - Plant details and controller for separate environment prediction (simplified).

12.6   CONCLUSION

12.6.1   Summary

An application of neural networks to the steering and navigation of non-holonomic MRs is introduced. Industrial MRs are highly nonlinear systems with kinematic constraints whose control is difficult to realise with conventional methods. BPTT is a neural network approach which has been successfully applied to control such complex systems. BPTT has the appealing property of training neural networks by self-learning in order to generate control signals that combine immediate and long-term error correction. In this way, with very little design effort, feasible motion trajectories for plant constraints are found.

Based on sensory information, a neural network controller learns to steer a vehicle around obstacles while performing abstract navigation actions extracted from a global task planner. No preprocessing of the sensory data is required. Consequently, the neural network performs a complex sensor-action behaviour. Inexpensive ultrasonic sensors may be employed, but any other sensory data are also applicable.

Due to the generalisation capabilities of neural networks, much of the high-level sequential planning activities (typical for artificial intelligence based navigation in robotics) were replaced by neural adaptive control mechanisms. Therefore, the complexity of the employed world model is reduced to a symbolic representation, since local trajectory "planning" is completed by the neural network controller. The world model is robust with respect to small and medium environment changes, since obstacle avoidance is performed automatically during local path execution. All this together with an implementation in parallel hardware, reduces the processing time dramatically and guarantees real-time performance. In addition, the possibility to import different weight matrices into one unique hardware allows us to perform various tasks, while keeping the control system structure very simple.

However, in the present form the NavS is restricted to man-made semi-regular environments. The system may also have some orientation problems in environments with much free space. Additional wide range perception systems should help to overcome these limitations.

Nguyen and Widrow [NW89, NW90] reported about 1000 to 2000 training cycles per lesson needed to train the neural network controller for the truck. In the present work the neural network controller convergence could be achieved in at most 150 training cycles, since, firstly, the forward kinematics of the employed vehicle model are much simpler, and secondly, some kind of reference trajectory could be utilised for training (whereas for the Truck Backer-Upper only the desired final state was known). However, it seems that the spreading of the input information over 25 sensory units also plays an important part in enabling fast controller training.

12.6.2   Future Research

Although the author claims that the introduced NavS is applicable to realistic vehicle models, the completed computer simulation still contains some simplifications. This makes it difficult to implement the NavS of the given form in a real MR. Future work will be concerned with removing these simplifications. Neural network controllers that output additional control signals should be investigated: besides the steering angle at least a signal controlling the vehicle speed.

The obtained simulation results give us enough evidence to believe that the system can easily be extended to control a MR with a trailer as illustrated in Fig. 12.5. Introducing a neural network controller with memory (recurrent net) may avoid the need to equip the trailer with sensors. Finally, future work will also be concerned with further investigations of the environment prediction nets. It is possible that such nets might be useful for the avoidance of movable obstacles.

REFERENCES

[Bie92]   Biewald, R., Application of Neural Networks for Steering and Navigation of Non-Holonomic Mobile Robots, MSc Thesis, UMIST, Control Systems Centre, 1992.

[BK91]   Borenstein, J. and Koren Y., The Vector Field Histogram: Fast Obstacle Avoidance for Mobile Robot, *IEEE Trans. on Robotics and Automation*, 7(3), 278-88, 1991.

[Elf89]   Elfes, A., Using Occupancy Girds for Mobile Robot Perception and Navigation, *Computer (IEEE)*, 22(6), 46-58, 1989.

[Gib79]   Gibson, J.J., *The Ecological Approach to Visual Perception*, Houghton Mifflin Company, Boston, 1979.

[KB88]   Kuipers, B.J. and Byun, Y.T., A Robust, Qualitative Method for Robot Spatial Reasoning, in *Proceedings of the AAAI '88 Conference*, 774-79, 1988.

[Kui82]   Kuipers, B.J., The 'Map in the Head' Metaphor, *Environment and Behaviour*, 14, 202-20, 1982.

[LT89]   Lozano-Perez, T. and Taylor, R.H., Geometric Issues in Planning Robot Tasks, in *Robotics Science*, Brady, M. (ed.), MIT Press, Cambridge, MA, 1989.

[NW90]   Nguyen, D.H. and Widrow, B., Neural Networks for Self-Learning Control Systems, *IEEE Control System Magazine*, 10(3), 18-23, 1990; *International Journal of Control*, 54.2(6), 1439-51, 1991.

[NW89]   Nguyen, D.H., and Widrow, B., The Truck Backer-Upper: An Example of Self-Learning in Neural Networks, in *Proceedings of IJCNN '89*, 2, 357-63, 1989.

[Opi90]   Opitz, R.,   Das Lernfahrzeug: Neural Network Application for Autonomous Mobile Robots, in *Advanced Neural Computers*, Eckmiller, R. (ed.), 373-79, Elsevier: North-Holland, 1990.

[Plu92]   Plumer, E.S., Neural Network Structure for Navigation Using Potential Fields, in *Proceedings of IJCNN '92*, Vol. 1, 327-32, 1992.

[Pom91]   Pomerlau, D.A.,   Rapidly Adapting Artificial Neural Networks for Autonomous Navigation, in *Advances in Neural Information Processing Systems 3*, Lippmann, R.P., Moody, J.E., Touretzky D.S. (eds.), 429-35, Morgan Kaufmann, San Mateo, 1991.

[SM88]   Shepanski, J.F., and Macy, S.A.,   Teaching Artificial Neural System to Drive: Manual Training Techniques for Autonomous Systems, in *Advances in Neural Information Processing Systems*,   Anderson, D.Z. (ed.), 693-700, American Institute of Physics, New York, 1988.

[SG91]   Shiller, Z. and Gwo, Y.R.,   Dynamic Motion Planning of Autonomous Vehicles, *IEEE Trans. on Robotics and Automation*, 7(2), 241-49, 1991.

[Tou88]   Tournassoud, P.,   Motion Planning for a Mobile Robot with Kinematic Constraint, in *Geometry and Robotics, Lecture Notes in Computer Science*, Boissonnat, J.D., Laumond, J.P. (eds.), 391, 150-71, 1988.

[War90]   Warren, C.W.,   A Technique for Autonomous Underwater Vehicle Route Planning, *IEEE Journal of Oceanic Engineering*, 15(3), 199-204, 1990.

[Wer90]   Werbos, P.J., Back-Propagation Through Time: What It Does and How To Do It, *Proceedings of the IEEE*, 78(10), 1550-60, 1990.

[ZL91]   Zhu, D. and Latombe, J.C.,   New Heuristic Algorithms for Efficient Hierarchical Path Planning, *IEEE Trans. on Robotics and Automation*, 7(1), 9-19, 1991.

Chapter 13

Measuring the Size Distribution of Emulsion Droplets in an Image Using Kohonen's Self-Organising Feature Map

Shail Patel, Eric Mahers and Mike Ashton

Unilever Research Laboratory, Port Sunlight, U.K.

Overview

This chapter describes a method of measuring the size distribution of similar objects in an image using Kohonen's Self Organising Feature Maps (SOM). In our application we are concerned with the distribution of droplet sizes in cream emulsions, such as hand creams. The droplets range from 0.5 to 20 microns in diameter. There are a number of current methods for this task, all of which have major drawbacks. In this system, we have used highly magnified Differential Interference Contrast (DIC) images of a cream sample. A number of Kohonen SOMs are trained to recognise the droplets, and categorise them by size. A key advantage of using the Kohonen SOM is its ability to self-organise. This cuts out the need for the time consuming hand marking of a training set. Essentially the SOMs act as feature extractors, where in this case the feature is size. The system has been tested on a number of different samples. The results are highly encouraging, and further developments are under way.

13.1   INTRODUCTION

Many physical properties of cream emulsions, such as stability, feel and absorption, depend on the size distribution of the constituent droplets. This size distribution is therefore an important parameter in the characterisation of such emulsions and is of great value as a measure for industrial processes concerned with the development and manufacture of cream emulsions. Current methods for measuring size distributions take indirect physical measurements, such as the light scattered by a sample, or attempt to count and size the droplets in an image. These, and their associated drawbacks, are outlined below.

13.1.1 Image and Ruler

Given an image of a sample, a straightforward method of measuring a size distribution is to use a ruler. Using the magnification, it is possible to scale these measurements to obtain the diameter in microns. However, this method is extremely time consuming and suffers from human inaccuracy.

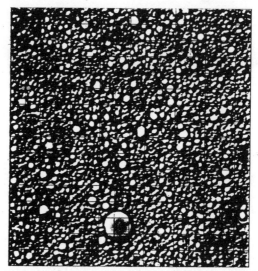

Fig. 13.1 - Grey scale image of emulsion droplets.

13.1.2 Malvern Mastersizer

This is an indirect method of measurement that uses the light scattered from emulsion samples to infer the size distribution. Its dynamic range is high, but it suffers from a number of inaccuracies. At the large end, measured droplets may be due to agglomerations of smaller particles scattering light as if they were a single particle. At the lower end the effects of dilution may physically affect particle sizes. In our experience the results produced by the Malvern technique are inconsistent with those observed on the microscope. Moreover this is a black box technique which is not directly verifiable, but has to be calibrated with known samples.

13.1.3 Brightfield Imaging

Images produced using Brightfield techniques may be used [Plu88]. This technique produces images in which the droplets have clear circular borders. They can easily be segmented and measured using conventional image analysis techniques. This is a direct measurement and is relatively accurate as far as the image is concerned. However its major drawback is that it cannot distinguish between droplets and air bubbles of varying sizes. These air bubbles may thereby lead to considerable inaccuracy.

13.1.4 Differential Interference Contrasting (DIC)

DIC is a double-beam interference light microscopy contrast system in which two polarised light beams fall on the object plane, i.e. the sample. These beams have an optical path difference similar to that of the resolution of the microscope configuration. This results in an image shear, such that one side of a particle is highlighted while the other is shadowed, giving the appearance of illumination by 45° incident light. This allows the observer to detect small sample variations, as well as to differentiate between circular droplets and air bubbles, thus affording a choice of view to be imaged. This technique provides clearer images for the human eye. However it creates a problem for conventional image analysis as there is not a clear demarcation of the objects total circumference. The difficult area of identification are the areas between the light and dark sides of the object, where the grey levels tend to merge with the background. These images are, however, truly representative of the sample, and we have therefore chosen to use these as the basis for our system using a Kohonen map.

13.2 SIZE DISTRIBUTION USING KOHONEN SOMs

Given the inadequacies of the above methods it was necessary to find an alternative method that is more accurate. The DIC images are clearly representative of the actual cream, and were therefore chosen as the input to our system. Conventional image analysis techniques are unable to segment the droplets from the background, i.e. they are unable to combine the light, dark and grey areas of each droplet as a distinct item separate from the grey background. For example, applying a convolution operator (Marr filter) to the image in Fig. 13.1 is given in Fig. 13.2. This demonstrates how the contrast contour lines run from object to object and are of no use in the object segmentation or recognition step. Interestingly, it is easy for humans to use the lighting effect to translate the 'flat' image into a bumpy surface, and to differentiate between droplet and background, even in very noisy images. It might be argued that we are biologically hardwired for this task.

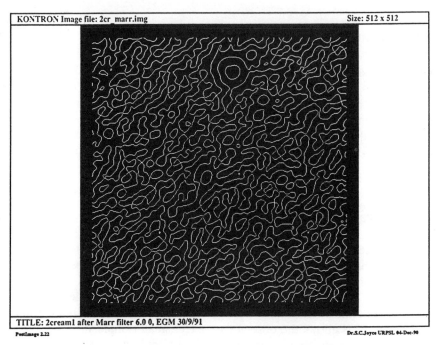

KONTRON Image file: 2cr_marr.img   Size: 512 x 512

TITLE: 2cream1 after Marr filter 6.0 0, EGM 30/9/91

PostImage 2.22   Dr.S.C.Joyce URPSL 04-Dec-90

Fig. 13.2 - Marr filter applied to grey scale image.

Kohonen's Feature Map [Koh88, Koh90] was developed for speech recognition. It has found uses in a many different areas including image analysis. At the time of writing the author is not aware of it's use for measuring the size distribution of similar objects. Interestingly, Kohonen himself makes the point that the Feature Map is not ideally suited for object recognition [Koh90], but that Learning Vector Quantisation (LVQ) should be used to fine tune the decision boundaries bringing them closer to the Bayesian ideal. This point is valid but has the drawback that it requires considerable human effort to handmark a training set for use in LVQ. It is worth noting that only those examples that lie near decision boundaries are used in training. In the same paper he makes the further point that it is not possible to "achieve invariances unless the primary image is first transformed using, e.g., various convolutions". Again the point is valid if one is considering the whole image. However we are here only interested in small parts of the image. It is possible with the centring algorithm described in this paper to centre candidate objects of interest, thereby solving the problem of translational invariance. In our system the issue of rotational invariance does not arise, as due to an effect of the DIC, all the droplet images are rotationally aligned.

The thrust of this paper is that, in an application sense, using the Feature Map to measure the size distribution of a large number of objects is sufficiently accurate for the characterisation of the physical properties of cream emulsions, and that this sufficient accuracy is a criterion that will apply in a number of other similar applications. It would be possible to cluster the data using cluster analysis, nearest neighbour or vector quantisation techniques. The major difference is that the Kohonen map offers an ordered set of representative nodes. In this particular application two advantages arise from this ordering. Firstly it takes less time to create a 'key' to the map, i.e. assign a value for the diameter represented by a particular node, as these follow in sequence (Figs. 13.6 and 13.7). Secondly, a number of nodes may represent the boundary between examples of droplets and noise, and these may give an indication of the degree of certainty with which the droplets have been classified in the image (e.g. first three nodes in third row of Fig. 13.6). This second feature has not been implemented at this stage, but will be included in future modifications.

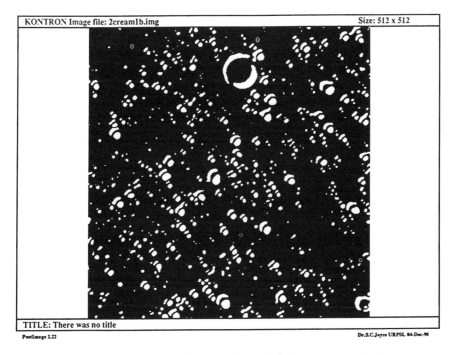

| KONTRON Image file: 2cream1b.img | Size: 512 x 512 |

| TITLE: There was no title |

PostImage 2.23   Dr.S.C.Joyce URPSL 04-Dec-90

Fig. 13.3 - Binarised image: light and dark are 1, grey is 0.

13.3 DESCRIPTION OF THE SYSTEM

The system as whole comprises Kohonen maps sandwiched between pre- and post-processes. Fig. 13.4 illustrates this for one such Kohonen map. The pre- and post-processes combine simple algorithms with algorithmically implemented heuristics. This combination makes for a greater efficiency and in this sense the system as a whole is a hybrid system [PD91].

There are three main stages to the system, illustrated in Fig. 13.5. These are

1) Preprocessing the images,
2) Training the Kohonen layers,
3) Running the system.

There are only two places at which human intervention is required, illustrated by the helpful TV presenter in Fig. 13.5. These are setting the levels for binarisation, and making the 'key' to the Feature Map.

13.3.1 Preprocessing the Images

There is a large variance between the number and size of droplets in different images of the same sample. Therefore for any given emulsion a number, of order 10, DIC images are taken (e.g. Fig. 13.1). The greyscale 512 x 512 pixel images are binarised using "top and bottom" thresholding. That is, very dark and very light areas are represented by 1, and intermediate grey areas are represented by 0 (Fig. 13.3). It is worth noting that some information is lost in the binarisation process, especially smaller droplets of diameter less than 7 pixels. For this reason images at different levels of magnification may need to be taken.

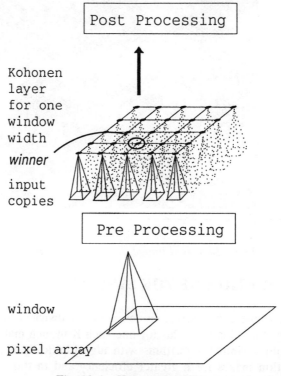

Fig. 13.4 - Kohonen map.

In order to isolate the droplets, windows of different sizes are passed over the 512 x 512 image. We need to take account of three effects

a)   a range of window sizes to cover the large range of droplet sizes,
b)   ensuring that the droplets are centred in each window,
c)   reducing the number of possible windows to a reasonable level.

These are described below.

Firstly, it is necessary to use a range of sizes as very small droplets will appear as noise for large windows, and very large droplets will be invisible to small windows. These windows are then passed to a set of SOMs, one SOM for each size of window chosen. A typical range is squares with side {45, 33, 23, 15}. A separate Kohonen map needs to be set up and trained for each window size.

Secondly, we need to ensure that the droplets are centred, that is, we need to ensure translational invariance. This can be achieved by a simple centring algorithm. First the pixel array is covered with a lattice of partially overlapped windows. Each window is taken in turn and moved so that it is centred on the centre of gravity of the pixels (previously) contained in it. This is repeated until convergence, or until the window has been moved a (user-defined) number of times. The effect is that the window is either centred on a droplet, or contains noise. The possibility of duplicates arises, and these need to be removed.

1. Preprocessing the images

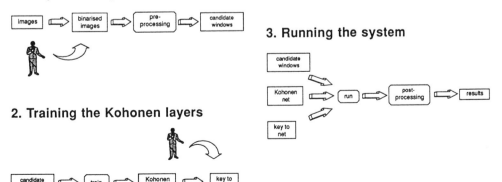

3. Running the system

2. Training the Kohonen layers

Fig. 13.5 - Stages of System.

Lastly, we can disregard a large proportion of the windows as not being worth processing unless a sufficient number of pixels are "on". A large amount of the image is empty space with small amounts of noise, and we can remove these by summing the number of "on" pixels and comparing this with a threshold. It was found that a threshold of 12.5% of pixels needed to be "on".

The combination of the above algorithms reduces the number of possible windows from O(100,000) to O(100) windows containing objects of interest, a significant reduction. For the purposes of implementation efficiency, the input windows are represented as structures containing a pointer to the relevant image, the window width, and the co-ordinates of the centres. The candidate droplets can thereby be stored and retrieved effectively as a list of their centres.

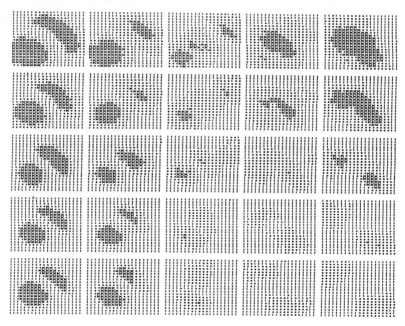

Fig. 13.6 - Kohonen map with 25 nodes, each weight vector graphically displayed as an input window.

13.3.2 Training the Kohonen SOMs

The Kohonen Feature Maps used vary from layers of 3 x 3 nodes to 7 x 7 nodes depending on the size of the windows. Note that these maps are trained in "parallel" in that their processes do not interact with each other in any way. The algorithms used in training are described elsewhere [Koh88, Koh90]. We can understand the process in the following way. The input windows are represented as vectors. Each node of the Kohonen layer has a weight vector attached to it, of the same dimension as the input. As each input is presented to the net, it finds the winner, i.e. the closest node to the input in a Euclidean sense. It then adjusts the weight vector of the winning node, as well as many of its neighbours, by moving them towards the presented input. The neighbourhood relationship, in this case a square, determines the topology of the map (Figs 13.4-13.6). This process is iterated through many steps, with the inputs presented in a random order, until the nodes in the Kohonen layer map the probability distribution of the inputs, i.e. each node acts as a representative for a subset of inputs. The nodes in the Kohonen map after training are ordered, and it is the ordering of the nodes that characterises a feature, in this case "size" and "degree of noise".

For each new sample, either a new set of Kohonen nets are trained, or a previously trained set is retrained to represent new inputs. The training parameters vary slightly from run to run but are in the region of: 200,000 cycles for training, or 50,000 for retraining; alpha, the learning parameter is initially 0.05 and decreases exponentially; $N_j(t)$ the neighbourhood relation is set up to be a square, and its area of influence starts out at half the dimension of the Kohonen layer (rounded up) and decreases linearly. On the DEC 5000/200 Workstation, and using a modified version of the OWL Neural Network 'C' Libraries, retraining takes approximately 10 minutes for each map.

During training the Kohonen layers adapt to the features present in the data. Fig. 13.6 illustrates the way in which the layer generalises the features of "size" and "degree of noise". Note that in Fig. 13.6 each weight vector is represented as a "window". Each node represents either droplets of different size, or noise. It is then necessary to create a 'key' to each map (Fig. 13.7). This needs to be done manually. Apart from setting the binarisation levels, this is the only part of the process that needs human intervention (Fig. 13.5). It is possible to assess the droplet diameter that each node represents to within a few pixels from the window representation of the weight vectors (Fig. 13.6). As can be seen from Fig. 13.10, there is a close correlation between the assessed size of droplets in an image, and their actual size as measured by counting the pixels.

0	0	0	0	0
0	0	0	0	0
0	0	0	0	0
19	17	14	13	14
19	17	14	13	14

Fig. 13.7 - Key to map, diameter in pixels.

13.3.3 Running the System

As the Kohonen layers are trained (or retrained) for every new batch of images, there is no distinction between training and test sets. Lists of centres of candidate droplets are created, by the pre-processing step, for each image as for the training step. These are presented to the Kohonen maps. Note that the Kohonen layers do not interact with each other until a final post-processing stage. Each candidate droplet is presented to the relevant Kohonen net only once, and the winning node is determined by the node whose weights are the nearest to the presented input. The system consults the 'key' to the Kohonen map, and assigns the window a value: 0 if it is not a droplet, or the diameter in pixels if it is.

At the final stage it is necessary to combine the information from the various Kohonen nets trained on the different window sizes. A problem that can arise at this stage is that occasionally the nets trained on different window sizes will assign different diameters to the same object. This is illustrated in Fig. 13.8, where a number of such conflicts can be seen as smaller circles inside larger ones. Each circle in the figure represents the assessment of a Kohonen layer, with an approximate indication of the assigned diameter. It is possible to resolve this conflict with a simple heuristic. A large droplet is often erroneously recognised by small window sizes as being a small droplet. The converse is extremely infrequent - no example of the converse has yet been identified. A simple heuristic rule is that the results from larger windows take precedence over those from smaller windows. The final result of the post-processing is shown in Fig. 13.9, and overlaid over the original grey scale image.

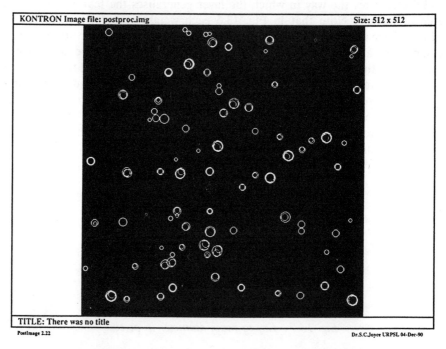

Fig. 13.8 - Example of conflicting diameter predictions.

13.4   RESULTS

There are a number of levels at which we need to assess the accuracy of such a system. We must also note that there is no reliable method of measuring size distribution of droplets. We have therefore compared our results against those obtained by hand. We have also been able to compare the predictions of the system for a sample composed of particles of a known diameter.

At the level of visual inspection, one can see from images such as Fig. 13.9 that our system is behaving "reasonably". It is correctly locating a fair proportion of the droplets and successfully ignoring the background noise. It is missing a few, but these tend to be of smaller diameter, and will be picked up by the images of higher magnification. Some others of these are not in the plane of focus, and therefore correctly ignored. Furthermore, the assigned diameters are as good, if not better, than one could do by hand.

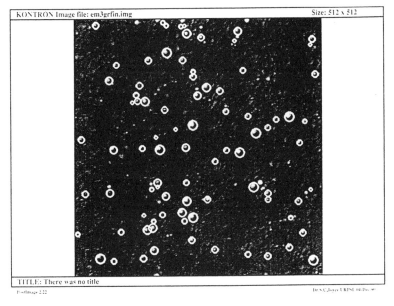

Fig 13.9 - Resolution of conflict superimposed on original.

We can put some figures to the above broad assessment. Firstly, to what extent does the Kohonen SOM correctly determine that a window presented to it contains a droplet, i.e. how well does the SOM categorise the presented input windows into "droplet" and "noise"? To measure this we need to consider both false positives (non-droplets that are counted and assigned a diameter) and false negatives (droplets that are completely missed). The results for some test images are given below.

	+ves	-ves	total
correct	164	257	421
false	21	219	50
total	185	286	471
accuracy	89%	90%	89%

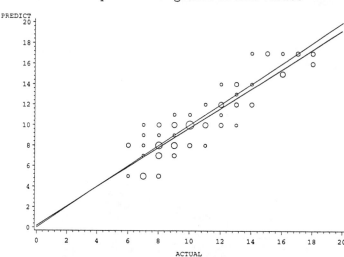

Fig. 13.10 - Bubble plot of actual against predicted diams (in pixels).

Secondly, how accurately does the system assign the diameter? The results, for a different sample, are shown in Fig. 13.10. The correlation between the diameters measured by the Kohonen map, and the diameters as measured by hand, are reasonably close. The thick line in the graph shows the regression line, and the thin line the desired relation (identity). The bubble plot shows the number of items at each point by the size of the bubble. The spread of the points is quite wide, but within a few pixels and so adequate for the purposes.

The system was also tested on a known sample. There are commercially available samples of latex with diameters given to within a nominal 10% accuracy. Each sample was diluted, and a test sample was made up consisting of approximately equal proportions, by weight, of latex particles of 2.5, 4.5 and 6 micron diameters. Five DIC images were taken. The predicted size distribution is shown in Fig. 13.11, the histogram bars show the contribution by volume each size makes. The curve gives a statistical indication what the underlying distribution might be. We can justifiably group the results into three groups and take the mean diameter predictions with the following results (in microns unless otherwise indicated).

actual	measured (mean)	inaccuracy (%)	inaccuracy (pixels)
2.5	2.1	16%	3.0
4.5	4.3	4%	1.6
6.0	5.8	3%	1.3

There would appear to be a structural underestimation of the diameters, which in the case of the 2.5 micron sample results in a great percentage inaccuracy. In a normal run, this would be rectified by carrying out a calibration step: superimposing the predicted results on the original image and checking the diameter estimations.

Lastly, to assess the measurement of the size distribution the table below shows the relative proportions of each of the three groups.

diam (microns)	A.sample	B.image	C.measured
2.5	33.3%	23.8%	27.7%
4.5	33.3%	22.5%	27.5%
6.0	33.3%	53.6%	44.8%

Key to column headings

A.sample:	proportions of the three latex sizes, by weight, in the made up sample.
B.image:	proportions of the three latex sizes in 5 images of the above sample, by volume.
C.measured:	proportions of the three latex sizes as measured by the described system in the 5 images of the above sample, by volume.

Latex: Volume distribution by diameter

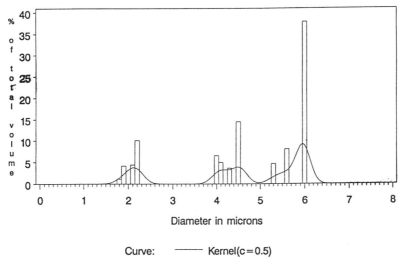

Fig. 13.11 - Size distribution of trimodal latex sample.

The described system has measured the size distribution of the latex samples as they appear in the images of the prepared sample. What is clearly evident here is the

droplets of 6.0 microns. This issue is dealt with at some length by British Standard 3406 [BS91]. However the above results show that while the data may not be truly representative of the underlying distribution, the described system is reasonably accurate with respect to the data it has to work on.

13.5 CONCLUSION

Current methods of measuring size distributions suffer from one or more of the following sources of inaccuracy

1)   black box measurements that are difficult to verify,
2)   agglomerations of small droplets measured as large ones,
3)   measurement of introduced air bubbles,
4)   human error,
5)   effects of dilution on droplet sizes.

The described system has eliminated these sources of error. It has been run on a number of different emulsion samples, and the results, as reported above, are very encouraging. We are in the process of developing a more user-friendly interface, and are porting the system to other hosts.

In this application it has not been necessary to use data that is pre-processed by a convolution filter. We have achieved translational and rotational invariance by other means, and shown further uses of Kohonen's Self-Organising Feature Map.

The effect of the Kohonen nodes is very similar to a conventional image analysis technique of template matching, whereby unknown objects are compared with known templates and if close to the template (in a Euclidean sense) are categorised as that object. The use of Kohonen's SOM has a number of advantages. It generates generalised templates rather than using examples, and finds these templates in a self-organised manner. This represents a tremendous saving in human time. The nodes in the Kohonen map are ordered by the feature of interest, in this case "size". This makes the task of labelling the nodes, i.e. creating a key to the map relatively straightforward.

ACKNOWLEDGEMENTS

We are indebted to colleagues Don Gregory for providing samples, and Phil Whittall for preparing the graphs.

REFERENCES

[BS91]   British Standards Institution BS 3406, Methods for Determination of Particle Size Distribution, Part 4, *Recommendations for Microscope and Image Analysis Methods* (Draft Revision of BS 3406, Part 4, 1963) 1991.

[Koh88]   Kohonen, T., *Self-Organisation and Associative Memory*, Springer-Verlag, Berlin, New York, 1984, 1988 (2nd edition).

[Koh90]   Kohonen, T., The Self-Organising Map, *Proceedings of IEEE*, 78(9), 1990.

[PD91]   Patel, S. and Denham, M., A Hybrid Neural Net/Knowledge-Based Approach to EEG Analysis, in *Proceedings of ICANN '91: Artificial Neural Networks, Helsinki, Finland,* 1991.

[Plu88]   Pluta, M., *Advanced Light Microscopy*, Vols. I and II, Elsevier: North-Holland, 1988.

Chapter 14

Location of Facial Features Using a Boltzmann Machine to Implement Geometrical Constraints

V. Popesco[1] [1] and **J.M. Vincent** [2]

Telecom Paris, France [1]
BT Laboratories, Ipswich, U.K. [2]

Overview

In order to comprehend real world signals, weak constraints usually need to be satisfied. Consider the location of features in an image of a particular type of object, such as a face. A constellation of uniquely identifiable localised features can be selected, such as the centres and corners of eyes and mouths. The co-ordinates, being subject to variability within a population of object shapes and poses, are weakly constrained. Knowledge of these geometric constraints in a specific application is invaluable and we have investigated using Boltzmann machines [HSA85] for learning and imposing them.

We have tested using a Boltzmann machine as a module in British Telecom Laboratory's Hierarchical Perceptron Feature Locator (HPFL) devised specifically for locating facial features although in principle modifiable for other objects [Vin91, Wai91, VWM91, VWM92]. The HPFL consists of two stages, one low resolution, the other high resolution. The first stage generates search regions for eyes and mouth and the second pin-points features within the confines of these regions; these features are

---

[1]Project undertaken at BT Laboratories March - August 1992

perceptually important essentially rigid parts such as corners of eyes and mouths. Both stages employ Multi-Layer Perceptrons (MLPs) trained to recognise the presence of specific features inside windows of pixels. The first stage has three MLPs to locate the centres of eyes and mouth at coarse resolution and their outputs are used to generate three coarse resolution images, called feature maps. However, in practice, these search regions are error prone, noisy and need to be post-processed.

A rule based post-processor was created from some geometric heuristics [Vin91]. Although successful, it is tailored to faces and it would be interesting to have an approach which is generalisable and automatically optimisable via training. Consequently we have been investigating a Boltzmann machine implementation as a connectionnist alternative.

The Boltzmann machine receives a set of thresholded raw feature maps and generates cleaned feature maps for the high resolution stage. Extra terms are added to the energy function that cause the cleaned search regions to expand slightly whilst the Boltzmann machine approaches equilibrium; this mechanism, which we call 'gathering', is an important error protection measure. Even though we have not used hidden units the network is sufficiently large to prevent feasible training. By building a translation invariant machine the number of parameters is reduced by a factor of 100. Moreover, by using 'parameterised weights' to define the random field, the number of parameters drops to about twenty. The initial parameters are fine-tuned using an adaptation of the common learning algorithm for Boltzmann machines. Although the model iHxheuristic, it is capable of being generalised and optimised.

This chapter is solely concerned with the low resolution stage and Section 14.1 discusses feature extraction by MLP and the symbolic approach to post-processing. Section 14.2 gives some definitions and properties concerning Boltzmann machines. In Section 14.3 we present the chosen model. We discuss the statistical analysis that made us choose this model as well as present the initial results that are very promising in Section 14.4.

14.1   REVIEW

14.1.1   Neural Feature Extraction

MLPs with a 5x5 input window, two hidden second degree neurones and a single linear output neurone are used as detectors to perform candidate feature point classification for the HPFL [Vin91]. Each detector is scanned across the 16x16 pixel image, and its thresholded output is used to create a 16x16 binary image known as a feature map. There are three feature maps, one each for the left eye, right eye, and mouth. After post-processing, these feature maps are passed to the high resolution stage, where they are used to define search regions for the feature detectors in the high resolution image.

As the MLP is scanned across the source image there is one occasion when the scanning window is closest to the desired feature. When this occurs the desired output of the MLP is a high value (1.0). In all other positions the MLP output is required to be low, ideally (0.0). The MLP is trained to accomplish this task at best. Results using raw MLP outputs for 30 training images and 30 test images are shown in Table 14.1.

14.1.2   Exploiting Knowledge to Prune the Search Space

Provided that the number of candidate search pixels is small, this scheme requires much less computation than scanning the entire high resolution image. However, as it stands it will still be prone to the location of spurious features, and fail to locate features that are present. These problems are ameliorated by post-processing using knowledge of geometric constraints. The post-processor has three consecutive stages: spatial pruning, temporal pruning and pixel expansion. The basic principles of spatial pruning and pixel expansion are described here, for further details see [VWM91].

Spatial Pruning

Spatial pruning is an intra-frame process that exploits geometric constraints imposed by facial structure on eye and mouth feature locations.

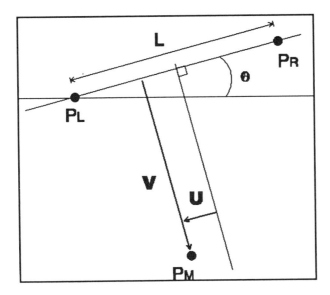

Fig. 14.1 - Notation for the supervisor.

Consider a triple combination of candidate feature points, one point being taken from each of the feature maps generated from a single frame. The pixels have co-ordinates P_L, P_R, P_M for candidate left eye, right eye and mouth positions respectively. A set of geometric feasibility criteria can be established, and each possible triple that can be generated from the feature map can be tested to establish whether it satisfies these criteria; if not, that triple is rejected.

The parameters used in the HPFL low resolution stage post-processor to establish a set of criteria are shown in Fig. 14.1. L is the spacing between the candidate eye points and θ is the angle that L makes with the horizontal. (U, V) are the co-ordinates of the candidate mouth point with respect to a frame of reference that has as its principal axes the line L, and an orthogonal line intersecting it at its midpoint. The following inequalities are tested

$$L_{min} \leq L \leq L_{max} \qquad (14.1)$$

$$|\theta| \leq \theta_{max} \qquad (14.2)$$

$$\left|\frac{U}{L}\right| \leq \left(\frac{U}{L}\right)_{max} \qquad (14.3)$$

$$\left(\frac{V}{L}\right)_{min} \leq \left(\frac{V}{L}\right) \leq \left(\frac{V}{L}\right)_{max} \qquad (14.4)$$

The maximum and minimum allowed values are calculated from the training set of images, and relaxed to allow for greater variability in test images.

Feature type	Rejections (/30)	Average search region (pixels /256)	Average connectivity
Training set (30 frames)			
Before post processing			
centre of left eye	0	11.43	4.47
centre of right eye	0	1.90	1.37
centre of mouth	0	3.93	2.53
After post processing			
centre of left eye	0	8.47	1.00
centre of right eye	0	8.93	1.00
centre of mouth	0	9.67	1.03
Test set (30 frames)			
Before post processing			
centre of left eye	1	11.37	4.37
centre of right eye	3	2.50	1.83
centre of mouth	6	5.13	3.37
After post processing			
centre of left eye	0	8.87	1.03
centre of right eye	0	8.87	1.03
centre of mouth	1	10.47	1.00

Table 14.1 - Results of the rule based post-processing.

Pixel Expansion

In the final post-processing stage, pixel expansion, the remaining candidate feature points are expanded by morphological dilation. Although this increases the areas of the search regions, it is necessary because the generation of a coarsely sub-sampled image can give rise to sampling problems, where the desired feature in the high resolution image lies across the boundary of two or more low resolution pixels.

Performance, before and after post-processing, is compared in Table 14.1. The one remaining rejected true feature was sufficiently close to the corresponding search region not to cause any problem for the high resolution stage.

The average search region size is given in pixels (out of 256) and the average connectivity is the average number of connected search regions per feature map. Low connectivity is good because it indicates compactness and low susceptibility to spurious MLP outputs.

14.2 GENERALITIES ABOUT BOLTZMANN MACHINES

A Boltzmann machine [GG84, HSA85, Aze92] is a network of formal neurones. Usually, these neurones or cells are called *sites* and they can take a binary value (0 or 1) called a *state*. A neurone in the state '1' is said to be active or firing.

The link between the sites is a quadratic energy function called the *Gibbs energy* of the machine and is symmetric. The lower the energy of a configuration of the network the higher the probability of this configuration.

14.2.1 Dynamics of Sequential Boltzmann Machines

Let S be the finite set of sites (formal neurones). The state x_s of a neurone takes its values from $\{0, 1\}$. Let us call $\Omega = \{0, 1\}^S$ the set of configurations of our network. The importance of the interaction between two neurones s and t of the network is given by the synaptic weight $w_{st} = w_{ts}$. A global configuration of the machine $x = (x_s)_{s \in S}$ has an energy

$$E(x) = -\sum_{s,t} w_{st} x_s x_t \tag{14.5}$$

The Dynamic of the machine is stochastic and controlled by a positive parameter T, called temperature. The target probability distribution (in the long run) is then given by the Gibbs distribution

$$P_T(x) = \frac{e^{-\frac{E(x)}{T}}}{Z_T} \quad where \quad Z_T = \sum_{x \in \Omega} e^{-\frac{E(x)}{T}} \tag{14.6}$$

The sites of the machine are visited sequentially. At each instant n, only one site is susceptible of having its state modified. If the site s is visited at instant n, the new value y_s of x_s is randomly selected as the following (this process is called the *Gibbs sampler*)

$$
\begin{cases}
P(y_s = 1 \mid x) = \dfrac{e^{\frac{1}{T}U_s(x)}}{1 + e^{\frac{1}{T}U_s(x)}} \\[2em]
P(y_s = 0 \mid x) = \dfrac{1}{1 + e^{\frac{1}{T}U_s(x)}}
\end{cases}
\tag{14.7}
$$

where

$$
U_s = \sum_{t \neq s} w_{st}x_t + w_{ss}
\tag{14.8}
$$

This stochastic dynamic reaches in the long run a probabilistic equilibrium that gives to each configuration x its Gibbs probability. Moreover, the *"simulated annealing theorem"* [GG85] ensures that, if one decreases the temperature T -one uses the temperature T_n at the instant n in the above changing probability, where $T_n \to 0$ slower than $1/\log(n)$- during this algorithm, one reaches the limit of P_T when T tends to 0, which is the uniform distribution over the configurations of minimal energy.

14.2.2 A Learning Algorithm for the Weights of a Boltzmann Machine

We describe hereafter a learning algorithm for the parameters (w_{st}) of the machine. This algorithm derived by Hinton, Sejnowski and Ackley [HSA85] has the advantage of using only local computations but does not apply to synchronous Boltzmann machines [Aze90].

The set S is generally divided into three (distinct) subsets

- the input sites, I, which have their values fixed from outside.
- the hidden nodes, H, which are a part of the machine that does not communicate with the outside world.
- the output neurones, O, which are the 'answer' of the machine to a given input.

We admit that an *a priori* law, υ, exists on $\{0, 1\}^I$, the set of input configurations. The behaviour of the machine is then characterised by the joint law $P(X_I, X_O)$.

Let $(F: \{0, 1\}^I \to \{0, 1\}^O)$ be the function we want to model. The 'ideal' machine accomplishing this task would have a law θ

$$P(X_I, X_O) = \theta(X_I, X_O) = v_I \, 1_{[x_0 = F(X_I)]} \qquad (14.9)$$

Let μ be the law of our real machine on $\{0, 1\}^I \times \{0, 1\}^O$.

The goal of the learning algorithm is to minimise the *Kullback distance* between both distributions

$$d(\theta, \mu) = - \sum_{z = (x_I \times x_O)} \theta(z) ln \left(\frac{\theta(z)}{\mu(z)} \right) \qquad (14.10)$$

A simple calculation shows that

$$-\frac{\delta}{\delta w_{st}} = \frac{1}{T} (E^{clamped}(x_s x_t) - E^{free}(x_s x_t)) \qquad (14.11)$$

where $E^{clamped}$ is the expectancy when the machine works on a *clamped regime* with $x_O = F(x_I)$, and E^{free} is the expectancy when only x_I is fixed.

This result suggests a simple gradient algorithm for optimising the parameters.

Implementation of the learning algorithm

At step n, start with weights (w^n_{st}) and two distinct machines, one which is clamped and one which is not, on an arbitrary configuration.

- Let the two machines stabilise (in distribution) for N_{stab} iterations of the whole sequence of S, in order to approach the limiting Gibbs distribution.
- Then, estimate the two values $E^{clamped}(x_s x_t)$ and $E^{free}(x_s x_t)$ for all s and t, at the same time, on N_{est} iterations of the whole sequence of S.
  Change (w^n_{st}) into (w^{n+1}_{st}) with a gradient descent method.

14.3 THE PARAMETERISED BOLTZMANN MACHINE

The idea is to express the *a priori* information regarding feature location as terms in the global energy function that the Boltzmann machine will minimise.

As an example, let us suppose we want the supervised search regions to contain mainly pixels satisfying the four inequalities from Section 14.2. Then, the Gibbs energy of the machine can be the following

$$E = \sum_{i=1}^{4} \alpha_i E_i \qquad (14.12)$$

where each term E_i is minimised only when the corresponding inequality is satisfied by the output neurones defining post-processed feature maps. The α_i are parameterswhich set the relative importance of the different terms in the global minimisation.

The main advantages of this method are

- One knows exactly what the neural network does.
- There are theoretical results about the convergence to a global minimum, when using a simulated annealing method.
- The energy is additive, so that one can add terms each expressing prior knowledge.
- By weighting the different terms of the global energy one can allow different types of output configurations according to what one puts most stress on.

The first implementation of a neural supervisor is a Boltzmann machine with a sequential dynamic, which is to be replaced in time by a parallel system for reasons of efficiency.

The weights of the connections between the different cells of the machine are parameterised according to *a priori* information (translation invariance and relative location of the features) and in order to solve roughly the same kind of inequalities as the rule based algorithm.

14.3.1   Structure of the Network

The Boltzmann machine has the following structure (see Fig. 14.2)

- One *input* layer which consists of the three feature maps received from the three MLPs trained to locate the eyes and the mouth at low resolution. These outputs are thresholded in order to have a binary input.
- An *output* layer which consists of three post-processed feature maps.
- There are no hidden units.

14.3.1.1   The Links Between the Different Units

As presented in Section 14.2, the links are symmetrical.

Each output cell represents a pixel and is bound to the following (and only to the following)

- Every cell of the other two output frames. These links are strongly related to the *a priori* information one has about the relative location of the different features.
- The corresponding cell on the corresponding input frame (e.g. the cell *(i, j)* of the left eye output frame is bound to the cell *(i, j)* of the left eye input frame). This binding is called *control*. Its aim is to give to those units which are found likely to contain a feature position by the MLPs, greater priority to be part of the final feature map.
- The eight, or less if the cell is on the border of the image, immediate neighbour cells in the feature map. These links are called *gathering* and tend to help both expansion and 'connectivity' of the search area.

Each cell also has a threshold which can be seen as a link to a clamped cell which is always on.

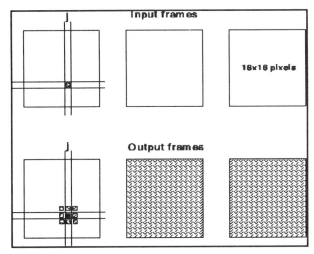

Fig. 14.2 - The parameterised Boltzmann machine: connections between the cells. Only the pixels shown in grey are connected to the black pixel on the output frame.

14.3.1.2   The Energy Function

Let us define the following

- L_i, R_i, M_i, L_o, R_o, M_o the six frames composing the network, where L, R, M stand for left eye, right eye and mouth respectively and the indices i and o stand for input and output frames.
- x_s the state of the cell s, $s \in [1..16]_N^2$, ($x_s \in \{0, 1\}$).

The energy function is the sum of four terms

$$E = E_g + E_c + E_t + E_l. \tag{14.13}$$

* E_c: *control* term

$$E_c = - \sum_{Ke\{L,R,M\}} \sum_s \alpha_c^K x_s^{K_I} x_s^{k_0} \qquad (14.14)$$

where $\alpha_c^L = \alpha_c^R = \alpha_c^E$ (E for eyes) for *a priori* reasons of symmetry. This term is called *control*, because it is the only direct link between the input and output frames. This term gives a higher probability of firing to those units -pixels- in the output frames which correspond to units firing in the input frames.

* E_t: *threshold* term

$$E_t = - \sum_{Ke\{L,R,M\}} \sum_{seK_0} h^K x_s \qquad (14.15)$$

where $h^L = h^R = h^E$

A threshold term in a Boltzmann machine is like a regulating link of the unit to a cell which is always on. The higher the threshold the less probability a neurone has of firing (regardless of other energy terms).

* E_g: *gathering* term

$$E_g = - \sum_{ke\{L,R,M\}} \sum_{\substack{s,teK_0 \\ neighbours}} \alpha_{st}^K x_s x_t \qquad (14.16)$$

where α_{st}^K is

$$\begin{cases} \alpha_g^K \ (constant) \ if \ s \ and \ t \ are \ at \ distance \ 1 \\ \dfrac{\alpha_g^K}{\sqrt{2}} \ if \ s \ and \ t \ are \ at \ distance \ \sqrt{2} \end{cases} \qquad (14.17)$$

and $\alpha_g^R = \alpha^L g = \alpha_s^E$.

This term describes the bindings between the pixels within an output frame. It encourages expansion of the search areas. Indeed, the more firing neighbours a unit has, the lower its energy and thereafter, the higher its probability of firing.

At the same time, this term helps the connectivity of the search regions on each feature map.

* E_l: term concerning the *relative location* of pixels. This term is the one which contains the most *a priori* information.

$$E_l = - \sum_{s \in L_0, t \in R_0} w_{st}^{LR} x_s x_t$$

$$- \sum_{s \in M_0, t \in L_0} w_{st}^{ML} x_s x_t \qquad (14.18)$$

$$- \sum_{s \in M_0, t \in R_0} w_{st}^{MR} x_s x_t$$

If we denote by $d(s, t)$ the Euclidean distance between the pixels s and t, e.g. $d((1,3),(5,6)) = \sqrt{16 + 9} = 5$ and $\theta(s,t)$ the angle of the vector $\underline{st}$ with the horizontal, the model which has been chosen to parameterise the weights is

$$w_{st}^{LR} = k^E e^{-(a^E(d(s,t) - d_0^E)^2 + b^E(\theta(s,t))^2) - k_0^E} \qquad (14.19)$$

$$w_{st}^{ML} = k^M e^{(a^M(d(s,t) - d_0^M) + b^M(\theta(s,t) - \theta_0^M)^2)3 - k_0^M} \qquad (14.20)$$

$$w_{st}^{MR} + k^M e^{-(a^M(d(s,t) - d_0^M) + b^M(\theta(s,t) - [\pi - \theta_0^M])2)} - k_0^M \qquad (14.21)$$

To summarise what precedes one can see that there are exactly seventeen parameters. We can distinguish these parameters into two classes

1.   The 'geometrical parameters'. These parameters are bound to the distribution of the relative location of the searched features. They can be worked out by the learning algorithm, but this is a waste of time, considering that their best approximation, in terms of a statistical approach, can be easily and precisely calculated. These parameters are

* a^E, a^M which represent the inverse of the variance allowed for the distance between two coarse pixels likely to contain two different features (half of this inverse to be precise).
* d_0^E, d_0^M which represent the mean distance between two coarse pixels which are part of search areas for two different features.
* b^E, b^M which represent the inverse of the variance allowed for the angle which the line joining two coarse pixels likely to contain two different features makes with the horizontal.
* θ_0^M which represents the mean angle that the vector defined by two coarse pixels

which are part of search areas for mouth and the left eye makes with the horizontal. By symmetry ($\pi - \theta_0^M$) is the mean angle for the right eye and the mouth.

The reason why we did not define θ_0^E and did not take into account any covariance terms between the distance and the angle is because the computed values for these terms are not significant as shown in Section 14.4.

2.   The other parameters determine the relative importance of the energy terms, which means that their variation can lead to completely different types of response by the machine.

* α_g^E, α_g^M set the importance of the *gathering* term in the energy.
* α_c^E, α_c^M set the importance of the *control* term in the energy.
* k^E, k^M set the importance of the *relative location* term in the energy.
* k_0^E, k_0^M add a penalty to the energy function which takes effect when the *relative location* of the coarse pixels supposed to contain features is far from what it is expected (*a priori*) to be.
* h^E, h^M are *thresholds* that prevent each pixel from arbitrarily turning on, that is, when the rest of the energy terms do not compensate this penalty.

All the parameters of this second category have no units, which in other terms means that there is a degree of freedom less than the number of parameters. This is because of the introduction of the temperature T which acts as a scale factor.

With the convention of sign that has been chosen all these parameters are positives.

14.3.2   The Modified Boltzmann Learning Algorithm

Despite the fairly reduced number of parameters, the optimisation seems to be a real problem. The first method implemented (on which there is still work to do) is an adaptation of the learning algorithm [HSA85] for Boltzmann machines as described in Section 14.2.

The main difference between the general algorithm and what is required here, is that the weights are not left totally free: the optimisation is done on a subspace of the global space of weights which is the parameterised weights space as described in the above section. This is a rather strong constraint, if we consider the respective dimensions of the two spaces: 17 dimensional subspace of parameterised weights for a total of 200,844 weights. Therefore, the optimal 'parameterised weights' can still provide the machine with results which are not exactly as expected.

However, the good results obtained with *manually* tuned parameters show that the minimum on the subspace will be very satisfactory (see Table 14.4).

As described in Section 14.2, the partial derivatives of the *Kullback distance* between the law L^{opt} of the optimal machine and the law L^{real} of our real machine -which we want to minimise- by the weight w_{st} are

$$-\frac{\delta}{\delta w_{st}}d(L^{opt},L^{real}) = \frac{1}{T}[E^{clamped}(x_s x_t) - E^{free}(x_s x_t)]$$

$$(14.22)$$

In this case, as there are no hidden units, the *clamped regime* is totally determined, so, there is no expectancy to approximate.

Let β be one of the parameters which define the energy. The derivative of our criterion is

$$-\frac{\delta}{\delta\beta}d(L^{opt},L^{real}) = \sum_{s,t}\left[\frac{\delta}{\delta w_{st}}d(L^{opt},L^{real})\right]\frac{\delta w_{st}}{\delta\beta}$$

$$(14.23)$$

The method which is then used is a gradient descent, which is, in the case of a Boltzmann Machine without hidden units, known [AKN92] to be theoretically convergent.

14.4 DISCUSSION OF THE MODEL AND RESULTS

14.4.1 Discussion of the Model

In this first subsection, we will discuss the choices we have made concerning the model of the Boltzmann machine.

a) Translation invariance

For very natural reasons like the difference of height and of position in the pictures of the subjects posing for the database, we had to build a translation invariant supervisor. Far from being a constraint difficult to deal with, this assumption makes the number of parameters of the system drop to 2892

- three terms of control (α_c).
- three terms of gathering (α_g.
- three terms of threshold (h).
- three 31x31 maps of links between the output feature maps (a feature map being a 16x16 pixels bitmap, the relative position of two pixels on two distinct feature maps can be described by a 31x31 grid).

b) Symmetry

Facial structure is mirror symmetric and this leads to the *a priori* idea that the statistics associated with the feature maps should have symmetrical properties.

The statistical data given in Tables 14.2 and 14.3 confirm this hypothesis as far as the links between the output features are concerned: the hypothesis fits with the usual tests [SC67] significant at the 5% level. This is also true when considering the 'gathering' and the threshold terms, since the estimation of these parameters depends essentially on the number of firing neurones on the desired output feature maps which we impose to be the same (9 per feature map) during the training.

When coming to the control parameter α_c, the validation of this 'symmetry hypothesis' depends very much on the quality of the training of the MLPs which give the input feature maps to the Boltzmann machine (see Section 14.1). Indeed, if the MLPs are not trained under the same hypothesis, it happens that the input feature maps for one eye is -on average- noisier than the input feature map for the other eye. In this case, the hypothesis fails.

Assuming that we are in a case in which we can validate our 'symmetry hypothesis', the number of parameters drops by one third.

c) Thresholded Gaussian distribution

We have chosen to model the 31x31 maps of links intra output frames by a thresholded Gaussian distribution. We characterise a pair of pixels from two different feature maps by a distance and an angle. The low correlation factor between the angle and the distance allows us to consider these variates to be orthogonal; we do not consider the covariance between distance and angle in our Gaussian function.

	inter-eyes	mouth-eyes (right eye mirrored)	mouth-left eye	mouth-right eye (mirrored)
average distance	2.59	3.22	3.25	3.18
average angle	0.04	1.99	2.06	1.92
variance distance	0.28	0.15	0.16	0.14
variance angle	0.01	0.03	0.03	0.02
covariance angle-dist.	0.03	0.00	0.00	-0.01
correlation factor	0.44	-0.06	-0.05	-0.20

Table 14.2 - Statistics on the relative location of the features: only the true pixel is kept on each feature map.

	inter-eyes	mouth-eyes (right eye mirrored)	mouth-left eye	mouth-right eye (mirrored)
average distance	2.88	3.43	3.47	3.40
average angle	0.04	1.98	2.05	1.91
variance distance	1.37	1.37	1.39	1.35
variance angle	0.29	0.19	0.19	0.19
covariance angle-dist.	0.02	0.03	0.03	0.02
correlation factor	0.04	0.06	0.06	0.04

Table 14.3 - Statistics on the relative location of firing neurones when considering feature maps defined by the true pixel and its eight geometrical neighbours.

So the link between the features A and B are modelled in the following way

$$w_{st}^{AB} = k^{AB} e^{-(a^{AB}(d(s,t) - d_0^{AB}) + b^{AB}(\theta(s,t) - \theta_0^{AB})^2)} - k_0^{AB} \qquad (14.24)$$

The parameters a^{AB}, b^{AB}, d^{AB}_0 and θ^{AB}_0 are estimated statistically, the learning algorithm optimising the values k^{AB} and k^{AB}_0.

To confirm the accuracy of these choices we have tested different types of training of our Boltzmann machine

1. Training on the 31x31 maps of links, unparameterised.
2. Training on all the parameters, including the geometrical ones.
3. Training on the non geometrical parameters, statistical estimation of the geometrical parameters.

The results of these trainings are given in the following subsection.

14.4.2   Results

Because a Boltzmann machine is a stochastic system, the performance of the machine is normally not quantifiable as in Table 14.1. However, for a practical use and in the desire of being able to compare the results of the machine with the rule based processor, we have presented in this section an average of the performance of the machine when practising a simulated annealing. In most cases, the results are similar for each simulation which holds with theory ensuring that the same configuration of minimal energy will be reached if it is unique.

Feature type	Average rejection rate (/30)	Average search region (pixels /256)	Average connectivity
Before post processing			
Training set (30 frames)			
centre of left eye	0	11.43	4.47
centre of right eye	0	1.90	1.37
centre of mouth	0	3.93	2.53
Test set (30 frames)			
centre of left eye	1	11.37	4.37
centre of right eye	3	2.50	1.83
centre of mouth	6	5.13	3.37
Manually selected parameters			
Training set			
centre of left eye	0.83	12.45	1.00
centre of right eye	0.83	12.45	1.00
centre of mouth	0.83	15.63	1.00
Test set			
centre of left eye	3.66	12.47	1.05
centre of right eye	4.17	12.53	1.00
centre of mouth	3.83	15.37	1.03
Unparameterised weights			
Training set			
centre of left eye	1.17	4.79	1.19
centre of right eye	1.33	3.75	1.03
centre of mouth	1.33	3.40	1.23
Test set			
centre of left eye	4.50	5.21	1.36
centre of right eye	6.33	3.73	0.98
centre of mouth	6.17	3.47	1.24
Parameterised + geometry			
Training set			
centre of left eye	0.00	5.73	1.68
centre of right eye	0.00	4.07	1.21
centre of mouth	0.00	3.73	1.34
Test set			
centre of left eye	2.83	5.93	1.57
centre of right eye	3.33	4.67	1.22
centre of mouth	3.83	3.97	1.31
Parameterised - geometry			
Training set			
centre of left eye	0.37	9.19	1.09
centre of right eye	0.37	9.13	1.08
centre of mouth	0.37	9.85	1.14
Test set			
centre of left eye	2.50	9.03	1.13
centre of right eye	3.50	8.97	1.10
centre of mouth	2.50	9.47	1.06

Table 14.4 - Results of the Boltzmann machine under different training schemes.

The main difference with the rule based processor is that, when 'missing' the true feature points, the Boltzmann machine can be very far from it. This is because some noise on two of the three input feature maps has been strong enough to bring the Boltzmann machine to converge to a configuration which is very unlikely if we consider only the third input feature map.

Table 14.4 presents the results.

Manually selected parameters: the geometrical parameters are the values computed, the other have been manually tuned. These parameters were the starting point for all the training cycles in order to accelerate convergence.

Unparameterised weights: the results of the Boltzmann machine without parameterising the 31x31 link maps, starting from the link maps produced by the manually selected parameters.

Parameterised + geometry: presents the results of the Boltzmann machine with all the parameters including the geometrical parameters updated by the training.

Parameterised - geometry: the geometrical parameters are calculated and fixed, the learning affecting only the parameters which weight the different terms of energy (see Section 14.3). One can see that the learning algorithm did not improve the performance of the machine by updating the geometrical parameters, on the contrary.

In any of the learning processes, the goal number of pixels for the output feature maps was 9: the true feature point and its eight direct neighbours.

14.5 CONCLUSION

The choice of a Boltzmann machine for solving our neural supervisor problem seems to be promising. On a sequence of frames, the temporal information would give even greater reliability to our system. If the built in energy function is convex or at least sufficiently sharp, an exponential annealing of the temperature (or even a start at a quasi null temperature) would not cause any problem.

The essential idea of this work is that when introducing constraints in the weights of a Boltzmann machine, training becomes more reliable. This is because the degrees of freedom are reduced in number making optimisation feasible since one is dealing with a stochastic learning algorithm which is extremely slow to converge.

The interest of the model is in its generality and its relationship to a rule based algorithm. Indeed, one can very easily change the number of constellation features, select a different class of object, choose a different type of geometrical parameterisation (e.g. Euclidean instead of polar) or even change the model of the links between frames of different objects.

REFERENCES

[AKN92]   Amari, S., Kurata, K. and Nagaoka, H., Information Geometry of Boltzmann Machines, *IEEE Transactions on Neural Networks*, 3(2), 1992.

[Aze90]   Azencott, R., Synchronous Boltzmann Machines and Gibbs Fields: Learning Algorithms, in *Neurocomputing*, Folgerman (ed.) NATO ASI. Vol. F68, Springer-Verlag, 1990.

[GG84]   Geman, S. and Geman, D., Stochastic Relaxation, Gibbs Distributions and the Bayesian Restoration of Images, *IEEE Transactions on Pattern Analysis and Machine Intelligence*, Vol. PAMI-6(6), 1984.

[HSA85]   Hinton, G., Sejnowsky, T. and Ackley, D.H., A Learning Algorithm for Boltzmann Machines, *Cognitive Science*, 9, 1985.

[SC67]   Snedecor, G.W. and Cochran, W.G., *Statistical Methods*, Iowa State University Press, 1967 (6th edition).

[Vin91]   Vincent, J.M., Facial Feature Location in Coarse Resolution Images by Multi-Layered Perceptrons, in *Proceedings of ICANN '91*, Vol. I, Elsevier Science, 1991.

[VWM91]   Vincent, J.M., Waite, J.B. and Myers, D.J., Precise Location of Facial Features by a Hierarchical Assembly of Neural Nets, in *Proceedings of the IEE 2nd International Conference on Artificial Neural Networks*, 1991.

[VWM92]   Vincent J.M., Waite J.B. and Myers D.J., Location of Feature Points in Images Using Neural Networks, *BTTJ*, 1992.

[Wai91]   Waite J.B., Facial Feature Location Using Multi-Layer Perceptrons and Micro-Features", in *Proceedings of IJCNN '91,* Vol. 1, 1991.

Chapter 15

Using Neural Networks in A CAD/CAM Application

Andreas Scherer [1] Thomas Berkel [1] Gunter Schlageter [1] Ralf Schultheiss [2]

FernUniversität Hagen [1], Germany and Ford AG Köln [2], Germany

Overview

In future CAD systems the reuse of already existing design objects becomes a key functionality. Typically, in many design domains solutions for new problems are derived from successful cases. In the first part of the chapter this requirement for future CAD systems is put in a more general context called concurrent engineering.

Then the chapter presents an application that supports the transfer of manufacturing information between different geometry specifications of CAD objects. Thus, the work of production planners is supported directly by automating routine work. As a consequence the time-to-market and the quality of the products are optimized in parallel.

15.1 INTRODUCTION

The great challenges for mechanical engineering of the nineties are the reduction of time-to-market and optimizing the quality standards in parallel. The main reasons are

- to introduce quickly new and innovative ideas to the market.
- to react directly to changing legislation (e.g. updated environmental regulations) and varying consumer demands.
- to guarantee high product quality over a long period of time.

Today's problem solving in design and production planning is characterized by the adaptation or variation of already existing solutions. This prevents the companies from expensive and time consuming development-from-scratch. Moreover it is worthwhile spending effort in reducing the iterations between design and manufacturing to minimize the amount of communication necessary to achieve global consistent results. Especially in the area of CAD/CAM this issue becomes increasingly important (e.g. because new techniques of tolerance analysis can be applied during the design process, especially before tooling is committed [Sch92]).

We suggest a neural network application that allows the designer to verify whether a drawing of a part can be machined without problems by cross-checking it against previous successful machining drawings. The latter are stored in databases and contain a lot of compiled domain knowledge implicitly represented in machining drawings, that are optimized through many iterations between designer and production planners.

The structure of this chapter is as follows. In section 15.2 general aspects regarding the complete engineering process are discussed. We explain the relation of concurrent engineering to our approach. In section 15.3 the principle usage of the system is introduced. Section 15.4 discusses some technical issues concerning the integration of neural networks in a CAD/CAM system. Finally in the last section some concluding remarks and an overview of our current work can be found.

15.2 CONCURRENT ENGINEERING

In mechanical engineering a variety of different methodologies exists which structure the complete engineering process. In [Kra92] these are compared with concurrent engineering (see Fig. 15.1). In reference to these one can subdivide the engineering process into different sub activities

- *problem specification*: information about requirements and functions to be embodied in the solution are collected.
- *concept development*: suitable solution principles have to be found. These are combined and lead to different concept variants.
- *design*: the layout and the form of the product are determined. Technical and economical aspects have to be considered.
- *detail design/production planning:* form, dimension and surface properties of all parts are defined, the type of material is specified, the technical and economical feasibility is checked and all technical drawings and documents that describe the machining and assembly process are produced.

Typically, all these activities have to be executed in a serialized way. However, because of the necessity to improve the time-to-market and quality we have to rethink about those methodologies and about the nature of the computer based systems to support the work of designers [KSS92, AWM92, TOS92, SS92]. In concurrent engineering among others the following aspects are important

- how can we join some activities in the engineering process in parallel?
- how can we use knowledge from later phases and take it as a constraint in generating design decision in earlier phases?

Without any doubt today's design methodologies help to identify specific design activities and in this way they structure the complete design process. On the other hand the designer's work becomes too constrained if s/he tries to execute his/her activities along with a particular serial methodology.   Along with case-based approaches (CBR) where specific solutions to previous problems were selected and transformed to be appropriate as solutions for a new problem by analogical reasoning [Mah90] we suggest an alternative technique.

The following improvements can be achieved

- *systematic reuse of already existing knowledge* (do not discover the wheel twice).
- *time*: the CAD/CAM-objects in the database are optimized by many iterations between the designers and the production planners. Using them as a basis for new problems means to reduce the amount of these iterations significantly.
- *quality*: currently produced CAD/CAM-objects represents a certain level of quality in a company. If new parts are designed and machined in a similar way as parts that have been successfully produced, then the same quality-standard can be achieved for the new part too.

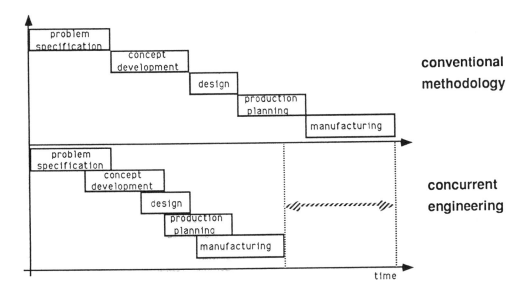

Fig. 15.1 - Conventional Methodologies vs Concurrent Engineering [Kra92].

We can use such a case based approach, because in our domain (production of motors and gears) the change of the technology to be designed is an evolutionary process, e.g. usually the versions no n+1 of a motor bases mainly on the version n. Some modules are exchanged or improved, most are taken from the previous version. Because of this domain characteristic CBR-like approaches can be reasonably applied. But note, the used techniques are not standard in CBR at all. We want to use neural networks for the selection of appropriate cases and also for the transfer of knowledge between the reference case and the new case.

The authors of this chapter have not found any references to similar approaches in CBR in the literature so far. In addition to that it can be seen that via the reuse of CAD/CAM objects we meet one of the issues in concurrent engineering by exchanging information between different phases of the whole engineering processes, namely design, production planning and manufacturing.

15.3 THE APPLICATION

Our approach is directly integrated in the CAD/CAM-system ADAPT (Analysis Tool for Design and Process Tolerancing) used at the Ford AG for years. ADAPT provides engineers with a tool to predict and optimize manufacturing and assembly tolerances

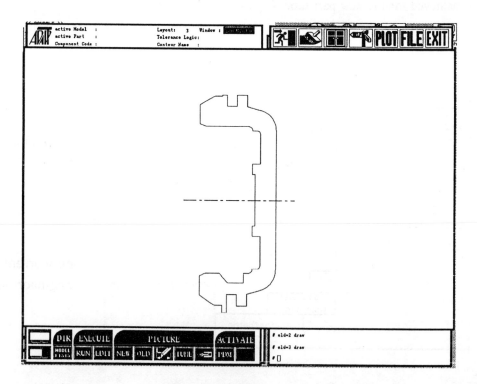

Fig. 15.2 - The new part.

before tooling is committed. The usage of ADAPT in early phases of the design process can eliminate potential geometrical, kinematics and tolerance problems. Expensive changes of the design or the manufacturing process are reduced significantly [Sch92].

The tool is used as follows. First the geometry of a part is specified by a parametric model. Then the designer determines every machining step/process that has to be shown in the particular drawing. The type of machining operation, the material removal and the tolerances are specified. By applying different analyzers the designer can verify whether this design and the associated machining process is feasible in principle. In addition the program checks whether there are any problems in the overall assembly in which the part shall be integrated. Critical areas of the assembly are visualized on the screen and the designer can react by changing the design and/or the machining operations.

This process is very time consuming. Also in most cases there exist parts in the CAD database that are very similar to the currently processed part. To speed up the generation of appropriate production plans the following scenario describes the aims of our project.

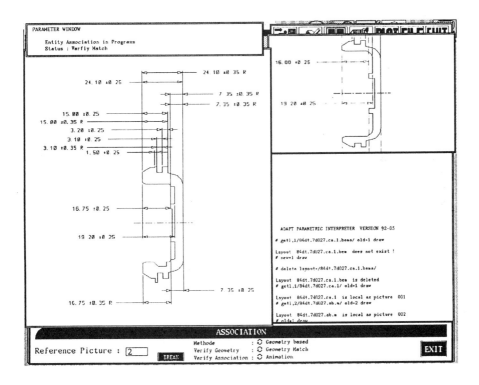

Fig. 15.3 - Transfer of Machining Operations.

15.3.1 The Scenario

On the basis of the functional requirements of the product the designer creates an initial parametric part model. In current practice the engineer searches manually through the database and looks for appropriate cases that are adaptable to the new problem. This procedure is very time consuming and depends strongly on the ability of the designer to recognize very fast structural similarities of part descriptions. By retrieving similar objects from a database a similar part is chosen and then the transfer of dimensioning and/or machining information (in process planning the material removal at every machining step, e.g. milling has to be defined) is performed automatically as far as the structural similarity between the reference part and the destination part allows it. Finally, the part description is post-processed by the designer by adding further dimensioning and machining information, respectively, to it. In this way it is possible to take advantage from previous design and machining solutions. Then ADAPT is used in the above described way. In an analysis step it is checked if the design and the manufacturing plan for the part are feasible. In addition it is verified whether there are problems in the assembly into which this part will be integrated. Because errors at the design and manufacturing planning phase are very expensive, the expert can never be replaced completely by a computer application in generating appropriate part designs and the associated production plans. Instead the designer is relieved from manual and cognitive routine matters; his/her work is focused on the *new* aspects of a CAD/CAM-problem.

15.4 INTEGRATING NEURAL NETWORKS IN A CAD/CAM SYSTEM

There are different reasons for using neural networks in the described project. Mainly we are using neural networks

- to learn the weighting of features to compute the overall similarity of two parts.
- to generalize during the transfer of manufacturing knowledge between structurally similar parts.
- to provide the user with high performance functions.

In this section we discuss first how the data from the CAD system are translated in an appropriate description. Then, we present the integration strategy.

15.4.1 The Data Representation

In the CAD/CAM system ADAPT the geometry of the objects is determined by points, lines and cycles. These entities are linked together and form a complex graph, that describes the CAD object. Some of the edges of this graph are enriched with further information (the machining operations mentioned in the previous section). If one tries to make use of the machining plans of previous successfully produced objects, then it is necessary to find ways to map the entities of the reference object to those of the new object.

Algorithm 15.4.1

u, v are entities of a CAD-OBJECT

TRAIN_SET is the training set used to train the network

FORALL (u, v) *IN* REFERENCE-OBJECT *AND NOT* MARK(u, v)

BEGIN
    d(u) := describe_entity(u);
    d(v) := describe_entity(v);
    IF (u, v) is linked with a MACHINE_OPERATION
    THEN TRAIN_SET:= TRAIN_SET + (d(u), d(v), MACHINE_OPERATION);
    ELSE TRAIN_SET := TRAIN_SET + (d(u), d(v), NO_OPERATION);
    mark(u,v)
END

From the training set we derive via algorithm 15.4.1 the architecture of the network. The input has always the same structure. The description of the entities u, v has a fixed length. In detail: in the description of a given entity the k neighbour entities on the left and the right side are listed. k is a fixed number greater or equal to two [EU90]. With this representation technique we represent the local context of an entity.

Algorithm 15.4.2

FORALL (u, v) *IN* NEW_OBJECT

BEGIN
    d(u) := describe(u);
    d(v) := describe(v);
    index := net(d(u), d(v));
    mop := look_up_table(index);
    IF mop *IS_NOT_A NO*_OPERATION *THEN* associate(u, v, mop)
END

Then the input is mapped to different output classes. Each class represents an index. With the ith class (or index) the associated information (machining operation: milling, drilling etc., and the required tolerance, e.g. +/- 0.25 mm) can be found in the ith row of a look-up-table.

Once a network is trained it represents the complete machining plan to produce a part. By using algorithm 15.4.2 such a network (net) is applied to a new part without the production specifications.

15.4.2 Integration of Neural Networks

In order to be able to characterize the "way of use" of networks we developed properties for differentiation [DSS92]; the primary properties are

- *stability*: a network N is said to be used in an ad hoc way if N is specially created for the treatment of a concrete problem instance p and exists only for the period of solving p; otherwise N is said to be used in a stable way.
- *dynamics*: N is said to be used in a dynamic way, if learning processes can be applied to N while using N in order to improve or adapt the computational behaviour of N to achieve adequate problem solving behaviour; otherwise N is said to be used in a static way. In the course of a static use of a network N topology and neuron-model of N are fixed (the neuron-model specifies the i/o-behaviour of each single neuron of a network). Therefore the computational behaviour of statically used networks will not change with time while using them to solve certain problems. Given a network N that is dynamically used, neuron-model and topology are modifiable. In the case of dynamically used networks we can further distinguish types of network uses referring to the dimension of requirement-stability.
- *requirement-stability*: N is said to be used in a requirement-stable way, if a function f with the following properties exists

    (i)   the computational behaviour of N should be organized according to f in order to produce optimal problem solutions (in a sense N would then realise f),

    (ii)   f is not a time dependent function.

    Otherwise N is said to be used in a requirement-variable way.

According to this classification we are using *static* networks for the transfer of machining operations. Once the network is trained a description of the network (topology and weights) is created and stored together with the look-up-table and the original CAD-object in a case database. Note, networks describing reference objects can be trained at any time. The user just executes trained networks. Thus, the transfer of the machining knowledge can be performed very efficiently. By selecting an appropriate case the knowledge of the production planner in generating correct machining plans can be used for new problems.

15.5 CURRENT WORK AND CONCLUSION

Section 15.4 presents the general strategy to use neural networks for the transfer of machining operations from a reference part to a new part. Our current activities focus on the following working packages

* analysis of different types of neural networks (back-propagation, Kohonen).
* experiments by varying the scaling parameters of networks.
* comparison of the achieved results with those of a conventional pattern recognition algorithm.

In the second phase of the project we will work on methods to automate the retrieval of appropriate reference cases from the case database.

Part drawings stored in CAD databases contain detailed knowledge on two levels

* design level: how to solve a given design problem satisfying all initial requirements.
* manufacturing level: how to process efficiently a part using existing machinery.

The main problem is that CAD objects are described by low level primitives that determine their geometry. We suggest a subsymbolic approach to make this kind of knowledge directly usable. First experiences with a prototype are promising. The designers find this tool, that was integrated into their conventional CAD environment helpful. Especially for the acceptance of a computer support it seems to be important that the designer can influence the information transfer process and is able to control the generated machining plans. We currently develop more flexible procedures to transfer information between reference parts and new parts.

ACKNOWLEDGEMENTS

We thank Mr. Schulze Schwering from Ford for his support. In addition we would like to thank the following students of the FernUniversität Hagen for the fruitful discussion and their participation on this project: Mr. Emmler, Mr. Hilbert, Mrs. Dr. Tuch and Mr. Weiland. This project is funded by a research grant from Ford AG.

REFERENCES

[AWM92]   Alberts, L.K., Wognum, P.M. and Mars, N.J.I., Structuring Design Knowledge on the Basis of Generic Components, in *Proceedings of the 2nd International Conference on Artificial Intelligence in Design '92*, Gero, J.S. (ed.), Kluwer Academic Publisher, 1992.

[DSS92]   Dunker, J., Scherer, A. and Schlageter, G., Integrating Neural Networks into a Distributed Knowledge-Based Systems, in *Proceedings of the 12th International Conference on Artificial Intelligence: Expert Systems and Natural Language, Avignon, France*, 1992.

[EU90]   Engels, C. and Ufer, S., Pattern Recognition, Master Thesis, Institüt for Informatik, Rheinische-Friedrich-Wilhelms Universität Bonn, 1990.

[Kra92]   Krause, F.L., The Change of Design Tasks for CAD Systems, in *Proceedings of CAD '92 Conference*, Springer Verlag (in German), 1992.

[KSS92]   Kemper, F., Scherer, A., Straube, M., Wilkes, W. and Schlageter, G., A Knowledge-Based Design Consultant: Model and Architecture, in *Proceedings of the 25th International Conference on Systems Sciences, Honolulu, Hawaii*, 1992.

[Mah90]   Maher, M.L., Process Models for Design Synthesis, *AAAI Magazine*, Maher, M.L., Gero, J.S. (eds.), Winter 1990.

[Sch92]   Schultheiss, R., Tolerance Analysis with ADAPT, *Internal Technical Report*, FORD AG Köln, 1992.

[SS92]   Scherer, A. and Schlageter, G., Concurrent Engineering: Towards the Integration of CAD/CAM by a Neural Network Application, in *ECAI-Workshop Notes on Concurrent Engineering, Vienna, Austria*, 1992.

[TOS92]   Taleb-Bendiab, A., Oh, V., Sommerville, I. and French, M.J., Collaborative Design: Knowledge-Based Systems for Concurrent Engineering, in *ECAI-Workshop Notes on Concurrent Engineering, Vienna, Austria*, 1992.

Chapter 16

A Self-Organising Logic Neural Network for Pattern Completion Tasks

G. Tambouratzis and T.J. Stonham

Department of Electrical Engineering, Brunel University, U.K.

Overview

In this chapter, a system which is able to perform pattern completion tasks is presented. The system is based on a logic neural network which has the advantages of being readily implementable and possessing a very high functionality. This network is trained using an self-organising algorithm, eliminating the need for supervision during learning.

16.1 INTRODUCTION

In information processing applications, data often contains a considerable amount of noise. In order to successfully perform the processing, as much noise as possible must be removed from the data. Hence, there is a need for a system which is able to recreate the noise-free pattern using the corrupted input as a starting point.

A neural network which performs pattern completion tasks and is able to remove noise has been presented by Hopfield [Hop82]. A conceptually similar system based on probabilistic logic nodes has been proposed by Kan [KA89]. Both these systems rely on supervised learning to store the stable state patterns in the system. Additionally, the reconstruction phase may require more than one cycle through the neural network, until the output is stabilised.

In the following sections, a self-organising pattern completion system is proposed and its application to a character reconstruction problem is described. Being based on a logic neural network, this system possesses the advantages of easy implementation and very high functionality. These are combined with the benefit of unsupervised learning which eliminates the need for both a supervisor during the training phase and the labelling (i.e. designation of the desired network output) of training patterns. The system promises to have a short response time as the pattern is reconstructed in a single cycle.

16.2 SYSTEM DESCRIPTION

The proposed system consists of RAM-based discriminators [AM90]. The discriminator contains logic functions, each of which samples a tuple of "n" pixels from the input image. In the case of a binary image, each function consists of 2^n memory locations where a binary number is stored. This number indicates whether the corresponding tuple combination has occurred during training (value "1" stored) or not (value "0" stored). Before training, all memory locations are set to "0" since no patterns have been presented to the system as yet. As training patterns are presented, "1"s are set in the locations addressed by the patterns. The basic discriminator structure is shown in Fig. 16.1.

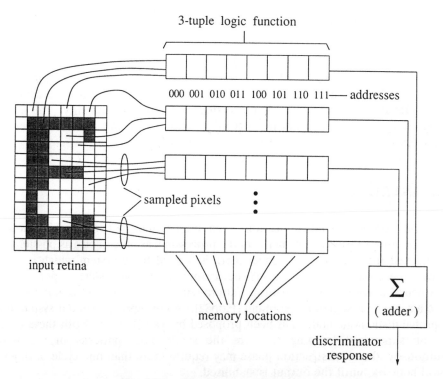

Fig. 16.1 - Discriminator Structure.

In the proposed system, the basic discriminator structure is retained though a number of modifications are introduced. The memory locations of each logic function occupy "k" bits instead of only 1, thus being able to store the frequency of occurrence of each pixel tuple (up to a limit of 2^k-1, imposed by the memory capacity of each location). The discriminator response to a pattern is generated by using the pixel values sampled by each function to access an address. The frequency of occurrence stored in the corresponding memory location is added to that of other functions to generate the actual response.

The training strategy also differs considerably. For each input pattern, all discriminators compete and the winner is assigned to that pattern. Originally, a simple winner-take-all strategy closely resembling the competitive learning paradigm [RZ86] was used for self-organisation. Experimentation showed that in hard self-organisation tasks (tasks where patterns belonging to different classes have a relatively high degree of similarity) this method by itself was not very effective, and the system performance could be considerably enhanced by adding lateral interconnections [TS92a]. These interconnections link the discriminators to form a one-dimensional (or higher-dimensional) network. The interconnections specify neighbourhoods of discriminators which get smaller as the training progresses. When a discriminator is selected to be adapted to one pattern, its neighbours (as defined by the active lateral interactions using a time-decaying neighbourhood function) are similarly adapted. The neighbourhood training has been claimed to be biologically plausible [Koh87, Mal73]. Such strategies have been shown to result in the topological ordering of input patterns, similar patterns being assigned to adjacent neurons [Koh84, Mal73].

16.2.1   Adaptive Algorithm Description

The unsupervised learning paradigm possesses significant advantages over the more conventional supervised learning. In supervised learning, a supervisor is required to guide the neural network. For each input pattern, the desired output must be specified. In contrast, in unsupervised learning no supervision or labelling of inputs is required. The network is presented with unlabelled data which it classifies according to internal criteria which are developed autonomously, as training progresses.

The algorithm used to train the proposed system belongs to the category of unsupervised learning and is particularly well-suited to digital neural networks [TS92b]. During training the system is presented with inputs to which all discriminators generate responses. According to these responses, a discriminator is selected and this, together with its neighbours, is adapted towards the current pattern by shifting units within each function towards the address designated by the sampled pixels.

For each logic function "j" of the discriminator being trained, an address a_j is generated depending on the values of the n-tuple pixels. As the memory location with that address is the one that corresponds to the input pattern, its content shall be increased by one. The address a_j' with the maximum Hamming distance from a_j is located and its content examined. If it is non-zero, then it is decreased by one and the content of a_j is increased by the same amount. If on the other hand the content of

a_j' is zero, then a new address a_j' with the next-highest Hamming distance from a_j is examined and so on. If all memory locations apart from a_j have zero contents, the discriminator is not modified. This adaptation operation can be formulated as follows

$$\text{for } 0 \le j < d \quad \begin{cases} m_{i,j}(a_j)(t) = m_{i,j}(a_j)(t-1) + 1 \\ m_{i,j}(a_j')(t) = m_{i,j}(a_j')(t-1) - 1 \end{cases} \tag{16.1}$$

where "i" denotes the discriminator, and "t" represents the current time step. An example of the adaptation procedure defined by (Eqn. 16.1) is depicted in Fig. 16.2. A 3-tuple function is shown before (upper function) and after (lower function) an input occurs. When input "111" is presented to the function, the content of address "111" is increased by 1 while the content of address "000" (which is the maximum Hamming distance) is decreased by 1 as it is non-zero.

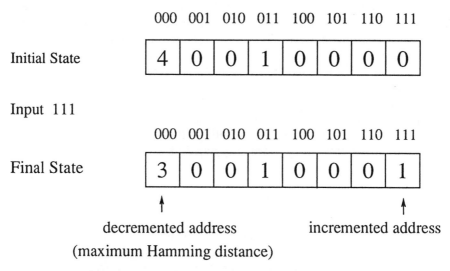

Fig. 16.2 - Example of the adaptive algorithm operation.

The total number of units in each logic function remains constant when the adaptation operation is performed, and thus the following equation holds during training

$$\sum_{j=0}^{d-1} m_{i,j} = constant \tag{16.2}$$

Due to (Eqn. 16.2), the system is prevented from saturating (a major problem in logic neural networks) even for training phases of unlimited length. At the same time, no additional normalisation step is required as is frequently the case in Kohonen Maps [Koh84] due to the fact that the algorithm automatically normalises the sum of weights in each function. The number of units inserted initially in each function together with the maximum storage capacity of each memory location (equal to 2^k-1) defines the bounds of the network's generalisation ability, which varies as training evolves.

16.2.2 Separation of Similar Patterns

In order to ensure separation of similar but distinct patterns in hard self-organising tasks, an additional constraint called *distribution constraint* is introduced [TS92b]. This has a function similar to Adaptive Resonance Theory's top-down expectation [CG88] in that it uses information already accumulated in the discriminator to reject input patterns which contradict the stored knowledge, resulting in a stable assignment of input patterns to discriminators. This constraint is implemented by examining how many functions contribute significantly to the response of the maximally-responding discriminator. If the number of these functions falls below a given threshold, this discriminator is considered unsuitable for the current input and the discriminator with the next-highest response is examined. Only if all discriminators in the system fail the distribution constraint will the input be assigned to the highest-responding discriminator which does not satisfy the constraint. By setting the distribution constraint limit, the operator is able to approximately define the degree of similarity between patterns assigned to the same discriminator and consequently dictate the selectivity of each discriminator and the range of the classes generated by the system.

It is worth noting that the violation of the distribution constraint signals that the system has not yet succeeded in fully separating the pattern classes. Thus, the constraint may be used to indicate whether the system has settled in a stable state or not. Experimentation has shown that if the distribution constraint is not satisfied after long training phases, this signifies that the storage capacity of the given system is too low to separate all the classes contained in the training set while complying with the distribution constraint.

16.2.3 Application to Pattern Completion Tasks

In pattern completion tasks, a contaminated pattern is presented to the system and each discriminator generates a response. The highest-responding discriminator is selected as it is most probably the one that has been trained to recognise the class the given pattern belongs to. The knowledge about the pattern class that has been accumulated in this discriminator during training is then used to reconstruct the noise-free input. This is achieved by locating for each function the address of the memory location with the highest content, which corresponds to the most frequent n-tuple value. This address then provides the values for the pixels sampled by the function. The ability to reconstruct the whole image is made possible by sampling all pixels in the retina once. By sampling each pixel only once, any conflicts caused by two functions generating different values for a given pixel are avoided.

The reconstruction phase is similar to the adaptive training phase in that in both cases all discriminators compete for the current input by generating responses. In both cases there is also a need to store for each function the address with the highest frequency of occurrence. Thus, the two mechanisms may be implemented efficiently in hardware, sharing a number of circuits. As described earlier, during training the distribution constraint is combined with the response magnitude in the discriminator selection. In pattern reconstruction, a similar constraint is not required as the system has (following the training phase) reached a stable state where different pattern classes have been separated and assigned to different discriminators.

During reconstruction, it is possible that the input pattern presented to the system does not belong to any of the classes encountered during training and thus should not be reconstructed. The occurrence of such an input may be detected by defining a threshold for the discriminator response. If this is not exceeded by any discriminator, the pattern is rejected as being unclassifiable. The introduction of this threshold helps avoid "impossible" reconstructions at the expense of limiting (to a small extent) the reconstruction capabilities of the system. In the following discussion on the system, we shall assume that only patterns belonging to classes from the training set are presented to the reconstruction system, eliminating the need for such a threshold.

16.3 SIMULATION RESULTS

The presented system was applied to a problem requiring the pattern completion of noise-contaminated characters. The data set consisted of 10 digitised machine-printed characters, shown in Fig. 16.3. The patterns were binary images with a size of 16x24 pixels. To generate the training set, each character was contaminated by random noise of a level equal to 6.25%. Thus though 10 characters were used, all training patterns were different, the characters forming the centroids of the training set classes. Eight-tuple functions were used because of their high selectivity in order to separate the letters.

The system comprised 30 discriminators, interconnected to form a one-dimensional string. Each pixel was sampled exactly once, the pixels sampled by each function being selected randomly from the image. The training consisted of 600 iterations, in each of which one noise-contaminated image of each letter was presented to the system. The neighbourhood function initially covered 5 discriminators (iterations 1 to 200), then being reduced to 3 (iterations 201 to 400) and finally to a single discriminator (iterations 401 to 600). This neighbourhood function was small in comparison to that normally used in Kohonen maps [KKL91], though it has been shown that the quality of the generated mapping is not adversely affected by such a small neighbourhood [TS92b].

ABCDEFGHJK

Fig. 16.3 - Character images used in simulations.

At the end of the training phase, the system had separated the characters by assigning them to different discriminators, while forming a topological mapping. The expected pattern for each discriminator after training (i.e. the pattern which would generate the highest response when presented to that discriminator) is shown in Fig. 16.4. This pattern was the result of the reconstruction process when the discriminator was selected. Even though these correspond to the stable state after the fine-tuning phase, the change in the expected pattern is progressive along the string. Patterns marked with an arrow correspond to the discriminators which generated the highest response for one of the ten letters. It is worth noting that in many cases, several neighbouring discriminators would, if selected, produce the same image. This was due to the topological ordering of inputs in the network nodes.

BBBHEFFFJJJEEEKGGGCCAAAAAAADDD

Fig. 16.4 - Expected patterns for the network discriminators.

In the experiments presented, three types of deformation were used

(i)   random noise, implemented by inverting the value of the noise-contaminated pixels,
(ii)   concentrated noise, implemented by setting entire rows of the character image to black, and
(iii)   concentrated noise, implemented by setting entire rows of the character image to white.

Random noise emulated errors introduced during the acquisition and/or digitisation of images. Concentrated noise replicated errors likely to occur during data transmission. The results obtained for each of these deformations shall be presented separately.

In each simulation, the system was trained using the same input patterns and with the same weight initialisation, the only difference being the type and level of contamination in the patterns to be reconstructed by the system. A noise level of approximately 25% seems to form the limit at which the human observer can recognise a pattern. However, higher noise levels (up to 50% noise) were used in the reconstruction phase so as to investigate the system's capabilities and limitations.

A sample of contaminated images of the letter "A", representative of the patterns presented to the system for reconstruction are depicted in Fig. 16.5. In the first row, random noise has been superimposed to the image while in the second and third row black and white lines respectively have been superimposed on the noise-free character. Images in the first row have 0%, 6.25%, 16.5%, 18.75%, 25%, 31.25%, 37.50%, 43.75% and 50.00% of their pixels corrupted (from left to right). In the two lower rows, the amount of corrupted lines is 0%, 8.33%, 12.67%, 25%, 33.33%, 41.67%, 50%, 58.33%, 66.67% and 75.00% respectively (again from left to right).

Fig. 16.5 - Examples of corrupted patterns presented to the system for reconstruction.

16.3.1 Random Noise Experiments

This first series of experiments consisted of presenting to the system patterns contaminated with random noise, the noise level varying from 6.25% up to 50%. For each letter, 100 different noisy patterns with the same noise level were presented to the pattern completion system. Ideally, for each letter all contaminated patterns would result in reconstruction of the noise-free patterns. However, as the noise level was increased, noise might cause a discriminator other than the one assigned to recognize this class to be used for reconstruction. In Table 16.1, the results of the simulations are shown. In this table, the term "d" has been used to denote the distance on the discriminator string between the discriminator corresponding to the input pattern's class and the discriminator selected for reconstruction. Hence, the second column (d=0) corresponds to the successful reconstructions, when the correct discriminator was selected. The third column (d=1) represents the cases for which the discriminator selected for reconstruction was next to the discriminator trained to recognise the class. Similarly, the fourth column corresponds to cases for which the selected and correct discriminators had a distance of 2, while the fifth column corresponds to distances larger than 2. Each row corresponds to a different noise level, the results from the ten characters having been combined to give a collective view which is as far as possible pattern-independent. Thus the sum of the entries in columns 2 to 5 for each row is equal to the number of patterns reconstructed by the system. Due to the lateral interactions connecting closely-positioned discriminators, a topology-preserving mapping has been achieved, and neighbouring discriminators have fairly similar contents and thus give rather similar reconstruction results. Hence, even if the discriminator selection is not correct and the selected discriminator has a small distance from the ideal discriminator, the reconstruction error is not very large.

Ideally, a distance "d" of 0 should be achieved for each pattern, but if that is not the case, a distance which is as small as possible is desirable.

From the results quoted in Table 16.1, it is evident that for low noise levels (less than 20%) all (or almost all) reconstructions were successful. Any errors were mainly confined to a radius of "d" equal to 1, representing a minimum and in many cases recoverable error. For higher noise levels, errors began to spread out at rather large distances from the "correct" discriminator, though a large number were still confined at a radius of "d" equal to 1. It is worth noting that errors with a distance "d" equal to 2 were few in comparison to those with a distance of 1, but more than for a random position in the discriminator string. Thus, errors involved mainly discriminators with a small "d". For 25% noise, the system successfully reconstructed over 90% of the corrupted patterns, while even for a noise exceeding 30%, the majority of patterns were successfully reconstructed.

Noise Level	Selections (d=0)	Selections (d=1)	Selections (d=2)	Selections (d>2)
6.250%	0	0	0	0
9.375%	1000	0	0	0
12.500%	1000	0	0	0
15.625%	999	0	0	1
18.750%	994	6	0	0
21.875%	961	22	2	15
25.000%	903	34	14	49
28.125%	759	79	32	130
31.250%	625	102	47	226
34.375%	467	93	83	357
37.500%	320	77	99	504
50.000%	76	10	96	818

Table 16.1 - Random Noise Simulations.

16.3.2 Black Line Deformation

The second type of deformation concerned concentrated noise, with whole rows of the binary image being changed to black. In all respects apart from the deformation, the system was similar to the one described previously. The results obtained by presenting patterns with different numbers of black lines are summarised in Table 16.2. It is worth noting that in this case the system appeared to be much more resistant to noise. In reality, the noise level was considerably less than the amount of black lines would suggest. The reason for that was that though in each black line all pixels were set to black, only the pixels which had originally been white were inverted, the rest remaining unchanged. Thus, even though the pixels in the dark rows conveyed no actual information, the amount of corrupted pixels was actually much lower than the number of black rows would suggest, and depended on the black-to-white pixel ratio in the original image. For an equal number of black and white pixels in the input image, the actual noise level would be equal to half the proportion of black lines. It is also worth noting that for a black-to-white pixel ratio considerably different to 50%, the system might be more (or less) susceptible to setting lines to black rather than white.

Black Lines	Selections (d=0)	Selections (d=1)	Selections (d=2)	Selections (d>2)
8.333%	1000	0	0	0
16.667%	1000	0	0	0
25.000%	999	1	0	0
33.333%	982	8	3	7
41.667%	916	36	17	31
50.000%	729	96	36	139
58.333%	528	113	67	292
66.667%	346	81	120	453
75.000%	211	39	177	573

Table 16.2 - Black Line Simulations.

The results presented in Table 16.2 indicate that the system is resistant to that type of deformation. With a third of the image rows being corrupted, over 98% of the presented patterns were successfully reconstructed, the system managing to identify the presented pattern from the remaining rows. Even when half of the rows provided no information whatsoever, the system was able to reconstruct correctly over 70% of the presented patterns.

The simulations performed indicate that some characters proved to be particularly resistant to such contamination, achieving a reconstruction success rate exceeding 94% even with 50% of rows being contaminated (character "H"), while for the same noise level other character had a success rate of 54% (character "F"). It turned out that characters "B", "C" and "H" were particularly resistant to this type of deformation, while characters "A", "F" and "J" had relatively low reconstruction success rates. This probably depends on the way the representative features of each character are distributed in the image as well as the ratio of black-to-white pixels in each pattern.

16.3.3 White Line Deformation

This type of deformation is the opposite of that presented in the previous paragraph. In this case the results (which are displayed in Table 16.3) are superior to these obtained for dark lines. This indicates that the character dataset is more resistant to this type of contamination than to the previous one, probably due to the fact that on average each character contains more white pixels rather than black ones. The system successfully reconstructed almost all contaminated patterns when 33.33% of rows are contaminated, the collective success rate being equal to 99.8%. Even when half of the rows conveyed absolutely no information, the reconstruction success rate exceeded 90%. The system behaviour was similar to the one described previously, with some characters being successfully reconstructed more frequently than others. Characters "A", "J" and "F" were consistently reconstructed for even high noise levels while characters "D", "K" and "H" were found to be highly susceptible to noise.

White Lines	Selections (d=0)	Selections (d=1)	Selections (d=2)	Selections (d>2)
8.333%	1000	0	0	0
16.667%	1000	0	0	0
25.000%	1000	0	0	0
33.333%	998	0	1	1
41.667%	984	4	2	10
50.000%	901	36	12	51
58.333%	771	40	38	151
66.667%	580	66	43	311
75.000%	383	83	51	483

Table 16.3 - White Line Simulations.

The experiments summarised in Tables 16.2 and 16.3 confirm that any reconstruction errors in the contaminated patterns are likely to result from an incorrect selection of a discriminator which is close to the correct one. Especially for low and medium noise levels, these errors were more often than not situated at a distance of 1 from the ideal discriminator, or if that is not the case almost always at a distance of 2. Thus, a considerable amount of misclassifications could be recovered by making use of the network's topology-preservation properties, as shall be described in the following paragraph.

16.4 DISCUSSION

The data-reconstruction system presented in this chapter has a number of significant advantages. It is trained by an noise-resistant, unsupervised learning algorithm; furthermore the reconstruction phase does not require a supervisor either. At the same time, the system is based on a digital neural network which is readily implementable in hardware while also possessing a very high functionality.

The training of the neural network consists of forming stable categories of inputs. These categories are assigned to the nodes in such a way as to preserve as many topological features as possible. Hence, nodes which are situated at a small distance from each other in the network lattice have similar weight contents and thus during reconstruction shall generate patterns with a high degree of similarity.

The simulations performed indicate that the system has a good performance for reasonable noise levels (up to around 25% noise). Furthermore, the simulations seem to indicate that for a wide range of noise levels (up to 25%) any misclassifications of corrupted patterns are likely to be of a distance of only one or two nodes from the class-representative node. This is attributable to the topology-preserving nature of the algorithm and can be utilised to recover a large amount of these errors with a simple strategy. After training, each discriminator is examined to find out which pattern class it recognizes. Whenever it is selected in the reconstruction phase, it shall activate the discriminator which has been optimally organised to recognise this class. Thus, a large number of otherwise slightly incorrect reconstructions will actually be transformed to correct ones, at only modest effort from a supervisor.

An interesting point is that when whole rows of the patterns were set to white or black, the results obtained were similar, though the system behaved markedly better for white rather than for black lines. This is related to the average black-to-white pixel ratio, as 56.5% of pixels in the noise-free letter images are white and 43.5% are black. Similarly, some characters were found to be more resistant to deformations with black or white lines than others. It turned out that those that were more resistant to black line deformation had a higher than average amount of black pixels. Similarly, letters that were more resistant to white line deformations turned out to have a higher than average amount of white pixels. Thus, as should be expected, the system's tolerance to such non-uniform deformations depends on the black-to-white pixel ratio of the binary image, which signifies how many pixels will actually be corrupted.

REFERENCES

[AM90]   Aleksander, I. and Morton, H., *An Introduction to Neural Computing*. Chapman and Hall, London, 1990.

[CG88]   Carpenter, G.A. and Grossberg, S.,   The ART of Adaptive Pattern Recognition by a Self-Organising Neural Network, *IEEE Computer*, 77-88, 1988.

[Hop82]   Hopfield, J.J., Neural Networks and Physical Systems with Emergent Computational Abilities, in *Proceedings of the National Academic Science, USA*, Vol. 79, 2554-58, 1982.

[KA89]   Kan, W. and Aleksander, I.,   A Probabilistic Logic Neuron for Associative Learning, in *Neural Computing Architectures*, Aleksander, I., (ed.), 156-71, North Oxford Academic Publishers, 1989.

[KKL91]   Kangas, J.A., Kohonen, T. and Laaksonen, J.T.,   Variants of Self-Organising Maps, *IEEE Transactions on Neural Networks*, 1(1), 93-99, 1991.

[Koh87]   Kohonen, T.,   Adaptive, Associative and Self-Organising Functions in Neural Computing, *Applied Optics*, 26, 4910-18, 1987.

[Koh84]   Kohonen, T., *Self-Organisation and Associative Memory*, Springer-Verlag, Heidelberg, 1984.

[Mal73]   von der Malsburg, C., Self-Organization of Orientation Sensitive Cells in the Striate Cortex, *Kybernetik*, 14, 85-100, 1973.

[RZ86]   Rumelhart, D.E. and Zipser, D.,   Feature Discovery by Competitive Learning, in *Parallel Distributed Processing: Foundations*, Vol. 1, Rumelhart, D.E., McClelland, J.L. (eds.), 151-93, MIT, Cambridge, 1986.

[TS92a]   Tambouratzis, G. and Stonham, T.J., A Logical Neural Network that Adapts to Changes in the Pattern Environment, in *Proceedings of the 11th IAPR Conference, Delft, The Netherlands*, Vol. 2, 46-49, IEEE Press, 1992.

[TS92b]   Tambouratzis, G. and Stonham, T.J., Implementing Hard Self-Organisation Tasks Using Logical Neural Networks, in *Artificial Neural Networks-II*, Aleksander, I., Taylor, J. (eds.), Vol. 1, 643-46, North-Holland, Amsterdam, 1992.

Chapter 17

Implementing an Associative Memory Environment

Ian Kelly and James Austin

Department of Computer Science, University of York, U.K.

Overview

Neural networks, if they are to be applied to many real-world problems, may require the development of large yet fast neural systems. Software solutions offer flexibility and the easy development of large systems but are generally impaired speedwise by the architecture of conventional computer systems. Hardware neural networks are fast but lack flexibility and remain relatively small. Here we outline an integrated software/hardware environment for the easy development of large neural systems, specifically aimed at binary associative memories.

17.1 INTRODUCTION

These are many different approaches to the implementation of neural networks in hardware [Mur89]. Digital VLSI approaches suffer from the large silicon area needed to implement digital multipliers and also to store weight values to the required precision in digital technology. The problem with analogue VLSI approaches are that of programmability, the difficulty of storing large numbers of variable weights in analogue circuitry without deterioration of the values with time. The disadvantage with all VLSI approaches are that they can only at present implement relatively small networks. While this is not a problem with all neural network applications, many of the application domains where the use of neural network technology is considered a possible solution are extremely complex and will require systems that can quickly process large quantities of data. Examples of these domains are vision, speech and other large pattern matching problems. Also many of these systems will probably require a large body of stored information to solve these problems and in the case of neural systems this will involve networks with large weight arrays. In addition, the many different areas that may have to be tackled in a particular application may require different approaches and networks for each task, leading to large heterogeneous systems.

This chapter describes work begun in building an environment for developing and running such a system for the *Vision by Associative Reasoning'* project by the Advanced Computer Architecture Group at the University of York. The major objective of this project is to provide a coherent framework for solving the problem of automated airborne vehicle guidance, or more specifically a system for determining the location of an aircraft by matching real-time infra-red camera images taken from an aircraft to stored digital maps. Different approaches to the various aspects of the project are being used and appraised, including relaxation methods and dynamic programming as well as neural networks.

The work described here is primarily focused on applying neural networks to this problem domain, specifically an associative memory under development at York, ADAM, the Advanced Distributed Associative Memory [AS87]. To this end we are developing an environment for building and running large ADAM systems. The approach that we have taken is to develop systems in software for ease of development and flexibility and to build a dedicated hardware platform for the execution of these systems.

17.2   ADAM

ADAM's principle features are its fast learning rate and it's ability to store large number of associations efficiently. To achieve this, ADAM, a development of both the Willshaw correlation matrix memory [WBL69] and the n-tuple network, employs binary weights within a two stage correlation matrix to store the associations and incorporates a training algorithm that has access to the 'hidden layer' in the network for fast training and implementing a special coding scheme for efficient thresholding. See Fig. 17.1 for a block diagram of an ADAM network in train and test modes.

The n-tuple pre-processing stage of the network is used to produce sparse pattern vectors to train on the correlation matrices. This helps prevent saturation of the memory and in addition to enable the memory to cope with the classification of non-linearly separable input patterns.

The ADAM memory is split into two stages for the addition of an intermediate 'hidden layer' in the network to allow implementation of a class vector that is used to associate the input and output patterns. Training of an association into the network involves the generation of a class vector that is used in separately training both the input and output vectors into the their respective correlation matrix. A recall cycle

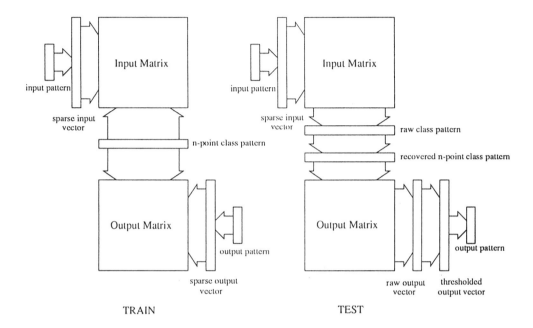

Fig. 17.1 - ADAM in train and test modes.

of the memory then involves the testing of the input matrix to recall a class pattern, which is in turn presented to the output matrix to recall the corresponding output pattern. The advantage to this system over the Willshaw matrix is that the training algorithm can choose class patterns that are optimised for efficient thresholding during a test of the memory. The training algorithm used chooses class vectors that are the subset where the number of bits set to 1 is some constant, known as an n-point pattern. The n-point thresholding of a raw class pattern produced during a test of the input matrix is performed by simply setting the n highest responses to 1 and the rest to 0. This thresholding process gives increased reliability of the classification of input vectors. In addition to this n-point coding of class patterns, the basic training algorithm can be adapted to choose particular n-point codes to increase the storage capability of the network [BA92].

The ADAM network has been applied to several tasks in the problem domain, including feature and texture recognition [SA92], and quick pattern matching on large databases to add rotation and scale invariance to any future vision system [Aus89].

To ease the development of pattern and image processing systems based around linking ADAM networks, and also to increase the speed of operating these systems, an integrated ADAM program library and hardware support is being developed.

17.3 THE ADAM LIBRARY

17.3.1 Introduction

The ADAM library is a standard set of 'C' data structures and a growing set of functions that operate on these to act as various types of ADAM associative memories. This enables a user to write usable ADAM systems very quickly. At present this library is capable of being used to create programs for building, training, running and storing ADAM systems in a conventional UNIX environment. Both ADAMs designed to associate binary and greyscale patterns or images are supported by the library. Work is also progressing on developing a simple X-Window graphical-user-interface for the library, to aid the building, running and displaying the results of ADAM systems. The use of a 'C' library over a neural network language was chosen as the functions in the library could be tailored to execute efficiently on the hardware platform being developed to execute the ADAM systems.

17.3.2 Example Application

The use of this library is being tested by using it in the development of a system for processing images using a two dimensional matrix of processing units that each takes its input from a section of the image. Processing units pass information about their input to neighbouring units and output a result based on a consensus of the patterns passed to them. Each of these units contains several ADAM networks for performing the pattern transformations required [Aus92]. Fig. 17.2 shows an example one-dimensional processor, containing four ADAM memories, and also shows how this one-dimensional processor is connected in a chain.

In this one-dimensional example, four ADAM units perform three pattern transformation tasks. The disperser transformation takes a pattern from the input image and transforms that to information patterns to pass to adjacent processors on the left and right. The combiner transformation takes patterns from the adjacent processors and produces an output pattern based on those. The passing transformation takes an input from an adjacent processor and produces an output to pass on to the opposite processor. The patterns produced by the disperser and passing transformations are logically OR'ed together to produce a combined pattern to pass to an adjacent processor that is based on the input pattern and patterns produced further down the processor chain.

A complete two dimensional network of similar processors could then take a section of an image as input. Each processor would pass information about their input to neighbouring processors and themselves produce an output based on the constraints imposed upon them by the patterns received from processors in their neighbourhood, in a similar manner to relaxation techniques. The advantage of this system over a programmed systems is that the behaviour of each processing unit is then determined by the training of transformations into each ADAM memory, giving greater flexibility.

If this technique is found to be useful it will be added to the library as a further suite of data structures and functions available to the programmer.

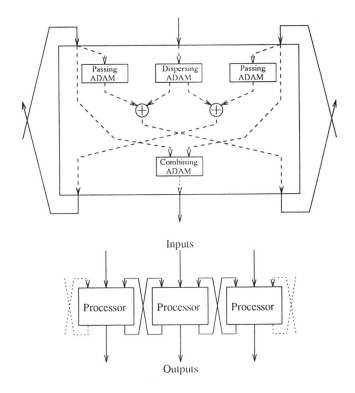

Fig. 17.2 - 1-dimensional processor and example chain of processors.

17.4 HARDWARE SUPPORT

17.4.1 Introduction

Software implementations of neural systems are limited in speed by the hardware platform they are executed on. The major goal of a dedicated platform is to increase this speed without compromising the maximum size of the network capable of being executed. Because of the distributed nature of information stored in neural networks a conventional cached system is not feasible as no 'working set' can be developed during execution, unlike conventional programs. No block of weights data for a network may have a statistically higher 'hit rate' than any other. Hence for very large networks, or systems of networks, which would be largely held in secondary storage, a simpler system that maximises the bandwidth between the processor and the secondary storage is needed [AJW91].

17.4.2 The DSPVME System

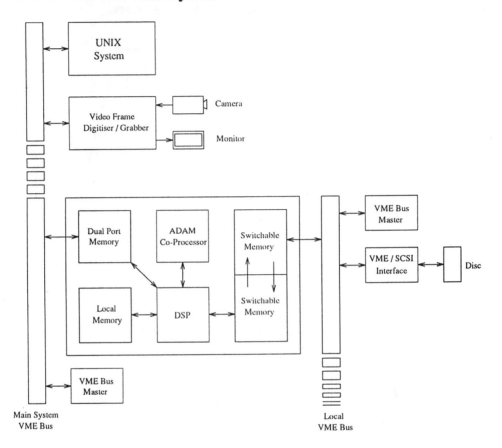

Fig. 17.3 - The DSPVME System.

The DSPVME system is one possible solution to this problem. It is intended to be individual processing boards optimised for executing neural network software which can be connected in parallel on an industry standard VME bus to other boards, peripheral hardware such as a video digitiser, and to a supervisory computer which is used for high level control and displaying final results of computation. The supervisory computer also runs the assembler, compiler and debugging programs for this DSP system. The system is designed to allow an array of several DSP boards to be connected to the VME bus to allow parallel processing. A block diagram of the hardware is shown in Fig. 17.3.

Each board is based around a Digital Signal Processor (DSP) as these are particularly suitable for the repetitive mathematical calculations found in neural network software. The board has three regions of memory, the dual-port memory, accessible by the DSP and the main VME bus for communication between boards, the local memory for programs and short term data, and the switchable memory. This last region of memory, which has a switchable address decoder to allow the addressing of banks of memory to be swapped, is intended to reduce the bottleneck between the DSP and the large amounts of image data and neural network weights that are stored on hard disc, by a simple memory paging system. It will allow the DSP to access one bank, while the other is accessed from the VME bus that is local to each board. Future versions of the system will have several banks of switchable memory, allowing several hard discs to access unused segments to allow a quicker update of the system virtual memory. This memory paging is an important part of the system as it produces a high data throughput and by allowing the quick paging of weight matrices used in very large trained ADAM systems will allow far larger networks to be implemented than was previously possible.

17.4.3 ADAM Co-Processor

Although the hardware platform as outlined above could be used for many types of large neural systems, reducing the bottleneck between the processor and secondary storage of weight data, and exploits the advantages of parallel processing by allowing arrays of these boards to be used, each board still suffers from the serial nature of the processor. The greatest increase in speed when running ADAM systems on this board comes from the addition of specialised hardware, built in Field Programmable Gate Array technology to perform some ADAM algorithms in parallel to the DSP itself. This ADAM co-processor has two functional parts. The first can sum the inputs to 16 ADAM neurons in parallel. This is performed simply by the DSP writing a 16 bit word to the co-processor for each 1 in the input vector to the correlation matrix being tested. This 16 bit word consists of the weights connecting that input 'line' to the 16 neurons being evaluated. As ADAM uses a binary weights system no complex multiplier is required and the word is then simply used to increment 16 different counters, one for each neuron being summed (see Fig. 17.4).

The counters are 16 bit and can hence sum up to 65536. Because of the n-tuple pre-processing of ADAM input patterns, which give a input vector with a single output set to 1 for each tuple unit, this system can then simply evaluate the sum of weights for 16 neurons connected to 65536 tuple units. This technique can be extended to sum in parallel a number of neurons equal to the width of the main processor data bus.

The second function of the ADAM co-processor is a state machine that can return the position of the highest counter value(s) of the 16 summations. This can greatly improve the speed of the ADAM n-point thresholding process, especially if n-point codes are chosen where one bit is set in every 16 bit grouping. This would greatly reduce the number of available codes for use in associating patterns but would greatly increase the speed of the summation and thresholding of the neurons by reducing it to a problem solvable simply by using the co-processing unit and not requiring any further calculation in software to recover the correct n-point code.

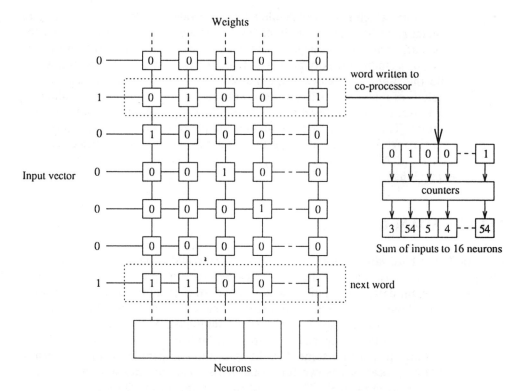

Fig. 17.4 - ADAM Co-Processor neuron summing function.

This co-processor is currently being constructed, but software simulation suggests an approximate speed improvement of 160 times over that of the equivalent operations performed in software by the DSP. This, in addition to the parallel DSP system is expected to greatly increase the speed of operation of the ADAM systems developed for the project towards that required.

ACKNOWLEDGMENTS

'Vision By Associative Reasoning' project supported by DTI/SERC Grant No. GR/F363300.

REFERENCES

[Aus89]   Austin, J., High Speed Invariant Pattern Recognition Using Adaptive Neural Networks, in *Proceedings of the Conference on Image Processing and Its Applications*, 28-32, 1989.

[Aus92]   Austin, J., Parallel Distributed Computation, *IEE International Conference on Artificial Neural Networks*, 1992.

[AJW91]   Austin, J., Jackson, T. and Wood, A., Efficient Implementation of Massive Neural Networks, *VLSI for Artificial Intelligence and Neural Networks*, 387-98, 1991.

[AS87]   Austin, J. and Stonham, T.J., An Associative Memory for Use in Image Recognition and Occlusion Analysis, *Vision and Image Computing*, 5(4), 251-61, 1987.

[BA92]   Brown, M. and Austin, J., Optimum Selection of Class Vectors for ADAM, in *IEE International Conference on Artificial Neural Networks*, 1992.

[Mur89]   Murray, A.F., Silicon Implementations of Neural Networks, in *First IEE International Conference on Artificial Neural Networks*, 1989.

[SA92]   Smith, G. and Austin, J., Analysing Aerial Photographs with ADAM, *Joint International Conference on Neural Networks, Baltimore, USA*, 1992.

[WBL69]   Willshaw, D.J., Buneman, O.P. and Longuet-Higgins, H.C., Non-Holographic Associative Memory, *Nature*, 222, 960-62, 1969.

Chapter 18

Neural Networks For System Fault Management

Janet Finlay and Julian Jones

Department of Computer Science, University of York, U.K.

Overview

The trend towards network-based systems brings with it an increased need to diagnose and manage system faults and their associated user problems. In large organizations, this help is often provided by a manned support service, a *Help Desk*, but this is a costly solution and user demand inevitably exceeds available resources. Although computer support, such as expert systems, can aid Help Desk staff and enable less experienced operators to do the job, the resource problem remains.

In this chapter we discuss the application of neural networks as a means of classifying user problems, based on natural language descriptions, within a support tool for the users themselves. This bypasses the Help Desk in cases where the solution to the problem is trivial and forwards the problem otherwise.

We describe an initial study which demonstrates the potential of the approach and discuss the role of the neural network within such a support system.

18.1 INTRODUCTION

As the trend in organizations swings towards network-based computer systems and, in particular, server-client configurations, the need to diagnose and manage system faults and their associated user problems becomes more pressing. Problems are more likely to be common to the network or related to centralized applications than confined to a single machine. In addition, the system administrator has the problem of maintaining software and managing version control, as well as remedying system errors.

One common solution to this problem is to provide a support service manned by human experts who can deal with user queries and pass details of system problems to the relevant support teams. However, this approach is costly in that it demands trained staff and is inefficient in that a significant proportion of the problems reported by users are trivial, requiring no external help to remedy. If these minor difficulties could be dealt with automatically, the support staff would be released to deal with more serious problems.

We propose the use of a neural network to filter common but trivial problems before they reach support staff. The system will allow users to describe their problem in their own words and would use an associative memory configuration [Aus87] to recognize the problem based upon keywords within the description. If the problem is identified as one of the common ones, diagnosis and advice can be given using simple advice templates; if not, the problem is forwarded to the support staff.

We discuss initial experiments using data from calls to a British Telecom (BT) Help Desk, in which problems were classified, using the keyword approach, from natural language transcripts of telephone conversations. The associative memory achieved up to 90% correct diagnosis of problems.

The associative memory approach has a number of advantages. Firstly, it is efficient and flexible. It does not require explicit representation of knowledge as with traditional expert system approaches, nor does it require iterative learning as in other neural paradigms. Examples are trained in a single pass. It has already been used successfully to model users based on patterns in usage [FB92] and to diagnose errors in interactive use [FH90]. A support system using this approach is therefore feasible in terms of resources and will allow rapid maintenance and updating, which is crucial to enable the administrator to include new problems as they occur. Secondly, the generalization properties of the network allow it to recognize examples of problem descriptions which have not been seen before. In addition, the network is tolerant of inconsistencies or *noise* within the example base. Finally, the method allows users freedom to describe the problem in their own terms, by utilizing keywords in a natural language description.

Having demonstrated the potential of the method in our initial experiments, we are now conducting more extensive testing and working towards a prototype system.

18.2 THE FAULT MANAGEMENT PROBLEM

The demand for increased resources and consistently available software has led to the widespread introduction of client-server system configurations, where multiple users access a common file store from a PC or local workstation. Typically, an organization may have several client-server networks which may be loosely connected to each other.

This provides the user with wider facilities but brings with it a number of problems for system support. Software is centralized and, consequently, so is fault management and user support. The problem of version control also occurs since different networks may run different versions of software within an organization. The networks themselves also introduce new problems for users.

In order to provide adequate support for users, organizations have to be able both to record problems as they arise and to handle their diagnosis and resolution efficiently. This involves both immediate remedial help for users, who are temporarily hampered by a system error, and longer term investigation of the root cause of recurrent errors.

18.3 HELP DESKS

In large organizations this support is often handled by providing a *Help Line* or *Help Desk*, manned by expert human operators. Users are able to call the Help Desk when a problem arises and the Help Desk operators will either resolve the problem immediately or refer it to alternative support staff. Calls to the Help Desk may be logged but this tends to be haphazard: problems which can be dealt with immediately are unlikely to be logged due to time pressures on operators. This means that the organization has no record of simple, but possibly highly recurrent, problems.

Help Desks are resource intensive, particularly in terms of operator time. The demand on these resources from users is high: many calls fail to reach a Help Desk operator as pressure on the service is too great.

Moreover, an informal study of calls to a BT Help Desk over one week shows that the majority of calls relate to problems which can be easily resolved by the user. These are often caused by misoperation (possibly due to an initial design flaw) rather than to system faults as such. The remaining problems relate to network and hardware faults which need to be handled by the relevant trained staff. The largest proportion of these problems relate to networks.

It is clear that Help Desk operators spend a large proportion of their time dealing with trivial problems or reporting network problems to the appropriate staff. If they could be freed from these duties they would be able to concentrate on handling the remaining, more difficult, problems and would be able to deal with the demand from users.

A second problem which effects the efficiency of Help Desks is the training requirements for its operators. In a large organization there are a wide range of systems in use as well as several versions of a piece of software operational at any time. Help Desk staff must be aware of changes to systems as they occur and problems that arise with them. The Help Desk is a primary source of information about problems with new systems or new versions of systems for the organization, so in addition to the pressures from users they are required to keep records of problems that occur. As previously noted, only problems which require specialist help to address are logged, resulting in trivial but common problems being left to recur. Therefore, there is no possibility of dealing with the problem at its cause (remedying the design) and user problems continue to arise.

18.4 SOFTWARE SUPPORT FOR HELP DESKS

A potential solution to some of the problems described is to provide software support, either for the Help Desk operator or for the users themselves. Currently, Help Desk operators at British Telecom use a form-based application to log calls but have no on-line support to help them diagnose the user's problem. A recent project investigated the possibility of using expert system technology to provide such information to the operator [Kre90]. If successful this would alleviate the need for skilled operators since the system would provide the necessary diagnosis. A basic expert system was developed for this task which enabled inexperienced operators to deal with queries but it was slow to use, particularly as operator skill increased, and was difficult to maintain since the information required changed frequently. While this approach should not be dismissed, particularly as support for the operator (see [BD92]), it seems unlikely to deal with the resource problem.

An alternative approach is to support the user rather than the operator. This has the advantage that it deals with problems before they ever reach the Help Desk, so releasing Help Desk resources. Such a system would be available directly to all users and would diagnose and treat simple problems and re-route others appropriately. In addition, the system would keep a record of all requests for help, including those which could be resolved easily, so improving overall fault management and correction. In effect, we are proposing a two tier organization of help, in which the first tier is provided by the support system. This is a parallel to the front-line Help Desk model in which the user accesses the Help Desk resources via a single entry point and is referred to appropriate support [BD92]. The distinction is that, in this proposal, the front-line helper is a computer not a human.

18.5 NEURAL NETWORKS: A SOLUTION?

Having established the need for a user-oriented fault diagnosis system, we can elaborate the requirements of this system more fully. We have seen that it is intended to perform three major roles

1. to diagnose and treat simple user problems,
2. to forward more complex problems to appropriate maintenance groups,
3. to record all problems reported.

It must also be updatable and easily maintainable, given the changing nature of the information. It must be efficient both in terms of speed of performance and memory requirements: users are unlikely to use a system which they perceive to be slow and will not tolerate it if it uses up large portions of their file store. Finally, it must be accessible to all users and require little expertise to use.

We can view the fault diagnosis problem as one of classification: there are a number of known faults which arise (classes) and each user report is diagnosed (or classified) as one of those faults. The user's report of the problem is the information upon which this classification is made. The solution we propose, therefore, is to use a neural network to perform this classification, trained upon examples of known faults as described by users.

By using example-based technology rather than knowledge-based or expert system technology, we can bypass the problem of knowledge acquisition. We do not need to develop a formal description of system faults; we can allow the network to detect significant features from the examples. Each class or fault can be associated with a particular help script which will provide the necessary advice when a fault has been diagnosed.

However, we need to use a network which is efficient in both training and recall, and can be updated. This rules out paradigms such as back propagation, due to its long training cycle. It is also unsuitable since it is difficult to update: adding examples to a trained net can corrupt the examples already trained, and retraining from scratch is not feasible due to the time required.

An alternative neural paradigm which does fulfil our requirements is the associative memory. It is a relatively small network which learns in a single iteration. Examples can be added without damage to a trained net and, if necessary, retraining is fast.

The associative memory model we use is ADAM, an Advanced Distributed Associative Memory [KA92]. It operates by *associating* a response to a particular known input, so that when that input (or a significant part of it) is presented to the memory the associated response is given. Each input pattern is translated into a bit pattern by *n-tupling*: the complete pattern is sampled by a number of tuples, each of which will set a unique bit in an input vector, according to its input. The mapping of elements onto the tuples may be random, or specific; for example, mapping each element of the original pattern onto a tuple which will set a unique bit in the input vector, as a function of the element's ASCII code. The advantages of tupling are twofold. Firstly, each element of the pattern is treated separately (rather than taking the pattern in its entirety) so that any pattern containing that element in that position will get a response from that tuple. This allows the system to recognize patterns that it has not seen before. Secondly, a sparse input is provided, avoiding saturation which would prevent the memory from being able to distinguish patterns accurately.

The memory can be visualized as a matrix of initially unlinked wires, a horizontal wire for each bit position in the input vector, and a number of vertical wires. In training, each of the input vector bit patterns is presented to the memory along with a unique, randomly generated, sparse bit pattern representing the class to which the example belongs. The class pattern has a known number of bits set. The input appears on the horizontal wires, while the class pattern is presented on the vertical wires. A link is made in the memory wherever an active vertical wire crosses an active horizontal wire. On recall, a pattern is presented as before, and the class pattern is calculated by summing the number of links in each column which are on an active horizontal wire. This is *n-point thresholded*, by retrieving the n highest values (where n is the number of bits set in the class pattern) to return the class pattern which matches the input most closely. It should be noted that the class pattern can be recovered even if not all the elements of the originally taught input pattern are present in the target pattern, since the thresholding provides us with the best match.

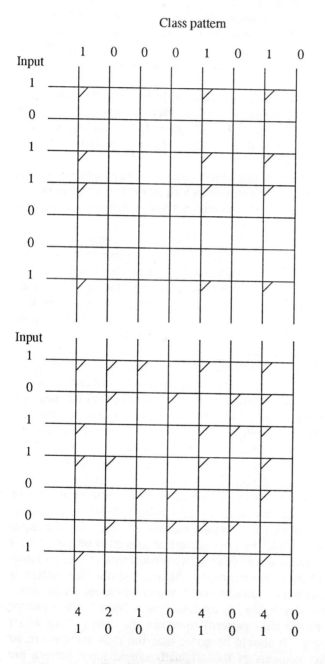

The matrix is initially empty. This shows the matrix after one pattern has been taught

Matrix after several patterns have been taught.
The input produces a response which is thresholded to recover the relevant class.

Fig. 18.1 - Training and recall in the ADAM memory.

This process is illustrated in Fig. 18.1 which shows an example of training and recall in the memory.

The first matrix shows the links set in the memory for the input pattern *1011001*, following the training of that pattern. The second matrix shows the same memory, after training with many more patterns (hence many more links are set). The first pattern is presented again and the correct class pattern recalled by n-point thresholding. The system also provides two measures of correctness: the confidence in the decision (which will be 100% only if all input lines are identical to the pattern trained), and a distance measure, which indicates how far the pattern is from the next nearest class.

18.6   A PILOT EXPERIMENT WITH ADAM

Before attempting to build a user support system we decided to test ADAM's performance on classifying user problems based on data provided from the BT Help Desk. ADAM has already been shown to be capable of classifying user expertise and tasks when trained on system logs [FB92], and has been used to analyse user errors [FH90]. However, in this case, we do not have system logs of the user behaviour, since monitoring all users in case a problem arises is unrealistic. Instead we want to allow users to describe the problem in their own words. The data for the pilot study comprised transcripts of telephone conversations between operator and user. Within these transcripts the user describes the problem that has arisen.

18.6.1   Representing the Transcripts

Our first problem is to present these natural language transcripts to ADAM in a suitable form. The transcripts are of actual telephone conversations and as such are imprecise and incomplete. ADAM requires a binary representation. We cannot map the transcripts directly to this representation for a number of reasons

1. they are incomplete and imprecise,
2. they represent wide variations in descriptive style,
3. the noise to information ratio in the transcripts is very high.

Instead we need to abstract the relevant features from the transcripts which identify the problem being described. We decided to do this using keywords from the transcripts. Help Desk operators identified keywords from a complete list of words used in the transcripts. These were then used to represent the transcripts themselves. The keywords represent the knowledge in the system. The use of keywords simplifies the process of knowledge acquisition from a knowledge intensive, descriptive task for a human expert to a mechanized filtering process (after the initial identification of keywords).

We considered two methods of representing the transcripts using the keywords. The first representation we call the *literal* vector, the second, the *feature* vector. In each case, the complete transcript is processed to convert it into a series of tokens, each token representing a keyword occurrence in the transcript. These symbolic representations are then mapped onto binary vectors, for input to ADAM, using two distinct mappings. These mappings are illustrated in Fig. 18.2. The symbol trace (which is kept short here for illustration) is transformed into an integer string, based on a function of its ASCII code. This is then used to determine which bits in the vector are set, using the mappings described.

Symbol trace	!#%
ASCII mapping	024
Feature vector	1010100
Literal vector	10000000 00100000 00001000

Fig. 18.2 - Literal and feature vector mappings.

The literal vector mapping represents the keywords as they actually appear in the transcript, including orderings and repetitions. The vector is constructed from a sequence of blocks, and each token is mapped onto a single block. Since ADAM requires fixed length input, a length limit was set on the transcripts (representing an average transcript length). Traces containing fewer tokens than this were filled using default tokens; traces containing too many tokens were curtailed. This introduces noise into the pattern. However, the mapping provides a sparse input pattern, which avoids memory saturation.

The feature vector mapping represents the *occurrence* of keywords in the transcript, ignoring ordering and repetition. In this case, each binary position in the vector represents a keyword, and the bit is set if the keyword appears in the transcript. As the number of keywords is constant, the length of this binary vector is fixed and therefore no information needs to be added or lost. The use of a smaller vector for the same amount of information means that the representation is less sparse, increasing the risk of memory saturation.

In spite of the potential saturation problem, the feature vector offers the most promising representation for the data. The transcripts vary considerably in the way that a problem is phrased, so there is likely to be little benefit in representing these conversations literally. However, although they may vary in the way the problem is described, similar problems tend to involve similar terminology, and so the occurence of keywords is a likely indicator of the problem class.

18.6.2 The Approach Taken

The data used in this pilot was recorded on audio tape in a previous study [Kre90], and only a limited number of transcriptions were available. In total we had transcripts of 30 telephone conversations, dealing with four problem classes. Given the fact that the majority of the time of Help Desk operators is spent dealing with a few recurring problem types, this is a reasonable set for a pilot study. The ADAM-based system is intended to deal with common problems and it is acceptable for it to pass on rarer examples.

Help Desk operators manually classified each transcript into a problem class. These expert-based classifications were used in the study both to delimit the data in training and as a measure of the success of recognition: if a trace was recognized by ADAM as belonging to the same problem class as the transcript from which it was taken, the classification has been successful.

For training, 2 examples per problem class were chosen randomly from the transcript set. The remaining traces were used as unseen test data for ADAM to classify. Each training and classification set was used with both the literal and the feature vector mapping.

In addition to the training sets of actual transcripts, we constructed a training example for each problem, which included the keywords which were common to all, or most, of the example transcripts in each class. These constructed examples represented a further training set, used with the feature vector mapping.

For each training set, ADAM was trained (as described previously) on the examples in the set, and presented with the unseen traces for recognition. The output for each example includes a measure of the confidence of the decision and of how distinct the example was from other classes. This allows us to distinguish definite correct responses from those which cannot be classified uniquely. Traces are sometimes classified as being close to a number of classes; these typically have very low confidences and distance measures. If a trace is not uniquely identified, it is deemed to be incorrectly classified, even if the correct class is among the examples matched. We do not insist on 100% confidence in a decision: any variation in a transcript from the trained examples will reduce the confidence of a decision. However, confidence measures for correct decisions tend to be above 60%.

18.6.3 Results

As expected, the literal vector mapping was inadequate to deal with the variation in data and results with this representation were poor. Using a vector length of 9 keyword symbols, ADAM was unable to classify correctly any of the examples from two of the four classes, and in the third class managed only 26%. The fourth class was correctly classified. The classification was adversely effected by the variation between transcripts. Half of the total traces were identified as belonging to the wrong class, the other errors (approximately 25% of the total errors) represented traces where a positive decision could not be made.

The feature vector mapping produced better results. In the two classes which ADAM failed to classify using the previous representation, all the examples in one are correctly classified and half in the other. In the remaining classes ADAM gets 67% and 73% correct respectively. The proportion of incorrect responses to uncertain responses is also reduced to 1 in 3. These results are more promising, suggesting that the feature representation is more viable, in spite of the saturation problem.

The constructed set produced the best results of all. Here three classes were classified correctly, while in the fourth, 87% of traces were identified successfully. Only one trace is incorrectly identified. This demonstrates the importance of a representative training set, and suggests that the approach to take may not be to use actual transcripts but to generate *super-transcripts* representing the commonalities within problem descriptions. The evidence from this study is that the more limited information in a given actual trace is sufficient to allow ADAM to classify it based on the more accurate and complete generated trace.

18.6.4 The Implications of the Study

The study described is limited by the small amount of data with which we had to work. The four classes represent a small subset of the problems that are reported to the Help Desk (albeit the most common ones), and even within these classes, there may be more variation within a larger data set. However, the results do indicate that ADAM is able to classify a high proportion of transcripts correctly and this augurs well for future experiments. Although this experiment deals with a subset of problems, these are the most common recurring errors reported to the Help Desk. The completed system would not be expected to recognize the full range of possible errors. Rather it would be trained to recognize the most common ones (which are simple to rectify) and to pass on any others, without necessarily diagnosing them, to the human operator.

The choice of training set is a crucial factor and, indeed, our current work indicates that significant improvements in performance can be achieved by changing the training set, even when using only actual traces. This suggests that the training set can be optimized. This clearly has implications for knowledge acquisition. An advantage of the ADAM approach is that knowledge acquisition is simplified. However, if the training set can be optimized, human expertise will be beneficial in the selection stage. This increases the burden on the human expert. It should be noted that this is a tradeoff between human effort and accuracy of recognition: the application of human expertise to selection may improve accuracy but it is still possible to achieve reasonable results using a randomly chosen training set.

The other limitation of the experiment is that it deals with transcripts of conversations between users and Help Desk operators, rather than with the user's free description. This is important since it is possible that the interaction with the Help Desk operator enables the user to describe the problem sufficiently accurately for ADAM to classify it. Left to themselves, users may be less precise. In order to work successfully in a user support system, ADAM must be able to handle users' own descriptions of their problems. However, these do not need to be completely unconstrained. An alternative approach is to provide the user with a constrained format in which to describe his problem, by using a form-based interface for example. The interface then acts in much the same way as the human operator, guiding the user through his description. This would ensure that descriptions contained certain information, while still allowing the user to describe the problem in his own words. We are currently investigating this using problem descriptions generated by users of a bibliographic database system. These traces should be more difficult to classify than Help Desk problem descriptions in that the problems that occur are all within the same domain and so they are less distinct. If ADAM can classify these descriptions correctly we are confident that it will be able to handle Help Desk type descriptions.

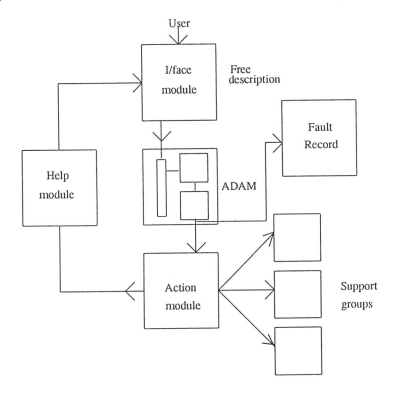

Fig. 18.3 - The architecture of the support system.

18.7 DESIGN FOR A SUPPORT SYSTEM

The experiment we have described demonstrates the potential for using a neural associative memory to diagnose faults based on abstractions of natural language descriptions. Although the results of this experiment are obviously limited due to the small amount of data available, it seems to be an approach worth pursuing. We are currently working on the design of a simple support system based on an ADAM memory. The aim is that the support system will be available on the user's terminal or workstation (or on that of a colleague if the user's problem is that his machine has locked up!). ADAM is trained on keyword descriptions of all problems with which it is to deal. Users will describe their problems in their own words, but will be encouraged to include information such as the machine and software being used. The description will then be filtered for keywords and the keyword abstraction presented to the trained ADAM. If ADAM is able to recognize the problem to an acceptable level of confidence, the decision will be passed to the response module which will either output a remedial help script giving the user recovery instructions, or will send a message to the appropriate support group (this can be done via email). If the problem cannot be recognized, the user is instructed to contact the Help Desk. The architecture of the design is shown in Fig. 18.3.

In addition to the user support facility, the system will be designed to facilitate maintenance and updating by the system administrator, and monitoring of problems. Information can be added to ADAM in two ways, by incremental training and by retraining. The former is appropriate when a small amount of information, such as a new problem, needs to be added; the latter, when information within the system changes. The training examples are stored and can be reused if required. The responses provided by the system are also stored to maintain a record of problems reported.

This system is initially being built to deal with problems in the bibliographic database domain, although, if it is successful there, we hope to develop a version to deal with the wider range of problems supported by a commercial Help Desk.

18.8 SUMMARY

The study reported in this chapter suggests that neural networks can be used to classify user problems, based on their own descriptions of their difficulty. Further experiments are in progress to test this on wider ranging data. A support system based on a neural classifier is being developed. The approach provides a means of relieving the pressure on human expert advisors by providing an advisory resource which users can access themselves. This will never replace human helpers, but by handling trivial items, will release them to deal with the problems which really require their expertise.

ACKNOWLEDGEMENTS

The authors would like to thank Richard Oppenheimer and members of the Leeds BT Help Desk for their help and cooperation in this work.

REFERENCES

[Aus87]   Austin, J., ADAM: A Distributed Associative Memory for Scene Analysis, in *Proceedings of the 1st International Conference on Neural Networks*, Caudill, M., Butler, C., (eds.) IEEE, 1987.

[BD92]   Bridge, D. and Dearden, A., Knowledge-Based System Support for Help Desk Operations: A Reference Model, *Knowledge-Based Systems*, 5, 217-34, 1992.

[FB92]   Finlay, J. and Beale, R., Pattern Recognition and Classification in Dynamic and Static User Modelling, in *Neural Networks and Pattern Recognition in HCI*, Beale, R., Finlay, J., (eds.), 65-90, Ellis Horwood, 1992.

[FH90]   Finlay, J. and Harrison, M., Pattern Recognition and Interaction Models, in *Human Computer Interaction, INTERACT '90*, Diaper, D., Gilmore, D., Cockton, G., Shackel, B., (eds.), 149-54, Elsevier: North-Holland, 1990.

[KA92]   Kelly, I. and Austin, J., Implementing an Associative Memory Environment, in *Techniques and Applications of Neural Networks*, Chapter 17, Ellis Horwood, 1993.

[Kre90]   Krening, S., An Expert System for British Telecom's Help Desk, MSc Dissertation, Department of Computer Science, University of York, 1990.

CONTRIBUTORS

Dr. M. Ashton
Unilever Research Laboratory
Port Sunlight
Wirral
Cheshire L63 3JW, U.K.

Mr. J. Austin
Department of Computer Science
University of York
Heslington
York YO1 5DD, U.K.

Professor P.G. Barker
Interactive Systems Research Group
School of Computing and Mathematics
University of Teesside
Middlesbrough
Cleveland TS1 3BA, U.K.

Dr. T. Berkel
FernUniversität Hagen
Applied Computer Science I
P.O. Box 940
D-5800 Hagen, Germany

Mr. R. Biewald
Fritz-Selbmann-Str. 68
0-1153 Berlin
Germany

Dr. D.J. Cornforth
Department of Computer Science
University of Nottingham
University Park
Nottingham NG7 2RD, U.K.

Mr. J.S. Curnow
Plymouth Postgraduate Medical School
Department of Obstetrics and
Gynaecology
Freedom Fields Hospital
Plymouth, U.K.

Dr. D. Diamond
School of Chemical Sciences
Dublin City University
Glasnevin
Dublin 9, Ireland

Dr. A.W.G. Duller
School of Electronic Engineering
and Computer Systems
University College of North Wales
Dean Street
Bangor, Gwynedd LL57 1UT
North Wales, U.K.

Dr. D.G. Elliman
Department of Computer Science
University of Nottingham
University Park
Nottingham NG7 2RD, U.K.

Dr. P.A. Errington
Department of Medical Biophysics
University of Manchester
Stopford Building
Oxford Road
Manchester M13 9PT, U.K.

Dr. J. Finlay
Department of Computer Science
University of York
Heslington
York YO1 5DD, U.K.

Mr. J.W. Gardner
Department of Engineering
University of Warwick
Coventry CV4 7AL, U.K.

Dr. J. Graham
Department of Medical Biophysics
University of Manchester
Stopford Building
Oxford Road
Manchester M13 9PT, U.K.

Ms. C. Gianna
Department of Engineering
University of Warwick
Coventry CV4 7AL, U.K.

Dr. K.R. Greene
Plymouth Postgraduate Medical School
Department of Obstetrics and
Gynaecology
Freedom Fields Hospital
Plymouth, U.K.

Mr. J.R. Griffiths
CRC Biomedical Magnetic Resonance
Research Group
Department of Cellular and Molecular
Sciences
Division of Biochemistry
St George's Hospital Medical School
Cranmer Terrace
London SW17 0RE, U.K.

Ms. M. Hartnett
School of Chemical Sciences
Dublin City University
Glasnevin
Dublin 9, Ireland

Dr. E.L. Hines
Department of Engineering
University of Warwick
Coventry CV4 7AL, U.K.

Ms. S.L. Howells
CRC Biomedical Magnetic
Resonance Research Group
Department of Cellular and Molecular
Sciences
Division of Biochemistry
St George's Hospital Medical School
Cranmer Terrace
London SW17 0RE, U.K.

Dr. E.C. Ifeachor
School of Electronic, Communication
and Electrical Engineering
University of Plymouth
Drake Circus
Plymouth
Devon PL4 8AA, U.K.

Mr. J. Jones
Department of Computer Science
University of York
Heslington
York YO1 5DD, U.K.

Mr. I. Kelly
Department of Computer Science
University of York
Heslington
York YO1 5DD, U.K.

Dr. P.J.G. Lisboa
Department of Electrical Engineering
and Electronics
University of Liverpool
P.O. Box 147
Liverpool L69 3BX, U.K.

Dr. E. Mathers
Unilever Research Laboratory
Port Sunlight
Wirral
Cheshire L63 3JW, U.K.

Dr. R.J. Maxwell
CRC Biomedical Magnetic
Resonance Research Group
Department of Cellular and Molecular
Sciences
Division of Biochemistry
St George's Hospital Medical School
Cranmer Terrace
London SW17 0RE, U.K.

Professor D. Partridge
Centre for Connection Study
Department of Computer Science
University of Exeter
Exeter EX4 4PT, U.K.

Dr. S. Patel
Unilever Research Laboratory
Port Sunlight
Wirral
Cheshire L63 3JW, U.K.

Mr. S.R. Patel
School of Electronic,
Communication and Electrical
Engineering
University of Plymouth
Drake Circus
Plymouth
Devon PL4 8AA, U.K.

Mr. A.C. Peet
CRC Biomedical Magnetic
Resonance Research Group
Department of Cellular and Molecular
Sciences
Division of Biochemistry
St George's Hospital Medical School
Cranmer Terrace
London SW17 0RE, U.K.

Dr. R. Perryman
University of Greenwich
Wellington Street
Woolwich
London SE18 6PF, U.K.

Dr. V. Popesco
Telecom Paris
16 rue Barrault
75013 Paris
France

Dr. A.N. Refenes
Department of Computer Science
University College London
Gower Street
London WC13 6BT, U.K.

Dr. A. Scherer
FernUniversität Hagen
Applied Computer Science I
P.O. Box 940
D-5800 Hagen, Germany

Professor G. Schlageter
FernUniversität Hagen
Applied Computer Science I
P.O. Box 940
D-5800 Hagen, Germany

Dr. R. Schultheiss
Ford AG Köln
CAM-Systems, Power Train,
Machinings and Forgings
P.O. Box 604002
D-5000 Köln 60, Germany

Dr. N.E. Sharkey
Centre for Connection Study
Department of Computer Science
University of Exeter
Exeter EX4 4PT, U.K.

Professor T.J. Stonham
Department of Electrical Engineering
Brunel University
Howell Building
Uxbridge
Middlesex UB8 3PH, U.K.

Mr. S.D. Strudwick
Power Group International Ltd
Ramsgate Road
Sandwich
Kent CT13 9NE, U.K.

Mr. G. Tambouratzis
Department of Electrical Engineering
Brunel University
Howell Building
Uxbridge
Middlesex UB8 3PH, U.K.

Dr. T. Tambouratzis
Department of Mathematics
Agricultural University of Athens,
Iera Odos 75
Athens 118 55, Greece

Dr. M.J. Taylor
Department of Computer Science
University of Liverpool
P.O. Box 147
Liverpool L69 3BX, U.K.

Mr. J.M. Vincent
British Telecom Laboratories
Martlesham Heath
Ipswich IP5 7RE, U.K.

Ms. J. Westgate
Plymouth Postgraduate Medical School
Department of Obstetrics and
Gynaecology
Freedom Fields Hospital
Plymouth, U.K.

Mr. P. Williams
School of Electronic Engineering
and Computer Systems
University College of North Wales
Dean Street
Bangor
Gwynedd LL57 1UT
North Wales, U.K.

Dr. A. Zaidi
Department of Computer Science
University College London
Gower Street
London WC13 6BT, U.K.

INDEX

a priori information   241-244

ADAM   278-284, 291-298

adaptive algorithm   265-266

address   36-41, 265-268, 283, 289

alcohol classification   135

analytic chemistry   155-156

associative memory   36, 62, 277, 278,
                      288, 291, 297

automatic neural network
      construction   135, 137

back-propagation through time   199,
                      204-208, 215

back-propagation   23, 63, 77, 128,
      135-145, 150-152, 155-158, 171-178,
                      191, 203

Bayes   35, 40, 41, 45, 222

binary associative memory   277

blocks world   48, 50

Boltzmann Machine   235, 236,
                      239-244, 246-251

CAD   253-261

CAM   253-256, 258

cancer   65, 77

cardiotocogram   93-95

cerebellar model articulation
      controller (CMAC)   35-45

chromosome analysis   77

clinicians   95, 97, 103, 105

cluster analysis   64-71, 223

competitive networks   88

concurrent engineering   253-256

condition based maintenance (CBM)
                      120, 130

condition monitoring   118, 119, 133

constraint propagation   47-53

constructive algorithms   135

constructive learning   113

contaminated pattern   267, 270, 273

control system   204, 213, 215

diesel engines   132

dimensionality   64, 173, 185, 191-193,
                      196

discriminator   35, 264-274

electrical fault indenfication   183

electrocardiogram (ECG)   97-99

electronic nose   135, 144, 153

expert system   156, 185

fault diagnosis   290

feature location   237, 241

feature map   183-193, 219-226,
                      235-251

fetal heart rate   93-98

fetal monitoring   93-97

flow injection analysis   155, 158-162,
                      168-170, 178, 179

foreign exchange trading   109

Gibbs sampler   240

growing algorithms   137

harmony theory   47, 52-56, 59-62

hashing function   36-41, 44

help desk   **287-290, 293, 295, 296**

hierarchical perceptron   **235**

human labour   **93, 95**

human experts   **93, 94, 184, 186, 288, 293-298**

image analysis   **221, 222, 232**

intelligent system   **50, 61, 93**

interpretation   **48-61, 65, 93-98, 156, 171**

ion selective electrodes   **161, 177**

knowledge acquisition   **291, 293, 296**

knowledge-based systems (KBS)   **120, 130, 132, 133**

Kohonen   **87, 183, 190-196, 219-232, 261, 266-268**

line-drawings   **50, 54, 58**

logic neural network   **263, 264, 266**

memory   **36-41, 60, 123, 136, 216, 264-267, 278-283, 290-297**

mobile robot navigation   **200**

modelling   **33, 35, 50-54, 60, 158, 205**

moving averages   **109-111, 113, 115**

multiversion programming   **22, 32**

natural language **32, 287-288, 293, 297**

neighbourhood training   **265**

network programming   **22**

neural net controllers   **210**

non-holonomic vehicles   **199**

nuclear magnetic resonance (NMR)   **63-67, 70, 74, 158**

obstacle avoidance   **199-201, 203, 215**

odour classification   **135**

olfactory system   **135, 144**

oscillators'   **109, 110**

parallel hardware   **54, 215**

parameter estimation   **125, 126**

parameterisation   **251**

pattern recognition **35, 40, 64, 94-98, 105, 157, 158, 183, 185, 261**

pattern completion   **263-270**

power generation   **117**

pre-processing   **93-98, 104, 227**

principal component analysis (PCA)   **63**

probability   **25-31, 35-44, 59, 157, 186, 190, 227, 239, 240**

production planning   **254, 256**

pruning algorithms   **137**

psychological evidence   **50**

RCE model   **137, 140, 141**

reconstruction   **263, 264, 268-274**

reuse of design object   **253**

scene analysis   **45, 47-51**

self-organisation   **183, 190, 219-232**

sensory data   **199-203, 214, 215**

similar objects   **219, 222, 258**

simulated annealing   **52, 53, 240, 242, 249**

size distribution   **219-222, 228-232**

software engineering   **21, 31**

subsymbolic level   **53, 61**

supervision   **263, 265**

symbolic route description   **199, 201**

system fault management   **287**

time series prediction   **125**

topological mapping   **203, 269**

trend analysis   **117, 121**

truck backer-upper   **215**

tumour   **63, 64, 66-68, 70-74**

ultrasonic sensors   **203**

unsupervised learning   **65, 190, 264,**

                               265, 274

user support   **288, 293, 296, 298**

vector quantizer   **190, 192**